Introduction to Engineering

The College of Engineering

The University of Texas at Arlington

A Pearson Custom Publication

Pearson Prentice Hall
Vice President and Editorial Director, ECS: *Marcia J. Horton*
Executive Editor: *Eric Svendsen*
Associate Editor: *Dee Bernhard*
Vice President and Director of Production and Manufacturing, ESM: *David W. Riccardi*
Executive Managing Editor: *Vince O'Brien*
Managing Editor: *David A. George*
Production Editor: *Barbara A. Till*
Director of Creative Services: *Paul Belfanti*
Creative Director: *Carole Anson*
Art Director: *Jayne Conte*
Art Editor: *Greg Dulles*
Manufacturing Manager: *Trudy Pisciotti*
Manufacturing Buyer: *Lisa McDowell*
Marketing Manager: *Holly Stark*

Pearson Custom Publishing
Director of Database Publishing: *Michael Payne*
Executive Marketing Manager: *Nathan L. Wilbur*
Operations Manager: *Eric M. Kenney*
Editorial Assistant: *Victoria L. Ravin*
Project Specialist: *Zach LaRosa*
Cover Designer: *Renee Sartell*

ISBN-13: 9780536421418
ISBN-10: 0536421412

Package ISBN-13: N/A
Package ISBN-10: N/A

Excerpts taken from:

Design Concepts for Engineers, 2/e by Mark N. Horenstein
0-13-093430-5 © 2002 by Prentice-Hall, Inc., a Pearson Education Company

Engineering Design and Problem Solving, 2/e by Steven K. Howell
0-13-093399-6 © 2002 by Prentice-Hall, Inc., a Pearson Education Company

Engineering Ethics by Charles B. Fleddermann
0-13-784224-4 © 1999 by Prentice-Hall, Inc., a Pearson Education Company

Engineering with Excel by Ronald W. Larsen
0-13-017696-6 © 2002 by Prentice-Hall, Inc., a Pearson Education Company

Engineering Success, 2/e by Peter Schiavone
0-13-041827-7 © 2002 by Prentice-Hall, Inc., a Pearson Education Company

Exploring Engineering, 2/e by Joe King
0-13-093442-9 © 2002 by Prentice-Hall, Inc., a Pearson Education Company

Graphics Concepts by Richard M. Lueptow
0-13-030687-8 © 2000 by Prentice-Hall, Inc., a Pearson Education Company

Introduction to AutoCAD® 2000 by Mark Dix and Paul Riley
0-13-016732-0 © 2000 by Prentice-Hall, Inc., a Pearson Education Company

Introduction to Engineering Analysis by Kirk D. Hagen
0-13-016733-9 © 2000 by Prentice-Hall, Inc., a Pearson Education Company

Introduction to Excel 2002 by David C. Kuncicky
0-13-008175-2 © 2003 by Pearson Education, Inc.

Introduction to MathCad® 2000 by Ronald W. Larsen
0-13-020007-7 © 2001 by Prentice-Hall, Inc., a Pearson Education Company

Introduction to MatLab® 6 by Delores M. Etter and David C. Kuncicky with Doug Hull
0-13-032845-6 © 2002 by Prentice-Hall, Inc., a Pearson Education Company

Introduction to PowerPoint 2002 by Jack Leifer
0-13-008179-5 © 2003 by Pearson Education, Inc.

Introduction to Unix® by David I. Schwartz
0-13-095135-8 © 1999 by Prentice-Hall, Inc., a Pearson Education Company

Introduction to Word 2002 by David C. Kuncicky
0-13-008170-1 © 2003 by Pearson Education, Inc.

Power Programming with VBA/Excel by Steven C. Chapra
0-13-047377-4 © 2003 by Pearson Education, Inc.

About ESource

ESource—The Prentice Hall Engineering Source— www.prenhall.com/esource

ESource—The Prentice Hall Engineering Source gives professors the power to harness the full potential of their text and their first-year engineering course. More than just a collection of books, ESource is a unique publishing system revolving around the ESource website—www.prenhall.com/esource. ESource enables you to put your stamp on your book just as you do your course. It lets you:

Control   You choose exactly what chapters are in your book and in what order they appear. Of course, you can choose the entire book if you'd like and stay with the authors' original order.

Optimize   Get the most from your book and your course. ESource lets you produce the optimal text for your students needs.

Customize   You can add your own material anywhere in your text's presentation, and your final product will arrive at your bookstore as a professionally formatted text. Of course, all titles in this series are available as stand-alone texts, or as bundles of two or more books sold at a discount. Contact your PH sales rep for discount information.

ESource ACCESS

Professors who choose to bundle two or more texts from the ESource series for their class, or use an ESource custom book will be providing their students with an on-line library of intro engineering content—ESource Access. We've designed ESource ACCESS to provide students a flexible, searchable, on-line resource. Free access codes come in bundles and custom books are valid for one year after initial log-on. Contact your PH sales rep for more information.

ESource Content

All the content in ESource was written by educators specifically for freshman/first-year students. Authors tried to strike a balanced level of presentation, an approach that was neither formulaic nor trivial, and one that did not focus too heavily on advanced topics that most introductory students do not encounter until later classes. Because many professors do not have extensive time to cover these topics in the classroom, authors prepared each text with the idea that many students would use it for self-instruction and independent study. Students should be able to use this content to learn the software tool or subject on their own.

While authors had the freedom to write texts in a style appropriate to their particular subject, all followed certain guidelines created to promote a consistency that makes students comfortable. Namely, every chapter opens with a clear set of **Objectives**, includes **Practice Boxes** throughout the chapter, and ends with a number of **Problems**, and a list of **Key Terms. Applications Boxes** are spread throughout the book with the intent of giving students a real-world perspective of engineering. **Success Boxes** provide the student with advice about college study skills, and help students avoid the common pitfalls of first-year students. In addition, this series contains an entire book titled *Engineering Success* by Peter Schiavone of the University of Alberta intended to expose students quickly to what it takes to be an engineering student.

Creating Your Book

Using ESource is simple. You preview the content either on-line or through examination copies of the books you can request on-line, from your PH sales rep, or by calling 1-800-526-0485. Create an on-line outline of the content you want, in the order you want, using ESource's simple interface. Insert your own material into the text flow. If you are not ready to order, ESource will save your work. You can come back at any time and change, re-arrange, or add more material to your creation. Once you're finished you'll automatically receive an ISBN. Give it to your bookstore and your book will arrive on their shelves four to six weeks after they order. Your custom desk copies with their instructor supplements will arrive at your address at the same time.

To learn more about this new system for creating the perfect textbook, go to www.prenhall.com/esource. You can either go through the on-line walkthrough of how to create a book, or experiment yourself.

Supplements

Adopters of ESource receive an instructor's CD that contains professor and student code from the books in the series, as well as other instruction aides provided by authors. The website also holds approximately **350 PowerPoint transparencies** created by Jack Leifer of University of Kentucky–Paducah. Professors can either follow these transparencies as pre-prepared lectures or use them as the basis for their own custom presentations.

Titles in the ESource Series

Design Concepts for Engineers, 2/e
0-13-093430-5
Mark Horenstein

Engineering Success, 2/e
0-13-041827-7
Peter Schiavone

Engineering Design and Problem Solving, 2E
ISBN 0-13-093399-6
Steven K. Howell

Exploring Engineering
ISBN 0-13-093442-9
Joe King

Engineering Ethics
0-13-784224-4
Charles B. Fleddermann

Introduction to Engineering Analysis
0-13-016733-9
Kirk D. Hagen

Introduction to Engineering Experimentation
0-13-032835-9
Ronald W. Larsen, John T. Sears, and Royce Wilkinson

Introduction to Mechanical Engineering
0-13-019640-1
Robert Rizza

Introduction to Electrical and Computer Engineering
0-13-033363-8
Charles B. Fleddermann and Martin Bradshaw

Introduction to MATLAB 6—Update
0-13-140918-2
Delores Etter and David C. Kuncicky, with Douglas W. Hull

MATLAB Programming
0-13-035127-X
David C. Kuncicky

Introduction to MATLAB
0-13-013149-0
Delores Etter with David C. Kuncicky

Introduction to Mathcad 2000
0-13-020007-7
Ronald W. Larsen

Introduction to Mathcad 11
0-13-008177-9
David W. Larsen

Introduction to Maple 8
0-13-032844-8
David I. Schwartz

Mathematics Review
0-13-011501-0
Peter Schiavone

Power Programming with VBA/Excel
0-13-047377-4
Steven C. Chapra

Introduction to Excel 2002
0-13-008175-2
David C. Kuncicky

Engineering with Excel
ISBN 0-13-017696-6
Ronald W. Larsen

Introduction to Word 2002
0-13-008170-1
David C. Kuncicky

Introduction to PowerPoint 2002
0-13-008179-5
Jack Leifer

Graphics Concepts
0-13-030687-8
Richard M. Lueptow

Graphics Concepts with SolidWorks 2/e
0-13-140915-8
Richard M. Lueptow and Michael Minbiole

Graphics Concepts with Pro/ENGINEER
0-13-014154-2
Richard M. Lueptow, Jim Steger, and
Michael T. Snyder

Introduction to AutoCAD 2000
0-13-016732-0
Mark Dix and Paul Riley

Introduction to AutoCAD, R. 14
0-13-011001-9
Mark Dix and Paul Riley

Introduction to UNIX
0-13-095135-8
David I. Schwartz

Introduction to the Internet, 3/e
0-13-031355-6
Scott D. James

Introduction to Visual Basic 6.0
0-13-026813-5
David I. Schneider

Introduction to C
0-13-011854-0
Delores Etter

Introduction to C++
0-13-011855-9
Delores Etter

Introduction to FORTRAN 90
0-13-013146-6
Larry Nyhoff and Sanford Leestma

Introduction to Java
0-13-919416-9
Stephen J. Chapman

http://www.prenhall.com/esource

About the Authors

No project could ever come to pass without a group of authors who have the vision and the courage to turn a stack of blank paper into a book. The authors in this series, who worked diligently to produce their books, provide the building blocks of the series.

Martin D. Bradshaw was born in Pittsburg, KS in 1936, grew up in Kansas and the surrounding states of Arkansas and Missouri, graduating from Newton High School, Newton, KS in 1954. He received the B.S.E.E. and M.S.E.E. degrees from the University of Wichita in 1958 and 1961, respectively. A Ford Foundation fellowship at Carnegie Institute of Technology followed from 1961 to 1963 and he received the Ph.D. degree in electrical engineering in 1964. He spent his entire academic career with the Department of Electrical and Computer Engineering at the University of New Mexico (1961-1963 and 1991-1996). He served as the Assistant Dean for Special Programs with the UNM College of Engineering from 1974 to 1976 and as the Associate Chairman for the EECE Department from 1993 to 1996. During the period 1987-1991 he was a consultant with his own company, EE Problem Solvers. During 1978 he spent a sabbatical year with the State Electricity Commission of Victoria, Melbourne, Australia. From 1979 to 1981 he served an IPA assignment as a Project Officer at the U.S. Air Force Weapons Laboratory, Kirkland AFB, Albuquerque, NM. He has won numerous local, regional, and national teaching awards, including the George Westinghouse Award from the ASEE in 1973. He was awarded the IEEE Centennial Medal in 2000.

Acknowledgments: Dr. Bradshaw would like to acknowledge his late mother, who gave him a great love of reading and learning, and his father, who taught him to persist until the job is finished. The encouragement of his wife, Jo, and his six children is a never-ending inspiration.

Stephen J. Chapman received a B.S. degree in Electrical Engineering from Louisiana State University (1975), the M.S.E. degree in Electrical Engineering from the University of Central Florida (1979), and pursued further graduate studies at Rice University.

Mr. Chapman is currently Manager of Technical Systems for British Aerospace Australia, in Melbourne, Australia. In this position, he provides technical direction and design authority for the work of younger engineers within the company. He also continues to teach at local universities on a part-time basis.

Mr. Chapman is a Senior Member of the Institute of Electrical and Electronics Engineers (and several of its component societies). He is also a member of the Association for Computing Machinery and the Institution of Engineers (Australia).

Steven C. Chapra presently holds the Louis Berger Chair for Computing and Engineering in the Civil and Environmental Engineering Department at Tufts University. Dr. Chapra received engineering degrees from Manhattan College and the University of Michigan. Before joining the faculty at Tufts, he taught at Texas A&M University, the University of Colorado, and Imperial College, London. His research interests focus on surface water-quality modeling and advanced computer applications in environmental engineering. He has published over 50 refereed journal articles, 20 software packages and 6 books. He has received a number of awards including the 1987 ASEE Merriam/Wiley Distinguished Author Award, the 1993 Rudolph Hering Medal, and teaching awards from Texas A&M, the University of Colorado, and the Association of Environmental Engineering and Science Professors.

Acknowledgments: To the Berger Family for their many contributions to engineering education. I would also like to thank David Clough for his friendship and insights, John Walkenbach for his wonderful books, and my colleague Lee Minardi and my students Kenny William, Robert Viesca and Jennifer Edelmann for their suggestions.

Mark Dix began working with AutoCAD in 1985 as a programmer for CAD Support Associates, Inc. He helped design a system for creating estimates and bills of material directly from AutoCAD drawing databases for use in the automated conveyor industry. This system became the basis for systems still widely in use today. In 1986 he began collaborating with Paul Riley to create AutoCAD training materials, combining Riley's background in industrial design and training with Dix's background in writing, curriculum development, and programming. Mr. Dix received the M.S. degree in education from the University of Massachusetts. He is currently the Director of Dearborn Academy High School in Arlington, Massachusetts.

Delores M. Etter is a Professor of Electrical and Computer Engineering at the University of Colorado. Dr. Etter was a faculty member at the University of New Mexico and also a Visiting Professor at Stanford University. Dr. Etter was responsible for the Freshman Engineering Program at the University of New Mexico and is active in the Integrated Teaching Laboratory at the University of Colorado. She was elected a Fellow of the Institute of Electrical and Electronics Engineers for her contributions to education and for her technical leadership in digital signal processing.

Charles B. Fleddermann is a professor in the Department of Electrical and Computer Engineering at the University of New Mexico in Albuquerque, New Mexico. All of his degrees are in electrical engineering: his Bachelor's degree from the University of Notre Dame, and the Master's and Ph.D. from the University of Illinois at Urbana-Champaign. Prof. Fleddermann developed an engineering ethics course for his department in response to the ABET requirement to incorporate ethics topics into the undergraduate engineering curriculum. *Engineering Ethics* was written as a vehicle for presenting ethical

theory, analysis, and problem solving to engineering undergraduates in a concise and readily accessible way.

Acknowledgments: I would like to thank Profs. Charles Harris and Michael Rabins of Texas A & M University whose NSF sponsored workshops on engineering ethics got me started thinking in this field. Special thanks to my wife Liz, who proofread the manuscript for this book, provided many useful suggestions, and who helped me learn how to teach "soft" topics to engineers.

Kirk D. Hagen is a professor at Weber State University in Ogden, Utah. He has taught introductory-level engineering courses and upper-division thermal science courses at WSU since 1993. He received his B.S. degree in physics from Weber State College and his M.S. degree in mechanical engineering from Utah State University, after which he worked as a thermal designer/analyst in the aerospace and electronics industries. After several years of engineering practice, he resumed his formal education, earning his Ph.D. in mechanical engineering at the University of Utah. Hagen is the author of an undergraduate heat transfer text.

Mark N. Horenstein is a Professor in the Department of Electrical and Computer Engineering at Boston University. He has degrees in Electrical Engineering from M.I.T. and U.C. Berkeley and has been involved in teaching engineering design for the greater part of his academic career. He devised and developed the senior design project class taken by all electrical and computer engineering students at Boston University. In this class, the students work for a virtual engineering company developing products and systems for real-world engineering and social-service clients.

Acknowledgments: I would like to thank Prof. James Bethune, the architect of the Peak Performance event at Boston University, for his permission to highlight the competition in my text. Several of the ideas relating to brainstorming and teamwork were derived from a

http://www.prenhall.com/esource

workshop on engineering design offered by Prof. Charles Lovas of Southern Methodist University. The principles of estimation were derived in part from a freshman engineering problem posed by Prof. Thomas Kincaid of Boston University.

Steven Howell is the Chairman and a Professor of Mechanical Engineering at Lawrence Technological University. Prior to joining LTU in 2001, Dr. Howell led a knowledge-based engineering project for Visteon Automotive Systems and taught computer-aided design classes for Ford Motor Company engineers. Dr. Howell also has a total of 15 years experience as an engineering faculty member at Northern Arizona University, the University of the Pacific, and the University of Zimbabwe. While at Northern Arizona University, he helped develop and implement an award-winning interdisciplinary series of design courses simulating a corporate engineering-design environment.

Douglas W. Hull is a graduate student in the Department of Mechanical Engineering at Carnegie Mellon University in Pittsburgh, Pennsylvania. He is the author of *Mastering Mechanics I Using Matlab 5*, and contributed to *Mechanics of Materials* by Bedford and Liechti. His research in the Sensor Based Planning lab involves motion planning for hyper-redundant manipulators, also known as serpentine robots.

Scott D. James is a staff lecturer at Kettering University (formerly GMI Engineering & Management Institute) in Flint, Michigan. He is currently pursuing a Ph.D. in Systems Engineering with an emphasis on software engineering and computer-integrated manufacturing. He chose teaching as a profession after several years in the computer industry. "I thought that it was really important to know what it was like outside of academia. I wanted to provide students with classes that

were up to date and provide the information that is really used and needed."

Acknowledgments: Scott would like to acknowledge his family for the time to work on the text and his students and peers at Kettering who offered helpful critiques of the materials that eventually became the book.

Joe King received the B.S. and M.S. degrees from the University of California at Davis. He is a Professor of Computer Engineering at the University of the Pacific, Stockton, CA, where he teaches courses in digital design, computer design, artificial intelligence, and computer networking. Since joining the UOP faculty, Professor King has spent yearlong sabbaticals teaching in Zimbabwe, Singapore, and Finland. A licensed engineer in the state of California, King's industrial experience includes major design projects with Lawrence Livermore National Laboratory, as well as independent consulting projects. Prof. King has had a number of books published with titles including MATLAB, MathCAD, Exploring Engineering, and Engineering and Society.

David C. Kuncicky is a native Floridian. He earned his Baccalaureate in psychology, Master's in computer science, and Ph.D. in computer science from Florida State University. He has served as a faculty member in the Department of Electrical Engineering at the FAMU–FSU College of Engineering and the Department of Computer Science at Florida State University. He has taught computer science and computer engineering courses for over 15 years. He has published research in the areas of intelligent hybrid systems and neural networks. He is currently the Director of Engineering at Bioreason, Inc. in Sante Fe, New Mexico.

Acknowledgments: Thanks to Steffie and Helen for putting up with my late nights and long weekends at the computer. Finally, thanks to Susan Bassett for having faith in my abilities, and for providing continued tutelage and support.

Ron Larsen is a Professor of Chemical Engineering at Montana State University, and received his Ph.D. from the Pennsylvania State University. He was initially attracted to engineering by the challenges the profession offers, but also appreciates that engineering is a serving profession. Some of the greatest challenges he has faced while teaching have involved non-traditional teaching methods, including evening courses for practicing engineers and teaching through an interpreter at the Mongolian National University. These experiences have provided tremendous opportunities to learn new ways to communicate technical material. Dr. Larsen views modern software as one of the new tools that will radically alter the way engineers work, and his book *Introduction to Math-CAD* was written to help young engineers prepare to meet the challenges of an ever-changing workplace.

Acknowledgments: To my students at Montana State University who have endured the rough drafts and typos, and who still allow me to experiment with their classes—my sincere thanks.

Sanford Leestma is a Professor of Mathematics and Computer Science at Calvin College, and received his Ph.D. from New Mexico State University. He has been the long-time co-author of successful textbooks on Fortran, Pascal, and data structures in Pascal. His current research interest are in the areas of algorithms and numerical computation.

Jack Leifer is an Assistant Professor in the Department of Mechanical Engineering at the University of Kentucky Extended Campus Program in Paducah, and was previously with the Department of Mathematical Sciences and Engineering at the University of South Carolina–Aiken. He received his Ph.D. in Mechanical Engineering from the University of Texas at Austin in December 1995. His current research interests include the analysis of ultra-light and inflatable (Gossamer) space structures.

Acknowledgments: I'd like to thank my colleagues at USC–Aiken, especially Professors Mike May and Laurene Fausett, for their encouragement and feedback; and my parents, Felice and Morton Leifer, for being there and providing support (as always) as I completed this book.

Richard M. Lueptow is the Charles Deering McCormick Professor of Teaching Excellence and Associate Professor of Mechanical Engineering at Northwestern University. He is a native of Wisconsin and received his doctorate from the Massachusetts Institute of Technology in 1986. He teaches design, fluid mechanics, an spectral analysis techniques. Rich has an active research program on rotating filtration, Taylor Couette flow, granular flow, fire suppression, and acoustics. He has five patents and over 40 refereed journal and proceedings papers along with many other articles, abstracts, and presentations.

Acknowledgments: Thanks to my talented and hard-working co-authors as well as the many colleagues and students who took the tutorial for a "test drive." Special thanks to Mike Minbiole for his major contributions to Graphics Concepts with SolidWorks. Thanks also to Northwestern University for the time to work on a book. Most of all, thanks to my loving wife, Maiya, and my children, Hannah and Kyle, for supporting me in this endeavor. (Photo courtesy of Evanston Photographic Studios, Inc.)

Larry Nyhoff is a Professor of Mathematics and Computer Science at Calvin College. After doing bachelor's work at Calvin, and Master's work at Michigan, he received a Ph.D. from Michigan State and also did graduate work in computer science at Western Michigan. Dr. Nyhoff has taught at Calvin for the past 34 years—mathematics at first and computer science for the past several years.

Acknowledgments: We thank our families—Shar, Jeff, Dawn, Rebecca, Megan, Sara, Greg, Julie, Joshua, Derek, Tom, Joan; Marge, Michelle, Sandy, Lory, Michael—for being patient and understanding. We thank God for allowing us to write this text.

http://www.prenhall.com/esource

Paul Riley is an author, instructor, and designer specializing in graphics and design for multimedia. He is a founding partner of CAD Support Associates, a contract service and professional training organization for computer-aided design. His 15 years of business experience and 20 years of teaching experience are supported by degrees in education and computer science. Paul has taught AutoCAD at the University of Massachusetts at Lowell and is presently teaching AutoCAD at Mt. Ida College in Newton, Massachusetts. He has developed a program, Computer-aided Design for Professionals that is highly regarded by corporate clients and has been an ongoing success since 1982.

Robert Rizza is an Assistant Professor of Mechanical Engineering at North Dakota State University, where he teaches courses in mechanics and computer-aided design. A native of Chicago, he received the Ph.D. degree from the Illinois Institute of Technology. He is also the author of *Getting Started with Pro/ENGINEER*. Dr. Rizza has worked on a diverse range of engineering projects including projects from the railroad, bioengineering, and aerospace industries. His current research interests include the fracture of composite materials, repair of cracked aircraft components, and loosening of prostheses.

Peter Schiavone is a professor and student advisor in the Department of Mechanical Engineering at the University of Alberta, Canada. He received his Ph.D. from the University of Strathclyde, U.K. in 1988. He has authored several books in the area of student academic success as well as numerous papers in international scientific research journals. Dr. Schiavone has worked in private industry in several different areas of engineering including aerospace and systems engineering. He founded the first Mathematics Resource Center at the University of Alberta, a unit designed specifically

to teach new students the necessary survival skills in mathematics and the physical sciences required for success in first-year engineering. This led to the Students' Union Gold Key Award for outstanding contributions to the university. Dr. Schiavone lectures regularly to freshman engineering students and to new engineering professors on engineering success, in particular about maximizing students' academic performance.

Acknowledgements: Thanks to Richard Felder for being such an inspiration; to my wife Linda for sharing my dreams and believing in me; and to Francesca and Antonio for putting up with Dad when working on the text.

David I. Schneider holds an A.B. degree from Oberlin College and a Ph.D. degree in Mathematics from MIT. He has taught for 34 years, primarily at the University of Maryland. Dr. Schneider has authored 28 books, with one-half of them computer programming books. He has developed three customized software packages that are supplied as supplements to over 55 mathematics textbooks. His involvement with computers dates back to 1962, when he programmed a special purpose computer at MIT's Lincoln Laboratory to correct errors in a communications system.

David I. Schwartz is an Assistant Professor in the Computer Science Department at Cornell University and earned his B.S., M.S., and Ph.D. degrees in Civil Engineering from State University of New York at Buffalo. Throughout his graduate studies, Schwartz combined principles of computer science to applications of civil engineering. He became interested in helping students learn how to apply software tools for solving a variety of engineering problems. He teaches his students to learn incrementally and practice frequently to gain the maturity to tackle other subjects. In his spare time, Schwartz plays drums in a variety of bands.

Acknowledgments: I dedicate my books to my family, friends, and students who all helped in so many ways.

Many thanks go to the schools of Civil Engineering and Engineering & Applied Science at State University of New York at Buffalo where I originally developed and tested my UNIX and Maple books. I greatly appreciate the opportunity to explore my goals and all the help from everyone at the Computer Science Department at Cornell.

John T. Sears received the Ph.D. degree from Princeton University. Currently, he is a Professor and the head of the Department of Chemical Engineering at Montana State University. After leaving Princeton he worked in research at Brookhaven National Laboratory and Esso Research and Engineering, until he took a position at West Virginia University. He came to MSU in 1982, where he has served as the Director of the College of Engineering Minority Program and Interim Director for BioFilm Engineering. Prof. Sears has written a book on air pollution and economic development, and over 45 articles in engineering and engineering education.

Michael T. Snyder is President of Internet startup Appointments123.com. He is a native of Chicago, and he received his Bachelor of Science degree in Mechanical Engineering from the University of Notre Dame. Mike also graduated with honors from Northwestern University's Kellogg Graduate School of Management in 1999 with his Masters of Management degree. Before Appointments123.com, Mike was a mechanical engineer in new product development for Motorola Cellular and Acco Office Products. He has received four patents for his mechanical design work. "Pro/ENGINEER was an invaluable design tool for me,

and I am glad to help students learn the basics of Pro/ENGINEER."

Acknowledgments: Thanks to Rich Lueptow and Jim Steger for inviting me to be a part of this great project. Of course, thanks to my wife Gretchen for her support in my various projects.

Jim Steger is currently Chief Technical Officer and cofounder of an Internet applications company. He graduated with a Bachelor of Science degree in Mechanical Engineering from Northwestern University. His prior work included mechanical engineering assignments at Motorola and Acco Brands. At Motorola, Jim worked on part design for two-way radios and was one of the lead mechanical engineers on a cellular phone product line. At Acco Brands, Jim was the sole engineer on numerous office product designs. His Worx stapler has won design awards in the United States and in Europe. Jim has been a Pro/ENGINEER user for over six years.

Acknowledgments: Many thanks to my co-authors, especially Rich Lueptow for his leadership on this project. I would also like to thank my family for their continuous support.

Royce Wilkinson received his undergraduate degree in chemistry from Rose-Hulman Institute of Technology in 1991 and the Ph.D. degree in chemistry from Montana State University in 1998 with research in natural product isolation from fungi. He currently resides in Bozeman, MT and is involved in HIV drug research. His research interests center on biological molecules and their interactions in the search for pharmaceutical advances.

http://www.prenhall.com/esource

Reviewers

We would like to thank everyone who has reviewed texts in this series.

ESource Reviewers

Christopher Rowe, *Vanderbilt University*
Steve Yurgartis, *Clarkson University*
Heidi A. Diefes-Dux, *Purdue University*
Howard Silver, *Fairleigh Dickenson University*
Jean C. Malzahn Kampe, *Virginia Polytechnic Institute and State University*
Malcolm Heimer, *Florida International University*
Stanley Reeves, *Auburn University*
John Demel, *Ohio State University*
Shahnam Navee, *Georgia Southern University*
Heshem Shaalem, *Georgia Southern University*
Terry L. Kohutek, *Texas A & M University*
Liz Rozell, *Bakersfield College*
Mary C. Lynch, *University of Florida*
Ted Pawlicki, *University of Rochester*
James N. Jensen, *SUNY at Buffalo*
Tom Horton, *University of Virginia*
Eileen Young, *Bristol Community College*
James D. Nelson, *Louisiana Tech University*
Jerry Dunn, *Texas Tech University*
Howard M. Fulmer, *Villanova UniversityBerkeley*
Naeem Abdurrahman *University of Texas, Austin*
Stephen Allan *Utah State University*
Anil Bajaj *Purdue University*
Grant Baker *University of Alaska–Anchorage*
William Beckwith *Clemson University*
Haym Benaroya *Rutgers University*
John Biddle *California State Polytechnic University*
Tom Bledsaw *ITT Technical Institute*
Fred Boadu *Duke University*
Tom Bryson *University of Missouri, Rolla*
Ramzi Bualuan *University of Notre Dame*
Dan Budny *Purdue University*
Betty Burr *University of Houston*
Dale Calkins *University of Washington*
Harish Cherukuri *University of North Carolina –Charlotte*
Arthur Clausing *University of Illinois*

Barry Crittendon *Virginia Polytechnic and State University*
James Devine *University of South Florida*
Ron Eaglin *University of Central Florida*
Dale Elifrits *University of Missouri, Rolla*
Patrick Fitzhorn *Colorado State University*
Susan Freeman *Northeastern University*
Frank Gerlitz *Washtenaw College*
Frank Gerlitz *Washtenaw Community College*
John Glover *University of Houston*
John Graham *University of North Carolina–Charlotte*
Ashish Gupta *SUNY at Buffalo*
Otto Gygax *Oregon State University*
Malcom Heimer *Florida International University*
Donald Herling *Oregon State University*
Thomas Hill *SUNY at Buffalo*
A.S. Hodel *Auburn University*
James N. Jensen *SUNY at Buffalo*
Vern Johnson *University of Arizona*
Autar Kaw *University of South Florida*
Kathleen Kitto *Western Washington University*
Kenneth Klika *University of Akron*
Terry L. Kohutek *Texas A&M University*
Melvin J. Maron *University of Louisville*
Robert Montgomery *Purdue University*
Mark Nagurka *Marquette University*
Romarathnam Narasimhan *University of Miami*
Soronadi Nnaji *Florida A&M University*
Sheila O'Connor *Wichita State University*
Michael Peshkin *Northwestern University*
Dr. John Ray *University of Memphis*
Larry Richards *University of Virginia*
Marc H. Richman *Brown University*
Randy Shih *Oregon Institute of Technology*
Avi Singhal *Arizona State University*
Tim Sykes *Houston Community College*
Neil R. Thompson *University of Waterloo*
Dr. Raman Menon Unnikrishnan *Rochester Institute of Technology*
Michael S. Wells *Tennessee Tech University*
Joseph Wujek *University of California, Berkeley*
Edward Young *University of South Carolina*
Garry Young *Oklahoma State University*
Mandochehr Zoghi *University of Dayton*

Contents

1

What Is Engineering?

If you're reading this book, you're probably enrolled in an introductory course in *engineering*. You may have chosen engineering because of your strong skills in science and mathematics. Perhaps you like to take things apart or use computers. Maybe you simply followed the advice of your high school guidance counselor. Whatever your reason for studying engineering, you are entering a career full of discovery, creativity, and excitement. Imagine yourself several years from now, after you've finished your college studies. What will your life be like as an engineer? How will the classes you've taken in school relate to your work and career? This book will help provide you with a vision of the future while teaching you the important principles of engineering design.

As an aspiring engineer, you have much to learn. You must master the foundations of all engineering disciplines: basic math, physics, and chemistry. You must study the specialized subjects of your chosen discipline, for example, circuits, mechanics, materials, or computer programming. You also must learn how to stay on top of technological advances by embracing a program of lifelong learning. The world embraces new technological advances almost on a daily basis, and the wise engineer keeps abreast of them all. Your

OBJECTIVES

In this chapter, you will learn about

- Engineering as a career.
- The relationship between the engineer and other professionals.
- Engineering professional organizations.
- The foundations of engineering design: knowledge, experience, and intuition.

college courses will provide you with the knowledge and mathematical skills that you will need to function in the engineering world. However, you also must learn about the primary mission of the engineer: the practice of design. The ability to build real things is what sets an engineer apart from professionals in the basic sciences. While physicists, chemists, and biologists draw general conclusions by observing specific phenomena, an engineer moves from the general to the specific. Engineers harness the laws of nature and use them to produce devices or systems that perform tasks and solve problems. This process defines the essence of design. You must become proficient at it if you want to become an engineer. This book will teach you the principles of design and help you to apply them to your class assignments, design projects, and future job activities.

ENGINEERING HAS MANY FIELDS

A perusal of the Web sites of engineering colleges around the world will reveal a wide variety of engineering programs. Although the names may vary slightly, most engineers are trained in one of the following traditional engineering degree programs (listed alphabetically): aeronautical, agricultural, biomedical, chemical, civil, computer, electrical, industrial, mechanical, naval, petroleum, and systems. From reading this list, one might get the impression that engineers are highly specialized professionals who have little interaction with people from other fields. In reality, the opposite is true. The best engineers are multidisciplinary individuals who are familiar with many different fields and specialties. The mechanical engineer knows something about electrical circuits, and the electrical engineer understands basic mechanics. The computer engineer is familiar with the algorithms used in industrial processes, and the industrial engineer knows how to program computers. Many of the great engineering accomplishments of the past century, including our global communication network; the Internet; life-extending biomedical technology; inexpensive, reliable air transportation; our ground transportation infrastructure; and the sequencing of the human genome were made possible by interactive teams of engineers from many disciplines.

Although engineers have multidisciplinary skills, most are trained in a specific degree program and spend much time using their specialized training. For this reason, we precede our study of design by reviewing the characteristic features of the various types of engineers and their fields of expertise.

Aeronautical Engineer

Aeronautical (or aerospace) engineers use their knowledge of aerodynamics, fluid mechanics, structures, control systems, heat transfer, and hydraulics to design and build everything from rockets, airplanes, and space vehicles to high-speed bullet trains and helium-filled dirigibles. Since the days of the Wright brothers, aeronautical engineers, working in teams with scientists and other types of engineers, have made possible human flight and space exploration. Aeronautical engineers find employment in many industries, but typically work for big companies on large-scale projects. Some of the more noticeable accomplishments of the aerospace industry have included the Apollo moon landings, the NASA Space Shuttle, deep space exploration, space stations, and the jumbo jet. The International Space Station, shown in Figure 1, for example, will be completed by teams of aeronautical and other engineers.

Figure 1 Artist's view of NASA's International Space Station. This station is being built by teams of aerospace and aeronautical engineers working together with other types of engineers and scientists. (*Photo courtesy of NASA.*)

Agricultural Engineer

Agricultural engineers apply the principles of hydrology, soil mechanics, fluid mechanics, heat transfer, combustion, optimization theory, statistics, climatology, chemistry, and biology to the production of food on a large scale. This discipline is popular at colleges and universities located in heavily agricultural areas. Feeding the world's ever-growing population is one of the most formidable challenges of the 21st century. Agricultural engineers will play an important role in this endeavor by applying technology and engineering know-how to improve crop yields, increase food output, and develop cost-effective and environmentally sound farming methods. Agricultural engineers work with ecologists and biologists, chemists, and natural scientists to understand the impact of human agriculture on the earth's ecosystem.

Biomedical Engineer

The biomedical engineer (or bioengineer) works closely with physicians and biologists to apply modern engineering methods to medicine and human health and to obtain a better understanding of the human body. Engineering skills are combined with knowledge of biology, physiology, and chemistry to produce medical instrumentation, prosthetics, assistive appliances, implants, and neuromuscular diagnostics. Biomedical engineers have participated in designing many devices that have helped improve medical care over the past several decades. Many biomedical engineers enter medical school upon graduation, but others go on to graduate school or seek employment in any of a number of health- or medical-related industries. The rapidly emerging world of biotechnology, which bridges the gap between engineering and molecular genetics, is also the province of the biomedical engineer (Figure 2). This discipline examines the fundamental functions of cells and organisms from an engineering point of view. The science of cloning, for example, has been made possible in part by the world of molecular engineers. Many of the secrets of future medicine lie at the genetic level, and the biomedical engineer will help lead the way to new medical discoveries. The biomedical engineer also is involved in the area of microfluidics, in which tiny bio-processing systems are built on small chips of silicon or other materials. This technology, part of the field of micro-electromechanical systems, or MEMS, is sometimes referred to as "lab on a chip." Another exciting area of biomedical engineering is the field of *bioinformatics* which combines computer science with the study of genomics, including the human genome.

Chemical Engineer

The chemical engineer applies the principles of chemistry to the design of manufacturing and production systems. Whenever a chemical reaction or process must be brought from the laboratory to manufacturing on a large scale, a chemical engineer is needed to design the reaction vessels, transport mechanisms, mixing chambers, and measuring devices that allow the process to proceed on a large scale in a cost-effective way. Chemical engineers are employed in many industries, including petroleum, petrochemicals, plastics, cosmetics, electronics, food, and pharmaceuticals. Their skills are needed wherever a manufacturing process involves organic or inorganic chemical reactions on a production scale. Typically, chemical engineers are employed by large companies that produce products for worldwide distribution.

Civil Engineer

The civil engineer is concerned with the design and construction of our nation's infrastructure. Civil engineers design transportation systems, roads, bridges, buildings, airports, and other large structures, such as water treatment plants, aquifers, and waste management facilities. One classic example of civil engineering on a grand scale is the Hoover Dam shown in Figure 3. Designing such a large structure requires knowledge of fluid and soil mechanics, strength of materials, concrete engineering, and construction practices. Civil engineers also may be involved in designing smaller structures such as houses, landscapes, and recreational parks. Over the next few decades, civil engineers will play a vital role in revitalizing aging infrastructures worldwide and in dealing with environmental issues, such as water resources, air quality, global warming, and refuse disposal. More than any other professional, the civil engineer has the unique handicap of having to rely heavily on physical scale models, calculations, computer modeling, and past experience to determine the performance of designed structures. This limitation exists because it is seldom possible to build a trial test structure on the scale of most civil engineering products. There are no full-scale prototypes in civil engineering. A civil engineer must be sure that a design will meet its specifications well before its final construction.

The civil engineer works closely with construction personnel and may spend much time at job sites reviewing the progress of construction tasks. Civil engineers often are employed in the public sector, but also may find work in large or small construction companies and private development firms. One renowned example of a large, public-sector civil engineering effort is the famed "Big Dig" in Boston, Massachusetts (Figure 4). This multibillion-dollar, 10-year effort, the most expensive and extensive single transportation infrastructure project in U.S. history, is formally known as Central Artery/Tunnel Project.

Figure 2 Genetics is one of the new frontiers of biomedical engineering. *(Graphic courtesy of the Center for Advanced Biotechnology, Boston University.)*

Figure 3 The Hoover Dam at the Nevada–Arizona border was designed by civil engineers.

Figure 4 Boston's Central Artery/Tunnel Project: The "Big Dig." Civil engineers will be responsible for revitalizing the nation's infrastructure in the 21st century. *(Photo courtesy of the Central Artery/Tunnel Project.)*

Computer Engineer

Computer engineering encompasses the broad categories of hardware, software, and digital communication (Figure 5). A computer engineer applies the basic principles of engineering and computer science to the design of computers, networks, software systems, and peripheral devices. The computer engineer also is responsible for designing and building the interconnections between computers and their components, including distributed computers, local area networks (LANs), wireless networks, and Internet servers. For example, a computer engineer might combine microprocessors, memory chips, disk drives, DVD drives, display devices, LAN cards, and drivers to produce computer systems. Graphical user interfaces, embedded computer systems, fault-tolerant computers, software systems, wireless interfaces, operating systems, and assembly language programming are also the responsibility of the computer engineer. Computer scientists, who traditionally are more mathematically oriented than are computer engineers, also become involved in writing computer software, including Web interfaces, database management systems, and client applications. Unlike the computer scientist, however, the computer engineer is fluent in both the hardware and software aspects of modern computer systems. Examples of which both hardware and software share equally important roles include CPU design, desktop and laptop PC design, cell-phone networks, global positioning systems, microcomputer- or Internet-controlled appliances, automated manufacturing, and medical instrumentation. Some of the more notable accomplishments of the computer industry include the invention of the microprocessor (Intel, 1982), the explosion of personal computing that began with the first desktop PC (IBM, 1984), and the advances in data communication networks that began with the U.S. Department of Defense Arpanet and grew into the Internet and the World Wide Web.

Electrical Engineer

Electrical engineering is a far-reaching discipline whose subjects are linked by a single common thread: the use and control of electricity. Because information can be expressed in electronic form, computers also fall into this broad category. Whether on a large or small scale, electrical engineers are responsible for many technology areas including microelectronics, data communication, radio, television, lasers (Figure 6), fiber optics, video, audio, computer networks, speech processing, imaging systems, electric power systems, and alternative energy sources, such as solar and wind power. The electrical engineer also designs transportation systems based on electric power, including mass transit, electric cars, and hybrid vehicles.

The typical electrical engineer has a strong background in the physical sciences, mathematics, and computational methods, as well as knowledge of circuits and electronics, semiconductor devices, analog and digital signal processing, digital systems, electromagnetics, and control systems. The electrical engineer also is fluent in many areas of computer engineering. Some of the more recent accomplishments that have involved electrical engineers include the microelectronic revolution (e.g., microprocessors and large-scale integration on a chip); wireless communications (e.g., cellular telephones, pagers, and data links); photonics (e.g., lightwave technology, lasers, and fiber-optic communication); and micro-electromechanical systems (e.g., laboratory on a chip).

Industrial Engineer

The industrial engineer (sometimes called a manufacturing engineer) is concerned with the total life cycle of a product, from the moment of its inception to its eventual disposal and recycling of its raw materials. Industrial engineers have the unique challenge of incorporating the latest technological advances in computing and machinery into production and manufacturing facilities. The industrial engineer is intimate with all aspects of the corporate environment, because much of what motivates the field of industrial engineering is the need to maximize output while minimizing cost. Skills required for this discipline include knowledge of product development, materials processing, optimization, queuing theory, production techniques, machining, fabrication methods, and engineering economy. Industrial engineers also become fluent in the techniques of computer-aided design (CAD) and computer-aided manufacturing (CAM). Global manufacturing, in which products are developed for a worldwide economy, is becoming increasingly important to the field of industrial engineering.

One of the more recent areas to emerge as the province of the industrial engineer is the use of robotics in manufacturing. Building, moving, and controlling robots requires knowledge of aspects of mechanical, electrical, and computer engineering. Most programs in industrial engineering include courses in these other areas. Another emerging area of industrial engineering is the field of "green manufacturing" in which an understanding of the environmental impact of a product over its life cycle is considered as part of the design process.

Figure 5 Computer engineers design the hardware and software for today's computer systems. (*Image courtesy of C. Moreira and L. Katz.*)

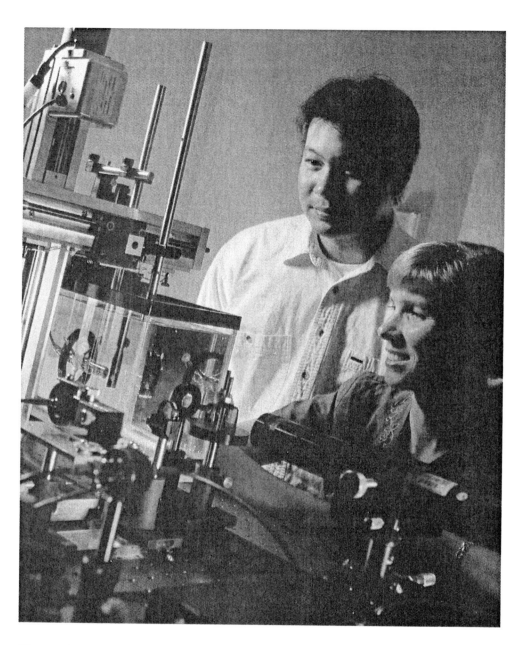

Figure 6 The laser, first invented around 1960, has become an indispensable tool for the electrical engineer. (*Photo courtesy of Boston University Photo Services.*)

Mechanical Engineer

The mechanical engineer is responsible for designing and building physical structures of all sorts. Devices that involve mechanical motion, such as automobiles, bicycles, engines, disk drives, keyboards, fluid valves, jet engine turbines, power plants, and flight structures, are all designed by mechanical engineers. Mechanical engineers are fluent in the topics of statics, dynamics, strength of materials, structural and solid mechanics, fluid mechanics, thermodynamics, heat transfer, and energy conversion. They apply these principles to a wide variety of engineering problems, including acoustics, precision machining, environmental engineering, water resources, combustion, power sources, robotics, transportation, and manufacturing systems. Compared with all engineering disciplines, the mechanical engineer interfaces most easily with other types of engineers because mechanical engineering requires such a broad educational background.

One of the newest areas of study involving mechanical engineers is the emerging field of micro-electromechanical systems, or MEMS, in which tiny microscopic machines are fabricated on wafers of silicon and other materials. Figure 7, for example, shows a tiny micromotor built on a silicon chip. MEMS has the potential to do for mechanics what the integrated circuit did for electronics, namely permit large-scale integration on single silicon chips of entire systems made from basic devices. Mechanical engineers work closely with electrical engineers in this exciting new discipline.

Mechatronics Engineer

The mechatronics engineer is fluent in mechanical engineering, electrical engineering, and robotics. As its name implies, the field of mechatronics involves the fusion of mechanical engineering, electronics, and computing toward the design of products and manufacturing systems. Engineers who work in this emerging field require cross-disciplinary training that can best be approached by majoring in either mechanical or electrical engineering and acquiring skills in the other needed disciplines through extra courses or technical electives. Mechatronics engineers are responsible for the innovation, design, and development of machines and systems that can automate production tasks, reduce production costs, reduce plant maintenance costs, improve product flexibility, and increase production performance. The typical mechatronics engineer solves design problems for which solely mechanical or electrical solutions are not possible. Sensing and actuation are important elements of mechatronics.

Naval Engineer

The naval engineer (or naval architect) designs ships, submarines, barges, and other sea-going vessels and also is involved in the design of oil platforms, shipping docks, seaports, and coastal navigation facilities. Naval engineers are fluent in many of the subjects studied by mechanical engineers, including fluid mechanics, materials, structures, statics, dynamics, water propulsion, and heat transfer. In addition, naval engineers learn about the design of ships and the history of sea travel. Many naval engineers are employed by the armed forces, but some work for companies that design and build large ships.

Petroleum Engineer

Over 70 percent of the world's current energy needs are satisfied by petroleum products, and this situation is unlikely to change for at least the next half century. The principle challenge of the petroleum engineer is to help produce oil, gas, and other energy forms from the earth's natural resources. In order to harvest these resources in an economical and environmentally safe way, the petroleum engineer must have a wide base of knowledge that includes mathematics, physics, geology, and chemistry, as well as aspects of most other engineering disciplines. Elements of mechanical, chemical, electrical, civil, and industrial engineering are found in most programs of study in petroleum engineering. Also, because computers are used with ever-increasing frequency in geological exploration, oil field production, and drilling operations, computer engineering has become an important specialty within petroleum engineering. Did you know that many of the world's supercomputers are owned by petroleum companies?

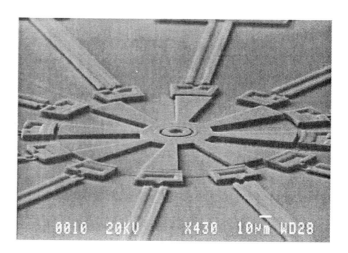

Figure 7 Tiny MEMS silicon micromotor measuring 100 micrometers in diameter. (*Photo courtesy of Cronos, Inc.*)

In addition to conventional oil and gas recovery, petroleum engineers apply new technology to the enhanced recovery of hydrocarbons from oil shale, tar sands, offshore oil deposits, and fields of natural gas. They also design new techniques for recovering residual ground oil that has been left by traditional pumping methods. Examples include the use of underground combustion, steam injection, and chemical water treatment to release oil trapped in the pores of rock. These techniques will likely be used in the future for other geological operations, including uranium leaching, geothermal energy production, and coal gasification. Petroleum engineers also work in the related areas of pollution reduction, underground waste disposal, and hydrology. Lastly, because many petroleum companies operate on a worldwide scale, the petroleum engineer has the opportunity to work in many foreign countries.

Systems Engineer

In the computer industry, the designation "systems engineer" has come to mean someone who deals exclusively with large-scale software systems. The traditional systems engineer, however, can be anyone who designs and implements complex engineering systems. Communications systems, transportation networks, manufacturing systems, power distribution networks, and avionics are but some of the areas in which systems engineers play a central role. Programs of study in this diverse field include courses in applied mathematics, computer simulation, software, electronics, communications, and automatic control. Because of their broad educational background, systems engineers are at home working with most other types of engineers.

PROFESSIONAL ENGINEERING ORGANIZATIONS

Most branches of engineering are represented by professional societies that bind together members with similar backgrounds, training, and professional expertise. These societies operate on a worldwide scale and publish one or more journals for which engineers write papers and articles of interest to members of the field. Each organization offers its members technical and informational services, including training, industry standards, workshops, and conferences. In some cases, other professional services are offered as well, including job networks, advertising, e-mail accounts, product information, Web page hosting, and even life and health insurance. All provide student membership at a discount, and student chapters at colleges and universities are common.

This section provides information about some of the principal professional organizations and the technical publications they produce. Each society has an official Web site from which you can obtain additional information. The text provided here has been taken from each organization's Web site.

Aeronautical and Aerospace Engineering

From the American Institute of Aeronautics and Astronautics (*www.aiaa.org*):

> "For more than 65 years, the American Institute of Aeronautics and Astronautics (AIAA) and its predecessors, has been the principal society of the aerospace engineer and scientist. Officially formed in 1963 through a merger of the American Rocket Society (ARS) and the Institute of Aerospace Sciences (IAS), the purpose was, and still is, 'to advance the arts, sciences, and technology of aeronautics and astronautics, and to promote the professionalism of those engaged in these pursuits.' Both ARS and IAS brought to the relationship a long and eventful history—stretching back to 1930 and 1932, respectively—and each left its mark on the Institute. The merger combined the imaginative, opportunistic, and risk-taking desire of those rocket, missile, and space professionals with the more established, well-recognized achievers from the aviation community."

> "Today, with more than 31,000 members, AIAA is the world's largest professional society devoted to the progress of engineering and science in aviation, space, and defense. The Institute continues to be the principal voice, information resource, and publisher for aerospace engineers, scientists, managers, policymakers, students, and educators. Also, many prominent corporations and governments worldwide rely on AIAA as a stimulator of professional accomplishment in all areas related to aerospace. Consider this: Since 1963, AIAA members have achieved virtually every milestone in modern American flight."

Key Publications: *Aerospace America, AIAA Bulletin, Aerospace Database, Student Journal*

Biomedical Engineering

From the Biomedical Engineering Society (*http://mecca.org/BME/BMES/society/index. htm*):

> "The Biomedical Engineering Society (BMES) is an interdisciplinary society established on February 1, 1968 in response to a manifest need to provide a society that gave equal status to representatives of both biomedical and engineering interests. As stated in the Articles of Incorporation, the purpose of the Society is: 'To promote the increase of biomedical engineering knowledge and its utilization.' Today, the society represents over 1,000 professionals and over 1,000 student members (undergraduate and graduate). There are 34 BMES student chapters and about two-thirds of the ABET-accredited bioengineering/ biomedical engineering undergraduate programs have BMES student chapters."

Key Publications: *Annals of Biomedical Engineering, BMES Bulletin*

Chemical Engineering

From the American Institute of Chemical Engineers (*www.aiche.org*)

"Founded in 1908, the American Institute of Chemical Engineers (AIChE) is a nonprofit organization providing leadership to the chemical engineering profession. Representing 57,000 members in industry, academia, and government, AIChE provides forums to advance the theory and practice of the profession, upholds high professional standards and ethics, and supports excellence in education. Institute members range from undergraduate students, to entry-level engineers to chief executive officers of major corporations. As AIChE approaches the 21st Century, technological, political, social, and economic changes in our society require that we evaluate and refine our strategic plan. This will assure relevance to our members, the profession, and society at large."

"Rapid changes in skill needs and career paths of chemical engineers create new opportunities for AIChE to assist its members. Institutional stakeholders are increasingly faced with the need for effective collaborations. At the same time, the explosive change in information and communication technology introduces challenges to deliver products and services more efficiently."

"In response, our leadership has revised our vision and mission and has developed objectives and strategies that address these changes and that consider the organizational and financial resources and the business processes needed to assure AIChE's relevance in the 21st Century."

Key Publications: *AIChE Journal, Chemical Engineering Progress, Environmental Progress and Process Safety Progress, Biotechnology Progress*

Civil Engineering

From the American Society of Civil Engineers (*www.asce.org*):

"Founded in 1852, the American Society of Civil Engineers (ASCE) represents more than 123,000 members of the civil engineering profession worldwide and is America's oldest national engineering society. ASCE's vision is to position engineers as global leaders building a better quality of life."

"ASCE's mission is to provide essential value to our members, their careers, our partners and the public by developing leadership, advancing technology, advocating lifelong learning and promoting the profession. From the building of the Parthenon in 432 B.C. to the building of the Petronas Towers today, the civil engineering profession has proven its sustainability. Withstanding the passage of time, civil engineers have built cultural landmarks that stand in tribute to the profession's creative spirit and ingenuity."

"Civil engineers are trained to plan, build and improve the water, sewer and transportation systems that you depend on every day. They build dams able to withstand the crushing pressure of a lake full of water. They build bridges able to resist the forces of wind and traffic. They develop environmentally friendly materials and methods, and they build things to last. So skilled is their work that we rarely stop to wonder how they design the mammoth skyscrapers we work in, the tunnels we drive in, and the stadium domes we sit beneath."

Key Publications: *ASCE News, Civil Engineering Magazine*, plus numerous journals on specialized topics in civil engineering

Computer Engineering

From the Association for Computing Machinery (*www.acm.org*):

> "Founded in 1947 Association for Computing Machinery (ACM) is the world's first educational and scientific computing society. Today, our members — over 80,000 computing professionals and students worldwide — and the public turn to ACM for authoritative publications, pioneering conferences, and visionary leadership for the new millennium."

> "ACM publishes, distributes, and archives original research and first-hand perspectives from the world's leading thinkers in computing and information technologies. ACM offers over two dozen publications that help computing professionals negotiate the strategic challenges and operating problems of the day. The ACM Press Books program covers a broad spectrum of interests in computer science and engineering."

> "*Communications of the ACM* keeps information technology professionals up to date with articles spanning the full spectrum of information technologies in all fields of interest including object-oriented technology, multimedia, the Internet, and networking. *Communications* also carries case studies, practitioner-oriented articles, and regular columns, the ACM Forum, and technical correspondence."

Key Publications: *The ACM Digital Library* (a collection online publications); *Communications of the ACM*; *Crossroads* (a student magazine); and various ACM Transactions journals, including: *Computer-Human Interaction, Computer Systems, Database Systems, Design Automation for Electronic System, Graphics, Information System, Mathematical Software, Modeling and Computer Simulation, Networking, Programming Languages and Systems*, and *Software Engineering and Methodology*

Electrical Engineering

From The Institute of Electrical and Electronics Engineers (*www.ieee.org*):

> "The Institute of Electrical and Electronics Engineers (IEEE) helps advance global prosperity by promoting the engineering process of creating, developing, integrating, sharing, and applying knowledge about electrical and information technologies and sciences for the benefit of humanity and the profession. IEEE provides the latest information and the best technical resources to members worldwide. Today, IEEE connects more than 350,000 professionals and students to the solutions to tomorrow's technology needs."

> "The IEEE is one of the world's largest technical professional societies. Founded in 1884 by a handful of practitioners of the new electrical engineering discipline, today's Institute is comprised of more than 350,000 members who conduct and participate in its activities in approximately 150 countries. The men and women of the IEEE are the technical and scientific professionals making the revolutionary engineering advances which are reshaping our world today."

> "The technical objectives of the IEEE focus on advancing the theory and practice of electrical, electronics, and computer engineering and computer science. To realize these objectives, the IEEE sponsors technical confer-

ences, symposia, and local meetings worldwide. It publishes nearly 25% of the world's technical papers in electrical, electronics, and computer engineering, and provides educational programs to keep its members' knowledge and expertise state-of-the-art."

Key Publications: *IEEE Spectrum; Proceedings of the IEEE;* plus over 40 specialized IEEE Transactions from its various societies, including (in alphabetical order): *Aerospace and Electronic Systems; Advanced Packaging; Antennas and Propagation; Applied Superconductivity; Automatic Control; Biomedical Engineering; Circuits and Devices; Communications; Computing in Science and Engineering Magazine (CiSE) Control Systems; Dielectrics and Electrical Insulation; Electromagnetic Compatibility; Electron Devices; Energy Conversion; Engineering Management; Geoscience and Remote Sensing; Image Processing; Industry Applications; Instrumentation and Measurement; Intelligent Systems; Lasers and Electro-Optics; Magnetics; Mechatronics; Medical Imaging; Microelectromechanical Systems; Microwave Theory and Techniques; Neural Networks; Parallel and Distributed Systems; Personal Communications; Photonics; Plasma Science; Power Electronics; Power Systems; Quantum Electronics; Reliability; Robotics and Automation; Semiconductor Manufacturing; Signal Processing; Software Engineering; Solid-State Circuits; Systems, Man, and Cybernetics; Ultrasonics, Ferroelectrics, and Frequency Control; Vehicular Technology; Very Large Scale Integration Systems;* and *Visualization and Computer Graphics*

Industrial and Manufacturing Engineering

From the Institute of Industrial Engineers (*www.iienet.org*):

"Founded in 1948, the Institute of Industrial Engineers is the society dedicated to serving the professional needs of industrial engineers and all individuals involved with improving quality and productivity. Its 24,000 members throughout North America and more than 80 countries stay on the cutting edge of their profession through IIE's life-long-learning approach, as reflected in the organization's educational opportunities, publications, and networking opportunities. Members also gain valuable leadership experience and enjoy peer recognition through numerous volunteer opportunities."

Key Publications: *IIE Solutions, Industrial Management, IIE Transactions, The Engineering Economist, Student IE, Journal of the Society for Health Systems*

Mechanical Engineering

From the American Society of Mechanical Engineers (*www.asme.org*):

"The 125,000-member ASME International is a worldwide engineering society. It conducts one of the world's largest technical publishing operations, holds some 30 technical conferences and 200 professional development courses each year, and sets many industrial and manufacturing standards. Founded in 1880 as the American Society of Mechanical Engineers, today ASME International is a nonprofit educational and technical organization serving a worldwide membership."

"The work of the Society is performed by its member-elected Board of Governors and through its five Councils, 44 Boards, and hundreds of Committees in 13 regions throughout the world. There are a combined 400 sections and student sections serving ASME's worldwide membership."

"Its vision is to be the premier organization for promoting the art, science and practice of mechanical engineering throughout the world. Its mission is to promote and enhance the technical competency and professional well-being of our members, and through quality programs and activities in mechanical engineering, better enable its practitioners to contribute to the well-being of humankind."

Key Publications: Mechanical Engineering; ASME News; Applied Mechanics Reviews; plus journals in numerous specialty areas; including Applied Mechanics; Heat Transfer; Biomechanical Engineering; Computing and Information Science; Dynamic Systems; Measurement and Control; Electronic Packaging Energy Turbines and Power Engineering Materials Technology Fluids; Manufacturing Science; Mechanical Design; Offshore Mechanics; Arctic Engineering; Pressure Vessel Technology; Solar Energy; Tribology; Turbomachinery; Vibration and Acoustics; and Mechatronics

PROFESSIONAL SUCCESS: CHOOSING A FIELD OF ENGINEERING

If you are a first-year student of engineering, you may already have decided upon a major field. After taking several required courses, however, you may not be sure if you've chosen the right type of engineering. Conversely, you may have entered school without committing yourself to any one field of engineering. If you find yourself in either of these situations, you're probably wondering how one goes about choosing a career direction in engineering.

One way to find out more about the different branches of engineering is to attend technical talks and seminars hosted by the engineering departments in your college or university. Such talks are usually aimed at graduate students and faculty, so much of the material will be over your head. Simply *exposing* yourself to these technical talks, however, will give you a feeling for the various branches of engineering and help you find one that most closely matches your skills and interests.

Most schools host workshops in career advising. Be sure to attend one. Talk with the experts in career planning and job placement. Many college campuses host student chapters of professional organizations. These groups often organize tours of engineering companies. Attending such a tour can provide valuable perspective about the activities of a particular branch of engineering and provide you with an idea about what life as an engineer will be like.

One of the most valuable resources for career advice is your own college faculty. Get advice from your advisor about which major is right for you. Also, professors love to talk about their work. Invite a professor to your dormitory or living unit to speak to students about choosing an engineering career. Speak to your department about hosting a career night in which a panel of professors answers questions about jobs in engineering. Learn to make use of all available resources for help in choosing your college major.

THE ENGINEER: CENTRAL TO PROJECT MANAGEMENT

When we think of the word "design," we may imagine a lone engineer sitting in a cubicle at a computer terminal, or perhaps in a workshop, crafting some marvelous piece of technical wizardry. As a student, you may be eager to pursue this notion of the rugged individual—the sole entrepreneur who single-handedly changes the face of technology. You might ask, "Why do I have to take all of these *other* courses? Why can't I just take courses that are of interest to me or important to my career goals?" The answer to these questions lies in the multidisciplinary nature of engineering. At times, an engineer does work alone, but most of the time, engineers must interface with individuals who come from different educational backgrounds. Engineering projects can be complex undertakings that require teamwork and the coordination of many people of different skills and personality traits. An engineer must learn the languages of physicists, mathematicians, chemists, managers, fabricators, technicians, lawyers, marketing staff, and secretaries. It's been said that a good engineer acts as the glue that ties a project together, because he or she has learned to communicate with specialists from each of these varied fields. Learning to communicate across all these occupations requires that the engineer have a broad education and the ability to apply a full range of skills and knowledge to the design process.

The Well-Rounded Engineer

To help illustrate the breadth of communication skills required of an engineer, imagine that you work for the fictitious company depicted in Figure 8. Each person shown in the outer circle brings to the company a different professional expertise and is represented by a famous person with an appropriate background. Notice that you, the design engineer, are in the center of the organizational circle. Other engineers on your design team may join you in the center, but each of you can easily communicate with any one specialist in the outer ring. As an engineer, you've taken courses or have been exposed to each of their various disciplines. This unique feature of your educational background enables you to communicate with anyone in the professional circle and positions you as the individual most likely to act as central coordinator.

The Physicist (*e.g., Albert Einstein, best known for his theory of relativity*).   The physicist of the company is responsible for understanding the basic physical principles that underlie the company's product line. He spends his time in the laboratory exploring new materials, analyzing their interactions with heat, light, and electromagnetic radiation. He may discover a previously unknown quantum interaction that will lead to a new semiconductor device or perhaps he will explore the potential for using superconductors in the company's product. Or, he may simply perform the physical analysis for a new micro-accelerometer. Because you've taken two or more semesters of basic physics and have learned some mechanics, thermodynamics, and electromagnetics, you can easily converse with the physicist and discuss how his basic discoveries relate to the practical interests of the company.

The Chemist (*e.g., Marie Curie, who discovered radium*).   The chemist analyzes materials and substances used in producing company products. She ensures that raw materials used for manufacturing meet purity specifications so that quality control can be maintained. In her laboratory, she directs a team of experimentalists who seek to discover improved materials that are stronger and more durable than those currently being used. She may perform research on complex organic compounds or perhaps work on molecular-based nanotechnology. As an engineer, you've taken one or more courses in chemistry and can speak her language. You understand such concepts as reaction rates, chemical equilibrium, molarity, reduction and oxidation, acids and bases, and electrochemical potential. Perhaps you're a software engineer writing a program that will control a chemical analysis instrument. Maybe you are a manufacturing engineer charged with translating a chemical reaction into a manufactured product. Whatever your role, you are an individual very well suited to bringing the contributions of the chemist to the design process.

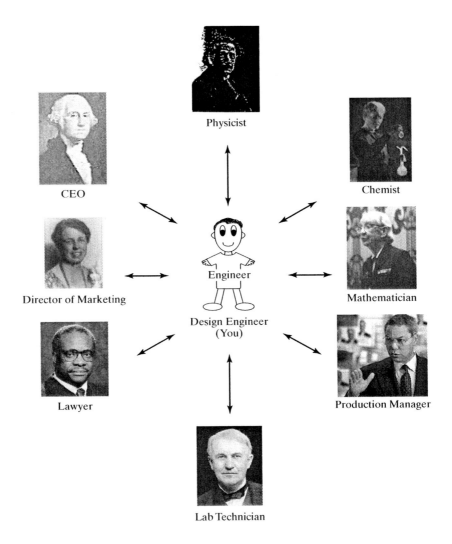

Figure 8 The professional circle with the design engineer at its center.

***The Mathematician** (e.g., Grace Hopper, former Navy admiral, mathematician, and computer specialist responsible for the term "computer bug").* The mathematician of the company, who might also be a computer scientist, worries about things such as modeling, statistics, databases, and forecasting. She may be involved in an intriguing new database algorithm or mathematical method for modeling an engineering system. Perhaps she uses mathematics to analyze the company's production line or to forecast trends in marketing. You converse easily with the mathematician, because you have taken numerous math courses as part of your engineering program. Although your emphasis has been on applied, rather than pure mathematics, you're familiar with calculus, differential equations, linear algebra, statistics, probability, vector algebra, and complex variables. You can easily apply the concepts of mathematics to problems in engineering design.

The Production Manager (*e.g., Colin Powell, U.S. Secretary of State, former U.S. Army general, military planner, and co-architect of Operation Desert Storm*). Like the army general in top command, the production manager is responsible for mobilizing materials, supplies, and personnel to manufacture company products. The production manager may worry about things such as job scheduling, quality control, materials allocation, quality assurance testing, and yield. As the engineer who designs products, you work closely with the production manager to make sure that your design approach is compatible with the company's manufacturing capabilities. Your training as an engineer and your exposure to machining, welding, circuit fabrication, and automation has given you the ability to understand the job of the production manager and has provided you with the vocabulary needed to communicate with him.

The Lab Technician (*e.g., Thomas Edison, famous tinkerer and experimenter, best known for inventing the incandescent light bulb*). The lab technician is an indispensable member of the design team. An habitual tinkerer and experimenter, the lab technician helps bring your design product to fruition. He is adept at using tools and has much knowledge about the practical aspects of engineering. The lab technician is masterful at fabricating prototypes and is likely to be the individual who sets up and tests them. The typical lab technician has a degree in engineering technology, hence you and he have taken many of the same courses, although your courses probably have included more formal theory and mathematics than his. You communicate easily with the lab technician and include him in each phase of your design project.

The Lawyer (*e.g., Clarence Thomas, lawyer and Supreme Court Justice*). The lawyer worries about the legal aspects of the company's products. Should we apply for a patent on the XYZ widget? Are we exposing ourselves to a liability suit if we market a substandard product? Is our new deal with Apex Corporation fair to both companies from a legal perspective? To help the lawyer answer these questions, you must be able to communicate with him and share your engineering knowledge. The logical thought that forms the basis of law is similar to the methods you've used to solve countless engineering problems. As an engineer, you easily engage in discourse with the lawyer and can apply his legal concerns about safety, ethics, and liability to the design process.

The Director of Marketing (*e.g., Eleanor Roosevelt, former First Lady of the United States*). The director of marketing is a master of imagery and style. Her job is to sell the company's products to the public and convince people that your products are better than those of your competitors. The marketing manager has excellent communication skills, some knowledge of economics, and an understanding of what makes people want to buy. You interface easily with the marketing manager because you've dealt with all aspects of design as part of your training as an engineer. Through this training, you have focused not only on technical issues, but also on things such as product appearance, the human-machine interface, durability, safety, and ease of use. Your familiarity with these important issues has prepared you to help the director of marketing understand your product and how it works. You can respond to her concerns about what the public needs from the product that you design.

The President/Chief Executive Officer (*e.g., George Washington, first president of the United States*). The CEO of the company probably has an MBA (Master's of Business Administration) or higher degree and a long history working in corporate financial affairs. The CEO worries about the economy and what future markets the company should pursue or whether to open a new plant in a foreign country. It's the

CEO who determines how your current project will be financed, and he needs to be kept up to date about its progress. The CEO also may ask you to assess the feasibility of a new technology or product concept. As an engineer, you have no difficulty conversing with the CEO, because the economic principles of profit and loss, cost derivatives, statistics, and forecasting are closely tied to concepts you learned in courses on calculus, statistics, and economics. You've learned to use spreadsheets in one or more engineering classes and have no trouble interpreting or providing the information that is part of the CEO's world. Likewise, your training as an engineer prepares you to communicate with the CEO about the impact of your design project on the economic health of the company.

ENGINEERING: A SET OF SKILLS

To be successful at design, an engineer must acquire technical, theoretical, and practical competency and must be a good organizer, and communicator. Three especially important skills that are at the foundation of engineering design are *knowledge*, *experience*, and *intuition*. These talents do not form an exhaustive set, but they are crucial to the well-rounded engineer.

Knowledge

Knowledge describes the body of facts, scientific principles, and mathematical tools that an engineer uses to form strategies, analyze systems, or predict results. An engineer's acquired knowledge can provide a deeper understanding of how something works. The natural sciences, for example physics, chemistry, and biology, help an engineer understand the physical world. Mathematics provides a universal technical language that spans various disciplines and can be understood by anyone regardless of spoken language or cultural background. Each field of engineering has its own traditional body of knowledge, but an engineer in one field also learns subjects from other fields. Areas of knowledge that are common to all engineers include mechanics, circuits, materials science, and computer programming.

As a student of engineering, you may ask why you are required to take subjects that seem irrelevant to your career aspirations. Any experienced engineer will tell you the answer: Engineers work in a multidisciplinary world where basic knowledge of many different subjects is necessary. Mechanical and computer engineers use electrical circuits. Electrical engineers build physical structures and use computers. Aeronautical engineers rely on software systems. Software engineers design airplane controls. Understanding the field of another engineer is critical to cross-disciplinary communication and design proficiency.

Although formal education is an important part of any engineer's training, the prudent engineer also acquires knowledge through on-the-job training and a lifetime of study and exploration. Tinkering, fixing, experimenting, and taking things apart to see how they work also are important sources of engineering knowledge. As a young person, did you disassemble your toys, put together model kits, write your own computer games, create Web pages, or play with building sets, hammers, nails, radios, bicycles, or computers? Without knowing it, you began the path toward acquiring engineering knowledge. The professional engineer engages in similar practices. By becoming involved in all aspects of a design project, by keeping up to date with the latest technology, by taking professional development courses and solving real-world problems, the practicing engineer remains current and competent.

Experience

Experience refers to the body of methods, procedures, techniques, and rules of thumb that an engineer uses to solve problems. For the engineer, accumulating experience is just as important as acquiring knowledge. As a student, you will have several opportunities to gain engineering experience. Cooperative assignments, assistantships in labs, capstone design projects, summer jobs, and research work in a professor's laboratory provide important sources of engineering experience. On-the-job training is also a good way to gain valuable professional experience. Many engineering companies recognize this need and provide entry-level engineers with initial training as a way of infusing additional experience. Developing experience requires "seasoning," the process by which a novice engineer gradually learns the "tricks of the trade" from other, more experienced engineers. Company lore about methods, procedures, and history is often passed orally, from one engineer to the another, and a new engineer learns this information by working with other engineers. The history of what *hasn't* worked in the past is also a key part of this oral tradition.

An engineer also gains valuable experience by enduring design *failure*. When the first attempt at a design fails in the testing phase, the wise engineer views it as a learning experience and uses the information to make needed changes and alterations. Experience is acquired by testing prototypes, studying failures, and observing the results of design decisions.

Engineers also must consider the issues of reliability, cost, manufacturability, ergonomics, and marketability when making design decisions. Only by confronting these constraints in real world situations can an engineer gain true design experience.

Intuition

Intuition is a characteristic normally associated with fishermen, fortunetellers, and weather forecasters. Intuition is also an essential element of engineering. It refers to an engineer's basic instinct about what will or will not work as a problem solution. Although intuition can never replace careful planning, analysis, and testing, it can help an engineer decide which approach to follow when faced with many choices and no obvious answer. An intuitive feeling for what will work and what will not work, grounded in extensive experience, can save time by helping an engineer choose the path that will eventually lead to success rather than failure. When intuition is at work, you may hear an engineer using phrases such as, "That seems reasonable" or "That looks about right." or "Oh, about this much."

Intuition is a direct by-product of design experience and is acquired only through practice, practice, and more practice. In the information age, where much of engineering focuses on computers, engineers are tempted to solve everything by simulation and computer modeling. While the use of computers has dramatically accelerated the design cycle and has dramatically changed the practice of engineering, using them makes it easy to forget that a product ultimately must obey the idiosyncrasies of the real physical world. Developing intuition about that world is an important part of your engineering education. The difference between a good engineer and an excellent one is often just an instinct for how the laws of nature will manifest themselves in the design process. Will too much heat overpower that circuit? Will friction rob that engine of too much power? How big should the vessel be for a production run of that new cosmetic? Developing intuition should be a key goal of your engineering education. How many times have you opened your computer to install new components? Do you alter hardware settings just to see what happens? Have you opened the hood of family car just to see what lies beneath it? Have you adjusted the gears on your bicycle? Have you put together a kit or built your science project from raw materials? Each of these tasks helps you acquire intuition. Observing the way in which other engineers have laid out the boards of a computer will acquaint you with the techniques of hardware design. Adjusting the gear and brake setting of your bicycle will help you to understand design trade-offs, such as the conflict between strength and durability versus lightweight construction. Becoming knowledgeable in the use of tools will help you to better understand the impact of your design decisions on manufacturing. Repetition, testing, careful attention to detail, working with more experienced engineers, and dedication to your discipline are the keys to developing design intuition. Design intuition is best acquired by "doing design," that is, by playing with real things.

PROFESSIONAL SUCCESS: HOW TO GAIN EXPERIENCE AS A STUDENT

Your experience as an engineer can begin while you are a student. If your school has one, a cooperative education program is an excellent way to gain experience as an engineer. The typical program places you as an intern in an engineering company for 6 to 12 months. You'll typically be assigned to a senior engineer to assist in such tasks as computer-aided design, software development, product prototyping, testing, laboratory evaluation, or other work. You'll get to see how the company works, and the company will get to evaluate you as a possible future hire. In addition, you'll be paid for the time you spend at the company.

Students also can gain valuable experience by working in research labs at school. Most professors are delighted to take eager undergraduates into their research laboratories. Most schools list the research interests of the faculty on departmental Web pages. Learn about the research activities of a professor whose class you have enjoyed. Don't be afraid to simply ask if she needs help in the lab. Many professors receive industry or government funding for their research, and many sponsor "Research for Undergraduates" programs, so you may even be paid an hourly wage or small stipend for your time. You'll be assigned tasks such as constructing experiments, wiring circuits, writing programs, obtaining data, preparing test samples, or assisting graduate students.

KEY TERMS

Engineering	Profession	Knowledge
Experience	Intuition	Management
Career		

2

What Is Design?

design n: Invention and disposition of the form, parts, or details of something according to a plan.[1]

Engineers have made tremendous contributions to the quality of life in the 20th and 21st centuries. The automobile, bicycle, airplane, transatlantic cable, heart pacemaker, radio and television, international shipping, national highway system, national power grid, personal computer, Internet, cellular telephone, fax machine, CD player, and global positioning system all began with the common thread of *design*. From a fundamental perspective, design can be defined as any activity that results in the synthesis of something that meets a need. A refrigerator keeps food cold; a bicycle provides transportation; a keyboard sends data to a computer; a muffler silences a noisy automobile. Although design is practiced by all sorts of individuals, technical and nontechnical alike, the notion of "design" in the context of engineering implies the application of knowledge and specialized skills toward the creation of something that meets a desired set of specifications. The object of design might be a device, machine, circuit, building, mechanism, structure, software program, operating system, manufacturing process, or other technical system. In an engineering context, the word "design" answers the simple question, "What do engineers do?"

[1] *Webster's II New College Dictionary.* Boston: Houghton-Mifflin Company, 1995, p. 307.

SECTIONS

- The Use of the Word "Design"
- The Difference Between Design, Analysis, and Reproduction
- Good Design Versus Bad Design
- The Design Cycle
- A Design Example

OBJECTIVES

In this chapter, you will learn about:

- The meaning of the word "design."
- The difference between design, analysis, and reproduction.
- The difference between good and bad design.
- The engineering design process.
- The design cycle.
- A design competition example.

THE USE OF THE WORD "DESIGN"

In this book, the word "design" will be used in several ways. It may be used as a verb, as in, "Design a widget that can open a soda can automatically." The word might be used as a noun that defines the creation process itself, as in, "Learning design is an important part of engineering education." Alternatively, design may be used as a noun that describes the end result of the process, as in "The design was a success and met the customer's specifications." The word may be used as an adjective, as in, "This book will help you learn the design process."

Sometimes, an alternative word is needed to describe the end result of a design effort. For this purpose, the word "product" may be used in its generic sense, even if the thing being designed is not a product for sale. Similarly, the word "device" may be used to describe the results of a design effort, even if the entity is not a physical apparatus. Thus, the words product and device can refer not only to tangible objects, but also to large structures, systems, procedures, or software.

THE DIFFERENCE BETWEEN DESIGN, ANALYSIS, AND REPRODUCTION

Students of engineering often are confused by the distinction between analysis, reproduction, and design. In science classes, students are asked to answer problems, observe phenomena in the lab, and perform calculations. In engineering classes, instructors instead may stress the importance of design. The difference between analysis and design can be defined in the following way: If only one answer to the problem exists, and finding it merely involves putting together the pieces of the puzzle, then the activity is probably analysis. For example, processing data and using it to test a theory is analysis. On the other hand, if more than one solution exists, and if deciding upon a suitable path demands being creative, making choices, performing tests, iterating, and evaluating, then the activity is most certainly design. Design can include analysis, but it also must involve at least one of these latter elements.

As an example of the distinction between analysis and design, consider the weather station shown in Figure 1. This remote-controlled buoy is located off the coast of California and is maintained by the U.S. National Oceanic and Atmospheric Administration (NOAA). It provides 24-hour data to mariners, the Coast Guard, and weather forecasters. Processing the data stream from this buoy, posting it on the Internet, and using the information to forecast the weather are examples of analysis. Deciding *how* to build the buoy so that it meets the needs of NOAA is an example of design.

Another example that illustrates the difference between analysis and design can be found in the medieval catapult of Figure 2. Determining the projectile's x-y trajectory is an analysis problem that involves computing the x and y components of Newton's law of motion $\mathbf{a} = \mathbf{F}/m$ that is,

$$\frac{d^2x}{dt^2} = \frac{dv_x}{dt} = 0 \tag{1}$$

and

Figure 1.   Automated weather buoy located off the coast of California provides information about local sea and weather conditions. (*Photo courtesy of National Data Buoy Center.*)

$$\frac{d^2y}{dt^2} = \frac{dv_y}{dt} = \frac{-mg}{m} = -g, \tag{2}$$

where v_x and v_y are the x- and y-components of the projectile's velocity, respectively. Here, g is the gravitational constant (9.8 m/s^2 in MKS units); m the mass of the projectile (e.g., a stone); and mg the gravitational force on the projectile in the $-y$-direction. The second derivatives d^2x/dt^2 and d^2y/dt^2 represent the x- and y-components of the projectile's acceleration. Note that the projectile experiences no x-directed force after its initial launch; hence, v_x will remain unchanged for $t > 0$.

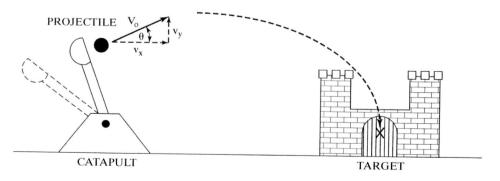

Figure 2.   A catapult sends a projectile along a trajectory toward a target. Computing the parameters needed to hit the target is an example of analysis. Determining how to best build the catapult is an example of design.

Equations (1) and (2) can be solved only if the initial values of V_o and θ, the so-called *initial conditions* at $t = 0$, are specified. The initial values of V_o and θ can be used to find initial conditions for the x- and y-components of velocity as well:

$$\frac{dx}{dt} = v_x = V_0 \cos\theta \tag{3}$$

and

$$\frac{dy}{dt} = v_y = V_0 \sin\theta, \tag{4}$$

where V_o is related to v_x and v_y by

$$V_0 = [v_x^2 + v_y^2]^{1/2}. \tag{5}$$

The launch speed V_0 and launch angle θ of the projectile are set by the user of the cata-pult. As suggested by Figure 2, the user must first choose the target point, then adjust V_0 and θ so that the stone hits the desired target. Although this process involves making decisions (*Which target shall I hit?*) and setting parameters (*Which V_0 and θ shall I choose?*), and although the problem has more than one possible solution, it requires analysis only and involves no design.

In contrast, determining *how to build* the catapult most certainly involves design. The machine can be built in more than one way, and the designer must decide which method is best. Should the structural members be made from oak or pine? Should twisted ropes, a hanging basket of rocks, or bent branches be used as the energy storage mechanism? How large should the machine be? Should it rest on wheels or skids? Answering these questions requires experimentation, analysis, testing, evaluation, and revision, which are all elements of the design process.

This example illustrates the difference between design and analysis. Design involves the creation of a device or product to meet a need or set of specifications. Analy-sis refers to the process of applying mathematics and other tools to find the answer to a problem. In contrast to both, the word *reproduction* refers to the process of recreating something that has already been designed. Reproduction may involve an exact replication, or it may involve minor revisions whose consequences have already been determined. For instance, copying an oscillator circuit from an electronics book and substituting resistor values to set the frequency is an example of reproduction rather than design. Similarly, building a backyard shed from a set of purchased plans involves reproduction, but no design. Reproduction is an important part of engineering and lies at the core of manufac-turing, but it does not require the same set of skills and tools as does true design.

EXAMPLE 1:
TRAJECTORY
ANALYSIS

Equations (1) through (4) form a set of *differential equations* that describe the motion of the catapult's projectile. Given an initial V_o and θ, these equations can be solved for the projectile's position coordinates $x(t)$ and $y(t)$ as functions of time. The techniques for obtaining such a solution are covered in math courses taken by most students of engi-neering; however, many first-year students do not yet have the math skills needed to solve differential equations. Another method by which solutions for the projectile coor-dinates $x(t)$ and $y(t)$ can be found as functions of time is to find them iteratively by com-puter. The flowchart of Figure 3 illustrates the basic roadmap for writing such a program.

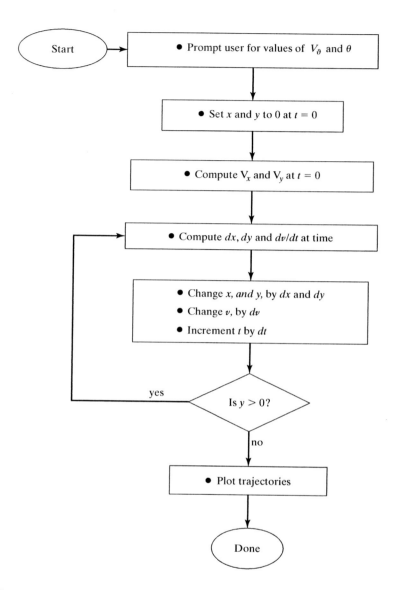

Figure 3.   Flowchart for the iterative solutions of Eqs. (1) through (4), given the initial conditions V_o and θ.

The listing shown below implements the program described by the flowchart of Figure 3 using the programming language MATLAB™. Many other programming languages can be used as well, but MATLAB is chosen here because of its widespread use in the engineering community and the generic nature of its commands and functions. MATLAB code is case sensitive. The percent symbols (%) denote comment lines, and the asterisks (*) denote multiplication. A semicolon (;) at the end of a line simply tells the program not to display the result of that particular calculation on the screen. The plot of x versus y for the initial conditions $V_o = 15$ m/s and $\theta = 60°$ is shown in Figure 4.

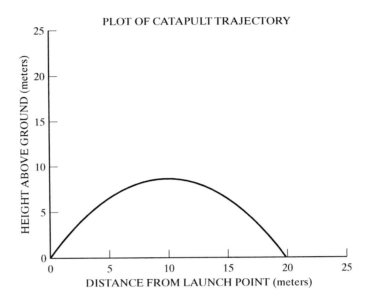

Figure 4.   Result of the computation of Figure 3 for the case V_o = 15 m/s and θ = 60°.

```
%%% MATLAB PROGRAM CODE %%%
%THIS PROGRAM CALCULATES and PLOTS the TRAJECTORY of a
CATAPULT PROJECTILE

%Prompt user for initial conditions:
Vo = input('Enter value of projectile launch velocity in
m/s ')
theta = input('Enter value of launch angle in degrees from
horizontal ')

%Convert launch angle from degrees to radians:
theta = (theta/180)*pi;

%set x and y to zero at t=0:
x=0; y=0; t=0;
%set value of time increment dt to 10 milliseconds:
dt=1e-2;
%set gravitational constant in meters/sec^2 (MKS units):
g=9.8;

%Compute x- and y-components of launch velocity at t=0:
vx = Vo*cos(theta);
vy = Vo*sin(theta);

%Declare initially empty vectors X, Y, and T
%(A construct in MATLAB for storing calculated plots for
latter plotting)
X=[ ]; Y=[ ]; T=[ ];

%THE LOOP BEGINS HERE: Iterate around the flow-chart loop
%while y is greater than zero
while y >= 0
```

```
%compute incremental changes to x, y, and vy at time t
dx = vx*dt;
dy = vy*dt;
dvy = -g*dt;%downward acceleration due to gravity

%update values of x, y,vy, and t:
x = x + dx;
y = y + dy;
vy = vy + dvy;
t = t + dt;

%save updated values for plotting when iteration is
finished
X = [X x];
Y = [Y y];
T = [T t];

end  %THE LOOP ITERATES HERE (exit if y is not greater than
zero)

%When calculations are finished, plot the results:
close;
axis([0 100 0 100]); axis manual; hold on;
%Set graph axes to fixed values
plot(X,Y);%plot trajectory of projectile (x and y values)
title('PLOT OF CATAPULT TRAJECTORY')
xlabel('DISTANCE FROM LAUNCH POINT (meters)')
ylabel('HEIGHT ABOVE GROUND (meters)')
```

PRACTICE!

For Exercises 1 to 7, determine whether the following tasks involve analysis, design, or reproduction:
1.   Find the best travel route between Chicago and Houston.
2.   Find a way to prevent people from burning their hands while removing a bagel from a toaster oven.
3.   Find the best dimensions of a 16-oz soup can so that a packing box for 24 cans has the smallest volume.
4.   Find a way to mount a cellular telephone on a bicycle to permit safe, hands-free operation.
5.   Find a way to produce bar-coded badges that can be handed out to the attendees of a technical conference.
6.   Find a way to produce 1,200 origami (folded paper) nut containers for a large alumni dinner.
7.   Find a way to use a global positioning system (GPS) receiver to automatically navigate a lawn mower around a nonrectangular yard.
8.   *Challenge Exercise*: Show by direct solution that Equations (1) through (4) yield a parabolic trajectory.

9. *Challenge Exercise*: A catapult target lies 100 m away. Determine at least one possible set of values for V_0 and θ in Figure 2 so that a 5-kg stone hits the target. How much energy must the catapult impart to the stone to meet this objective? (Hint: the kinetic energy of the stone when it first leaves the catapult is $mV_0^2/2$.)

10. Modify the MATLAB program shown above so that it plots (a) the height of the projectile as a function of time, and (b) the angle of the trajectory relative to the horizontal as a function of time.

GOOD DESIGN VERSUS BAD DESIGN

Anyone who has taken a car in for repair recognizes the difference between a good mechanic and a bad mechanic. A good mechanic diagnoses your problem in a timely manner, fixes what's broken at a fair price, and makes repairs that last. A bad mechanic fails to find the real problem, masks the symptoms with expensive solutions that don't last, and charges too much money for needless repairs. Engineers are a bit like auto mechanics in this respect. The world is full of both good engineers and bad engineers. Just because an engineer has produced something does not mean that the product has been designed well. Just because the design works initially doesn't mean that the product will last over time. Although the criteria by which a product is judged varies with the nature of the product, the success of most design efforts can be judged by the general characteristics summarized in Table 1.

TABLE 1   Characteristics of Good Design Versus Bad Design

GOOD DESIGN	BAD DESIGN
1. Meets all technical requirements	1. Meets only some technical requirements
2. Works all the time	2. Works initially but stops working after a short time
3. Meets cost requirements	3. Costs more than it should
4. Requires little or no maintenance	4. Requires frequent maintenance
5. Is safe	5. Poses a hazard to users
6. Creates no ethical dilemma	6. Raises ethical questions

The contrast between good and bad design is readily illustrated by the catapult of Figure 1. Suppose that the Apex Catapult Corporation has been asked to produce this device (actually called a *trebuchet*) for a brigade intent on recapturing their castle. The buyers will judge the worthiness of the catapult based on the considerations outlined in Table 1, as illustrated by the following discussion.

1. Does the Product Meet Technical Requirements?

It might seem a simple matter to decide whether or not a catapult meets its technical requirements. Either the stone hits its target, or it does not. But success can be judged in many ways. A well-designed catapult will accommodate a wide range of stone weights, textures, and sizes. It will require the efforts of only one or two people to operate, and will repeatedly hit its target, even in strong wind or rain. A poorly designed catapult may meet its launch specification under ideal conditions, but it may accommodate stones of only a single weight or require that only smooth, hard-to-find stones be used. It may not work in the rain, or it may not produce repeatable trajectories. When the arm of a poorly designed catapult is released, it may hit its own support structure, causing the stone to lose momentum and fall short of the target. The catapult might work fine for the first few launches, only to fail at a later time.

2. Does the Product Work?

During the development stage, a product need not be "bug"-free the very first time it is tested. However, it *must* work perfectly before it can be delivered to the customer. It must be durable and not fail after only a short time in the field. The catapult of Figure 5 provides an excellent example of this second principle. Even a bad designer could produce a catapult capable of meeting its specifications upon initial delivery. The Apex Corporation could make the catapult from whatever local timbers were available.

Figure 5.   Reproduction of a medieval catapult called the "trebuchet." (*Photo courtesy of Middelaltercentret.*)

It might use a simple trigger mechanism made from vines and twigs. The bad designer would build the catapult as he went along, adding new features on top of old ones without examining how each feature interacted with those before it. The catapult would likely pass inspection upon delivery and be able to hurl stones several times before fraying a line, cracking a timber, or breaking its trigger mechanism. After a short period of use, however, the ill-designed timbers of its launch arm might weaken, causing the projectile to fall short of its target.

A good designer would develop a robust catapult capable of many long hours of service. This conscientious engineer would test different building materials, carriage configurations, trigger mechanisms, and launch arms before choosing materials and design strategies. The catapult would be designed as a whole, with consideration given to how its various parts interacted. The process typically would require stronger and more expensive materials, but it would prove more reliable and enable the user to hit the target repeatedly.

3. Does the Product Meet Cost Requirements?

Some design problems can be approached without regard to cost, but in most cases, cost is a major factor in making design decisions. Often a trade-off exists between adding features and adding cost. A catapult made from cheap local wood will be much less expensive than one requiring stronger, imported wood. Will the consumer be willing to pay Apex a higher price for a stronger catapult? Durable leather thongs will last longer than links made of less expensive hemp rope. Will the consumer absorb the cost of the more durable thongs? Painting the catapult will make it visually more attractive but will not enhance performance. Will the customer want an attractive piece of machinery at a higher price? An engineer must face questions such as these in just about every design situation.

4. Will the Product Require Extensive Maintenance?

A durable product will provide many years of flawless service. Durability is something that must be planned for as part of the design process, even when the cost of the final product is important. At each step, the designer must decide whether cutting corners to save money or time will lead to component failure later on. A good designer will eliminate as many latent weaknesses as possible. A bad designer will ignore them as long as the product can pass its initial inspection tests. If the Apex Catapult Corporation wishes to make a long-lasting product worthy of its company name, then it will design durability into its catapult from the very beginning of the design process.

5. Is the Product Safe?

Safety is a quality measured only in relative terms. No product can be made completely hazard free, so when we say that a product is "safe," we mean that it has a significantly smaller probability of causing injury than does a product that is "unsafe." Assigning a safety value to a product is one of the harder aspects of engineering design, because adding safety features usually requires adding cost. Also, accidents are subject to chance, and it can be difficult to identify a potential hazard until an accident occurs. An unsafe product may never cause harm to any one user, while statistically, some fraction of a large group of users is likely to sustain injury. The catapult provides an example of the trade-off between safety versus cost. Can a catapult be designed that provides a strategic advantage without injuring people? When a stone is thrown at the door of a castle, a probability exists that it will hit a person instead. Designing a device that can throw, say, large bags of water instead of stones would reduce the potential for human injury, but at the added cost of producing water bags. Features also could be added to the catapult to protect its users. Guards, safety shields, and interlocks would prevent accidental misfirings, but would add cost and inconvenience to the finished product.

6. Does the Product Create an Ethical Dilemma?

The catapult has been chosen as an example for this section because it poses a common ethical dilemma faced by engineers: Should a device be built simply because it *can* be built? A catapult, for example, can be a lethal device. When asked to build a catapult, is Apex obligated to build it? Is Apex responsible for suggesting alternatives to the rescue brigade? A less destructive battering ram might help recapture the castle while sparing innocent lives. Quiet diplomacy in lieu of force may lead to resolution and peaceful cooperation. As contrived as this fictitious example may be, it exemplifies the ethical dilemmas that may confront you as an engineer. If asked by a future employer to design offensive military weapons, will you find it personally objectionable? If your boss asks you to use cheaper materials but bill the customer for more expensive ones, will you comply with these instructions or defy your employer? If you discover a serious safety flaw in your company's product that might lead to human injury, will you insist on costly revisions that will reduce the profitability of the product? Or will you say nothing and hope for the best? Questions of these sorts are never simple to answer, but engineers face them regularly. As part of your training as an engineer, you must learn to apply your own ethical standards, whatever they may be, to problems that you encounter on the job. This aspect of design will be one of the hardest to learn, but it is one that you must master if you wish to be an engineer.

PROFESSIONAL SUCCESS: CHOOSE A GOOD DESIGNER TO BE YOUR MENTOR

There is a difference between good designers and bad designers. Practicing engineers of both types can be found in the engineering profession, and it's up to you to learn to distinguish between the two. As you make the transition from student to professional engineer, you are likely to seek a mentor at some point in your career. Be certain that the individual you choose follows good design practices. Seek an engineer who has an intrinsic feeling for why and how things work. Find someone who adheres to ethical standards that are consistent with your own. Avoid "formula pluggers" who memorize equations and blindly plug in numbers to arrive at design decisions but have little feeling for what the formulas actually mean. Avoid engineers who lack vision and perspective. Likewise, shun engineers who take irresponsible shortcuts, ignore safety concerns, or choose design solutions without thorough testing. In contrast, do emulate engineers who are well respected, experienced, and practiced at design.

THE DESIGN CYCLE

Design is an iterative process. Seldom does a finished product emerge from the design process without undergoing changes along the way. Sometimes, an entire design approach must be abandoned and the product redesigned from the ground up. The sequence of events leading from idea to finished product is called the *design cycle*. Although the specific steps of the design cycle may vary with the product and field of engineering, most cycles resemble the sequence depicted in Figure 6. The following section explores this diagram in more detail.

Define the Overall Objectives

You should begin any new project by defining your design objectives. This step may seem a nuisance to the student eager to build, test, or write software, but it is one of the most important steps. Only by viewing the requirements from a broad perspective can an engineer determine all factors relevant to the design effort. Good design involves more than just making technical choices. The engineer must ask the following questions: Who will use the product? What are the needs of the end user? What will the product look like? Which of its features are critical, and which are only desirable? Can the product be manufactured easily? How much will it cost? What are the safety factors? Who will decide how much risk is acceptable? Answering these questions and similar ones at the outset will help at each subsequent stage of the design process.

Gather Information

In the early stages of a new project, much time should be devoted to gathering information. Learn as much as possible about related technology. Identify off-the-shelf items, systems, or software components that can be incorporated directly into your design, so that you don't have to "reinvent the wheel." Look for product descriptions, data sheets, and application notes on the Web. Keep this information in a file folder (either hard copy or on a computer) where you'll be able find it easily. Also look for reports or project descriptions in the same general area as your own project. Detailed specifications about most component parts and devices are available on company Web sites. Over the past several years, these electronic databases have largely supplanted printed catalogs as the primary source of information for design engineers.

Perusing advertisements in trade magazines and journals can be a good way to learn what types of products are available that might be relevant to your project. Each field of engineering has many such publications. Examples include *Biomedical Products, Compliance Engineering, Computer Design, Electronic Component News, Electronic Design, Industrial Product Bulletin, Machine Design, Manufacturing Engineering, Mechanical Engineering*, and *OEM Technology News* (OEM: "original equipment manufacturer"). A good directory of technical magazines can be found at *www.techexpo.com/toc/tech_mag.html*.

Choose a Design Strategy

The next step in the design process of Figure 6 involves the selection of a strategy for meeting design objectives. At this stage of the project, the engineer (or, more likely, the design team) might decide whether the design will involve an electrical, mechanical, or software solution, and whether the product will be designed from the ground up or synthesized from off-the-shelf components. If the system is complex, it should be broken up into simpler, smaller pieces that can be designed independently and later interconnected to form the complete product. These subsections, or modules, should be designed so that they can be tested individually before the entire system is assembled.

Subdividing a large job into several more manageable tasks simplifies synthesis, testing, and evaluation. In a team design effort, the modular approach is essential. The various components of an automobile, for example, such as the engine, cooling system, electrical system, suspension, braking system, chassis, and drive train, are each designed and tested individually before the entire automobile is assembled. This same modular strategy applies to large software systems, where each section should be designed as an

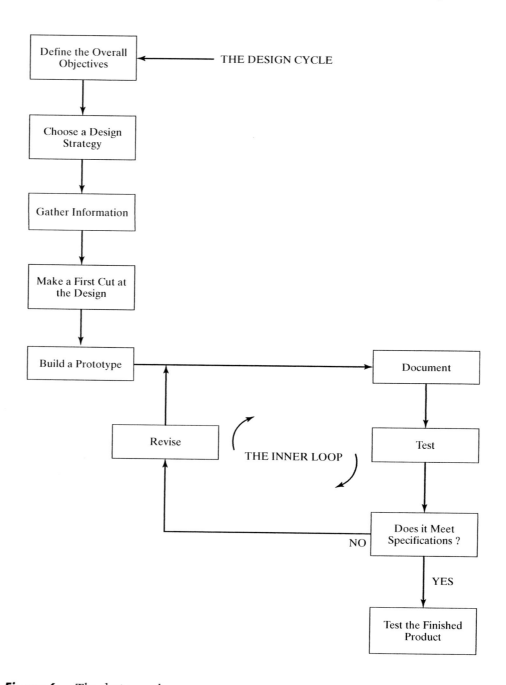

Figure 6.   The design cycle.

independently testable module. In all cases, however, individual modules must always be designed with the overall design strategy in mind. Otherwise, the end product may consist of a collection of working but incoherent modules. In much of modular design, the integrated final product is more than the sum of its individual parts.

The design strategy also should consider similar efforts that may have been attempted in the past. Does a new technology exist that will be useful for the design? Perhaps a partial solution is already available in commercial form. For example, suppose that your design solution includes the amplification of voice or music. Many inexpensive off-the-shelf kits exist for constructing board-level amplifiers (see, for example, *www.rainbowkits.com,*) so that designing your own amplifier from raw electronic parts would be an unnecessary duplication of effort. The wise engineer makes use of existing products and components to simplify the design task. There is no shame in using off-the-shelf ingredients or subsystems if they can help achieve your design objectives more quickly and inexpensively. Typically, labor is the most expensive part of any development effort, so it's often cheaper (and sometimes more reliable) to buy something ready-made than it is to design it from scratch. Imagine how needlessly complex the task would be of designing a desktop computer without making use of the disk drives, memory chips, power supplies, monitors, and central processors available from other vendors. One caution: Be certain that using another company's product does not create patent infringement problems if your product is destined for commercial sale.

Make a First Cut at the Design

Once a design strategy has been identified, it's time to make an initial attempt, or "first cut" at the design. If the product is to be a physical entity, a layout or engineering drawing is helpful at this stage. Tentative values of dimensions, construction materials, part numbers, electronic component values, and other relevant parameters are specified. This step typically involves rough approximations and gross estimates. Its primary purpose is to determine whether or not the design approach has a chance of working, and it should result in a rough, tentative prototype for the system or each of its subsections. If the object of the design effort is a software product, its outer shell, overall structure, and user interface are laid out as part of the first-cut attempt. If the design involves a system (a manufacturing procedure, for example) than its overall flowchart should be specified at this time.

Build, Document, and Test

After the design team has reached a consensus on a first cut, a facsimile of the product is built as a working prototype. The typical first prototype is destined to be revised many times before the design cycle has been completed. This first prototype should be functional, but need not be visually attractive. Its primary purpose is to provide a starting point for evaluation and testing. For example, if the product is software, the prototype might consist of the main calculation sections without the fancy graphical interfaces that the user will expect in the final version. If the product is mechanical, it can be built up as a mock-up from easy-to-modify materials, such as wood or pre-punched metal strapping. For instance, a prototype for a new washing machine mechanism might be built inside an open wooden box made from framing lumber and hinged plywood. Such a structure would permit easy access to the inner machinery during testing, but obviously would never make it to the sales floor. If the product is electrical, its prototype could be wired on a temporary circuit breadboard. A new digital clock, for example, might be built in this way so that the designer could have easy access to its timing and display signals for test purposes. This arrangement would allow for circuit revisions before final construction and packaging.

During the prototyping phase of design, computer simulation tools such as AutoCAD™, ProENGINEER™, Solidworks™, PSPICE™, Electronics Workbench™, or Simulink™ can save time and expense by allowing you to predict performance before actual construction of the prototype. These software packages can help you identify hidden flaws before the product is built and give you some indication of the success of your design approach. However, computer simulations should never be used as a substitute for actual physical testing unless the product is very similar to one you've designed before. "Glitches," "bugs," and other anomalies caused by physical effects not modeled by the simulator have a nasty habit of appearing when a new product is tested. Despite the usefulness of computer-aided design tools and simulators, there is simply no substitute for constructing and testing a real physical prototype when the design is the first of its kind.

Note that documentation is part of the inner loop of the design cycle of Figure 6. The typical engineer faces considerable temptation to leave documentation to the very end of the design process. Pressed with deadlines and project milestones, many inexperienced engineers think of documentation as an annoying intrusion rather than as an integral part of the design process. After working diligently on a design project, the unseasoned engineer then faces with panic the reality of having to write documentation. ("Now I have to write this up?") Documentation added as an afterthought often is incomplete or substandard, because most of the relevant facts and steps have been forgotten by the time the writing takes place. Haphazard, after-the-fact documentation is the cause of many design failures. Many products, developed at great cost but delivered with pathetic documentation, have found their way to the trash heap of engineering failures because no one could figure out how to use or repair the product. Poor documentation also leads to subsequent duplication of effort and reinvention of the wheel, because no one can remember or interpret the results of previous work.

A good engineer recognizes that documentation is absolutely critical to every step of the design process. He or she will plan for it from the very beginning, keeping careful records of everything from initial feasibility studies to final manufacturing specifications. As the design progresses, it's a good idea to write everything down, even if it seems unimportant at the time. Information should be written in such a way that another engineer with the same technical background as your own could pick up your work at any time simply by reading your documentation. Careful documentation also will aid in writing product literature and technical manuals should the product be destined for commercial sale. Good documentation provides the engineer with a running record of the design history and the answers to key questions that were asked along the way. It provides vital background information for patent applications, product revisions, and redesign efforts, and it serves as insurance in cases of product liability. Above all, documentation is part of an engineer's professional responsibility. Its importance to engineering design cannot be overemphasized.

Revise and Revise Again

One of the characteristics of design that distinguishes it from reproduction is that the finished product may be totally different from what was envisioned at the beginning of the design cycle. Elements of the system may fail during testing, forcing the engineer to rethink the design strategy. The design process may lead the engineer down an unexpected path or into new territory. A good engineer will review the status of a product many times, proceeding through many revisions until the product meets its specifications. In truth, this revision process constitutes the principal work of the engineer. An experienced engineer recognizes it as a normal part of the design process and does not become discouraged when something fails on the first or second try. The revision cycle may require many iterations before success is achieved.

Thoroughly Test the Finished Product

As the design process converges on a probable solution, the product should be thoroughly tested and debugged. Performance should be assessed from many points of view, and the design should be modified if problems are identified at any stage. If the product is a physical entity, the effects of temperature, humidity, loading, and other environmental factors, as well as the effects of repeated and prolonged use, all must be taken into account. A physical product should be subjected to a "burn-in" (extended use) period to help identify latent defects that might cause the product to fail in the field. The human response to the product also should be assessed. No two people are exactly alike, and exposing the product to many different individuals will help identify problems that may not have been apparent during the development phase, when the product was examined by the design team only. Only after a comprehensive test period is the product ready to be put into actual service. Nothing will kill a new product faster than a few instances of malfunctioning in the field.

Like their physical counterparts, software products should be tested by a variety of different users who can discover hidden bugs. One of the characteristics of software is that different individuals will exercise the product in very different ways. Hence, extensive testing by a multitude of users is necessary if all software bugs are to be discovered. Commercial software is sometimes released to a control group of customers before widespread distribution. This control group understands that bugs may exist in the preliminary version of the software and are usually given incentives (reduced cost or a jump on competitors) to serve as real-world testers. A software trial of this type is sometimes called a *beta test* in the software industry.

PROFESSIONAL SUCCESS: HOW TO TELL A GOOD ENGINEER FROM A BAD ENGINEER

As you pursue your engineering career, you will encounter many colleagues. Some will be good engineers, and others will be bad engineers. In your quest to identify and emulate only good engineers, you should learn the differences between the two. The following list highlights the traits of both types of engineers:

A GOOD ENGINEER

- Listens to new ideas with an open mind.
- Considers a variety of solution methodologies before choosing a design approach.
- Does not consider a project complete at the first sign of success, but insists on testing and retesting.
- Is never content to arrive at a set of design parameters solely by trial and error.
- Uses phrases such as, "I need to understand why," and "Let's consider all possibilities."

A BAD ENGINEER

- Thinks he/she has all the answers; seldom listens to the ideas of others.
- Has tunnel vision; pursues with intensity only the first design approach that comes to mind.
- Ships the product out the door without thorough testing.
- Uses phrases such as, "good enough", and "I don't understand why it won't work. So-and-so did it this way."
- Equates pure trial and error with engineering design.

PRACTICE!

1. Without looking at Figure 6, draw a diagram of the design cycle that includes the following steps: define, gather, choose, first cut, build, document, test, revise.

2. Suppose that you are asked to build a recumbent bicycle (a low-profile bicycle in which the pedals are in front of the seat). Make a list of the various ways in which you might gather information as part of the design cycle.

3. Draw a modified design cycle, similar to Figure 6, that includes feedback from a test group of individual users.

4. Define the design strategy that might have gone into the invention of the first personal computer. Imagine yourself before the days of small hard disk drives, graphical drivers for monitors, compact disks, and inexpensive memory chips. (In the early days of computers, random-access memory chips were one of the most expensive components of the PC.).

5. Describe the various elements of the design cycle as they might have applied to the development of the ball point pen.

6. Write a chronicle of the design cycle applied to a simple medieval catapult.

A DESIGN EXAMPLE

The typical engineering design cycle is made up of the following seven steps; 1) Define the objectives; 2) gather information; 3) choose a strategy; 4) make a first cut; 5) build, document, test; 6) revise (and revise again); and 7) test. Steps 5 and 6 form an iterative loop that may be repeated many times before the design effort is deemed successful. "Success" in this case is measured by how well the finished product meets the desired specifications. Imagine that your professor has announced a design competition as part of an introductory engineering course. The rules of the contest are outlined in the following flyer.

COLLEGE OF ENGINEERING PEAK-PERFORMANCE DESIGN COMPETITION

OBJECTIVE

The goal of the competition is to design and construct a vehicle that can climb a ramp under its own power, stop at the top of the ramp, and sustain its position against an opposing vehicle coming up the other side of the ramp. The illustration in Figure 7 shows the approximate dimensions of the ramp. The 30-cm width of the carpet-covered track may vary by ±0.5 cm as the vehicle travels from the bottom to the top of the ramp. A vehicle is considered to be on "top of the hill" if its body, plus any extensions, strings, or jettisoned objects, lie completely within the two 120-cm lines after a 15-second time interval.

PEAK PERFORMANCE DESIGN COMPETITION
RAMP SPECIFICATIONS

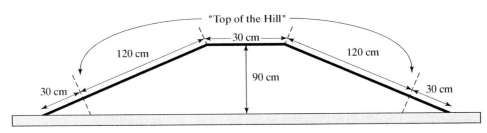

Figure 7.   Ramp specifications for the Peak Performance Design Competition.

**VEHICLE
SPECIFICATIONS**

1.   The vehicle must be autonomous. No remote power, control wires, or remote-control links are allowed.

2.   The vehicle's exterior dimensions at the start of each run must not extend beyond the sides of an imaginary 30-cm cube. A device, such as a ram, may extend beyond this limit once activated, but cannot be activated before the start of the run.

3.   The vehicle must be started by an activation device (e.g., switch or mechanical release) on the vehicle. Team members may not activate any device before the start. Vehicles cannot have their motors running before the start and dropped after the start.

4.   The vehicle can be powered by the following energy sources only:

   •   One battery of up to 9 volts
   •   Rubber bands (4 mm × 10 cm maximum size in their unstretched state)
   •   Mouse-traps (spring size 3 cm × 6 cm maximum)

5.   The vehicle's weight, including batteries, must not exceed 2 kg.

6.   The vehicle must not use chemicals or dangerous substances. No rocket-type devices, CO_2 propulsion devices, or chemical reactions are allowed. No mercury switches are permitted. (Mercury is a toxic substance, and a risk exists that a mercury switch will break during the competition.)

7.   The vehicle must not be anchored to the ramp in any way before the start. At the end of the run, the vehicle and all its parts, including jettisoned objects, extensions, etc., must lie completely within the top of the hill and the 30-cm track width.

8.   The vehicle must run within the 30-cm-wide, carpet-covered track. The vehicle may not run on top of the guide rails.

9.   The vehicle must compete in six 15-second runs against opposing vehicles. The vehicles with the most wins after six runs will be selected for the Grand Finale. The latter will determine the winner of the competition. Modifications to the vehicle are permitted between (but not during) runs.

Applying Design Principles to the Design Competition

Let's now examine the Design Competition problem in the context of the seven steps of the design cycle. Remember that the problem can be addressed in many different ways. Some design solutions, however, will work better than others.

Define the Overall Objectives

When faced with the task of designing something, an inexperienced engineer is tempted to begin with construction right away without taking the time for a careful planning stage. Building things is fun and satisfying, while estimating, sketching, calculating, simulating, and checking design parameters seem less glamorous. It's important, however, to begin any project by taking time to define its objectives. In this case, your objectives might take the following form:

1. *Design for speed.* The fastest vehicle will not necessarily be the winner, but in order to win, your vehicle must reach and maintain the center line well before the 15-second time limit. Otherwise, it may be blocked from reaching the top of the ramp by the other vehicle.

2. *Design for defensive and offensive strategies.* Not only must your vehicle reach the top of the ramp and stop on its own, but it also must maintain its position as your opponent tries to do the same. Although offensive and defensive strategies are not necessarily mutually exclusive, you've decided (somewhat arbitrarily) that defense will be given a higher priority than offense. You may need to modify this choice if tests show it to be infeasible.

3. *Design for easy changes.* The rules state that modifications to the vehicle are permitted between runs. During the contest, you may see things on other vehicles that will prompt you to make changes to your own vehicle. Similarly, you may choose to modify your vehicle in mid-competition should any of its features make it needlessly vulnerable. Adopting an easy-to-change construction strategy will facilitate on-the-fly changes to your vehicle. The likely trade-off in choosing this approach is that your car will be less durable and more likely to suffer a disabling failure.

4. *Design for durability.* The vehicle must endure six, and possibly more, trips up the contest ramp. Opposing vehicles and accidents can damage a fragile design. You must weigh the issue of durability against your desire to produce a vehicle that's flexible and easy to modify.

5. *Design for simplicity.* By keeping your design simple, you will be able to repair your vehicle quickly and easily. An intricate design might provide more performance features, but it also will be more prone to breakdowns and will be more difficult to repair.

Note that goals (1) through (5) are not independent of one another. For example, designing for easy changes may conflict with building a durable vehicle. Designing for both offensive and defensive strategies will lead to a more complicated vehicle that is harder to repair. Engineers typically face such trade-offs when making design decisions. Deciding which pathway to take requires experience and practice, but making any decision at all means that you've begun the design process.

Choose a Design Strategy

Many different design strategies will lead to a vehicle capable of competing. Building a *winning* design, however, requires making the right choices at each step in the design process. How can you know ahead of time what the right choices will be? In truth, you cannot, especially if you have never built such a vehicle before. You can only make educated guesses based on your experience and intuition. You test and retest your design choices, making changes along the way if they increase your vehicle's performance. This process of *iteration* is a crucial part of the design process. Iteration refers to the process of testing, making changes, and then retesting to observe results. Good engineering requires many iterations, trials, and demonstrations of performance before a design effort is completed. In the world of engineering, the first cut of a design seldom resembles the finished product.

In the case of the Design Competition described here, the rules provide for many alternatives in vehicle design. Regardless of the details of the design, however, all vehicles must have the same basic components: *energy source, propulsion mechanism, stopping mechanism,* and *starting device.* Although not required, a defense mechanism that prevents an opponent from pushing the vehicle back down (or off) the ramp will increase your chances of winning. After some discussion with your teammate, you develop the *choice map* shown in Figure 8.

This diagram displays some of the many design choices available to you and the consequences of making these design choices. For example, choosing battery power for propulsion constrains the stopping mechanism to one of the choices listed in the third

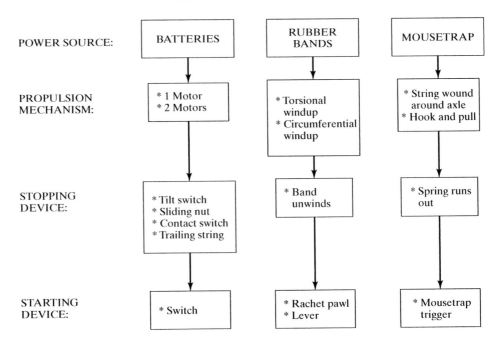

Figure 8.   Choice map that outlines the decision tree for the first phase of the design process.

box down. Although the diagram does not provide an exhaustive list of possible design choices, it serves as an excellent starting point for your design attempt. As your team-mate points out, "We have to start somewhere." You remark in return, "Let's begin with our best guess as to what will work." The choice map of Figure 8 includes some of the following elements:

Energy Source   According to the rules of the competition, you may power your vehicle from standard nine-volt (9V) batteries, rubber bands, or mousetrap springs. Batteries are attractive because they require no winding or preparation other than periodic replacement. They will, however, be more expensive than the other two alternatives. Rubber bands will require much less frequent replacement, but will store the least amount of energy among the three choices. Like a rubber band, a mousetrap needs no frequent replacing. It stores more energy than a rubber band, but because of its physical form, it offers the fewest options for harnessing its stored energy.

Propulsion Mechanism   Your choice of the propulsion device, or *prime mover*, will depend entirely on your choice of energy source. If a battery is used as the energy source, an electric motor seems the obvious choice for turning the vehicle's wheels. Rubber bands can be stretched to provide linear motion or twisted for torsional energy storage that turns an axle or power shaft. Alternatively, a rubber band can be stretched around a shaft or spool like a fishing reel and used to propel the vehicle's wheels. A mousetrap can provide only one kind of motion. When released, its bale will retract in an arc, as depicted in Figure 9. This motion can be harnessed and used to propel the vehicle.

Stopping Mechanism   Your vehicle must stop when it arrives at the top of the ramp. This requirement can be met by interrupting propulsion power precisely at the right moment and relying on a combination of gravity and friction to stop the vehicle. A braking device to augment these forces also might be considered. If the vehicle is powered by batteries, there are many possibilities for a device to interrupt the flow of power to the vehicle. A simple tilt switch that disconnects the battery when the vehicle is level, but connects the battery when the vehicle is on a slope, will certainly do the job. For safety reasons, however, the rules prohibit the use of mercury switches (elemental mercury is toxic to humans), hence any tilt switch used in the vehicle must be of your own design. A metal ball bearing that rolls inside a small cage and makes contact with two electrodes, as illustrated in Figure 10, might serve as a suitable tilt switch. Other choices might be a spring loaded contact switch, such as the one shown in Figure 11, or a system that cuts off power to the wheels after the car has traveled a preset distance as measured by wheel rotations. This scheme will work well only if the wheels do not slip.

One interesting alternative to a mechanical switch would be to use an electronic timer circuit that shuts off power from the battery after a precise time interval. Through trial and error, you could set the elapsed time to just the right value so that the vehicle stops at the top of the ramp. One problem inherent with this open-loop timing system is that the vehicle does not actually sense its own arrival at the top of the hill, but rather infers it by precise timing. Because the speed of the vehicle may decrease with each successive run as battery energy is depleted, this timing scheme might cause problems. On the other hand, it is likely to be more reliable than solutions that involve mechanical parts.

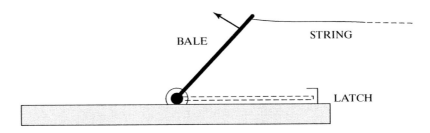

Figure 9.   Harnessing the stored mechanical energy of a mousetrap. The bale retracts in an arc when the mousetrap is released.

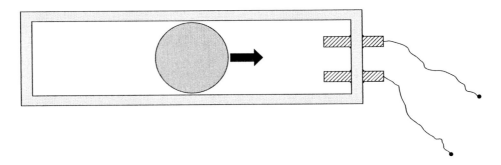

Figure 10.   Tilt switch made from a small enclosure, a ball bearing, and two contact points.

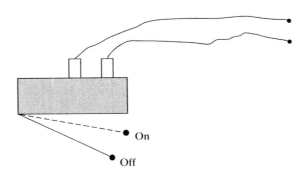

Figure 11.   Spring-loaded contact switch.

If a rubber band or mousetrap is chosen as the power source, then stopping the vehicle will require something other than an electrical switch. One crude way of stopping a vehicle propelled by mechanical energy storage is simply to allow the primary power source to run out (e.g., by allowing the rubber band to completely unwind). However crude this method, it is reliable because power input to the vehicle will *always* cease when the source of stored energy has been depleted.

Starting Device   If the vehicle is powered by a battery, then an electrical switch becomes the most feasible starting device. A rubber-band power source will require a mechanical device such as a pin or trip lever to initiate power flow to the wheels. A mousetrap can make use of its built-in trigger mechanism or any other starting mechanism that you can devise.

Make a First Cut at the Design

The first design iteration begins with rough estimations of the dimensions, parameters, and components of the vehicle to make sure that the design is technically feasible. After discussing the long list of design choices, you and your teammate decide upon a battery-powered vehicle. This decision makes available the many choices for a stopping device and power train. You feel that this design flexibility far outweighs the advantages of mechanical propulsion schemes. You decide upon a defensive strategy and agree to build a slower-moving, wedge-shaped vehicle driven by a small electric motor. The advantage of this design strategy is that the motor can be connected to the wheels using a small gear ratio, thereby providing higher torque at the wheels and a mechanical advantage that would be unavailable to a very fast vehicle. You plan to use plastic gears and axles purchased from an on-line Web site. The gear box will reduce the speed of the wheels relative to the motor shaft speed, providing added mechanical torque that will significantly increase the force available to push the opposing vehicle off the ramp. Because your vehicle will be slower than the others, it may not reach the top of the ramp first, but its wedge-shaped design will help to dislodge the front of any opposing vehicle that arrives first at the top of the hill. If your vehicle should happen to arrive first at the top of the hill, your car's defensive wedge shape will cause your opponent's car to ride over your car's body, allowing you to maintain your place at the top of the ramp.

You decide to use one motor with a single driven axle attached to both rear wheels. An alternative strategy would be to drive each rear wheel separately, thereby allowing the driven wheels to turn at different speeds. Such *differential* capability is essential for vehicles that travel curved paths, but in this case the vehicle must travel along a straight path only. By driving the wheels from a common shaft, you will reduce slippage, because both wheels will have to lose traction before forward motion is impaired. You briefly consider front-wheel drive, because you assume from hearing many car advertisements that front-wheel drive is superior to rear-wheel drive. Your teammate is quick to point out, however, that the advantage of front-wheel drive lies in its ability to help the car negotiate curves. Despite the media-driven message of "better traction," the advantages of front-wheel drive have nothing to do with your application. In fact, front-wheel drive may be a disadvantage to your wedge-shaped design, because it may cause your car to flip over forwards if another car travels on top of it (Figure 12). Your teammate draws the sketch of Figure 13 to illustrate this scenario. You abandon the idea of front-wheel drive.

Build, Document, Test, and Revise

A rough preliminary sketch of your car is shown in Figure 13. You've entered this sketch into a notebook in which you've been recording all information relevant to the project. Included in your notebook are design calculations, parts lists, and sketches of various pieces of the car. Shown in Figure 13 are the car's wedge-shaped design, a single drive shaft driven by a motor, belt, and pulleys, and a single switch to turn off the motor when the vehicle arrives at the top of the hill. Your design concept represents a trade-off between several competing possibilities, but you and your teammate have decided that the car's electric motor drive and defensive shape have the best chance of winning the competition.

REAR WHEEL DRIVE:

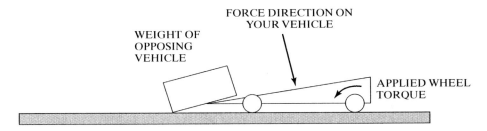

FRONT WHEEL DRIVE:

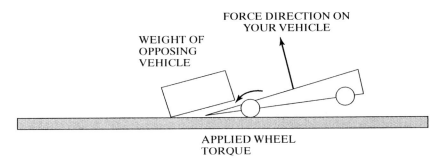

Figure 12.   Front- and rear-wheel drive options for a moving wedge vehicle.

The sketch in Figure 13 represents a beginning, but it is not the finished product. You still have many hurdles to overcome before your vehicle will be ready to compete. The next step in the design process involves building and testing a "first-cut" prototype. To help you in this phase of the design process, your professor has built a test ramp available to all contestants. You begin by constructing a chassis shell in the form of a wedge, without a motor drive or stopping mechanism.

You run your wedge-shaped vehicle up the ramp by hand. You soon discover that the bottom of the vehicle hits the ramp at the top of the hill, as depicted in Figure 14(a). The change in angle of the ramp is large, and all four wheels do not always maintain contact with the ramp surface. You discuss several solutions to this problem with your teammate. One solution would be to increase the size of the wheels, as shown in Figure 14(b). This change would decrease the mechanical advantage between the motor and the wheels, requiring you to recalculate the torque required from the motor. Another solution would be to make the vehicle shorter, as in Figure 14(c), but you realize that this solution would lead to a steeper angle for the wedge shape of the vehicle and reduce its effectiveness as a defensive strategy. (The sharper the wedge, the more capable the car will be of wedging itself under opposing vehicles. However, the largest thickness of the vehicle must stay the same to leave space for the motor and gear box.)

Revise Again

Your teammate suggests keeping the wheels and shape of the wedge the same and simply moving the rear wheels forward, as depicted in Figure 15. You rebuild the vehicle by moving the rear shaft mount forward, and you test the vehicle again. The redesigned vehicle no longer bottoms out on the ramp, and you claim success. Your professor sees your design changes and suggests that you test your vehicle under more realistic conditions. For example, what will happen when another vehicle rides over the top of your wedge-shaped body? You proceed to simulate such an event by placing a weight at various positions on the top of the car. The results of these additional tests suggest that moving the wheel location may not be the best solution to your problem. When you move the rear wheels forward, you change the base of support for the car's center of gravity. You discover that if an opposing vehicle rides over the top of your car, the net center of gravity moves toward the rear, eventually causing your car to topple backwards, as depicted in Figure 16.

Reality Check

These discoveries and setbacks may seem discouraging, but they are a normal part of the design process. Some things work the first time, while others do not. By observing and learning from failure and by building, testing, revising, and retesting, you can converge on the best solution that will meet your needs.

More Revisions

After some thought, you decide that increasing the size of the wheels may be the best option after all. Your teammate points out that you can simply change the ratio of the

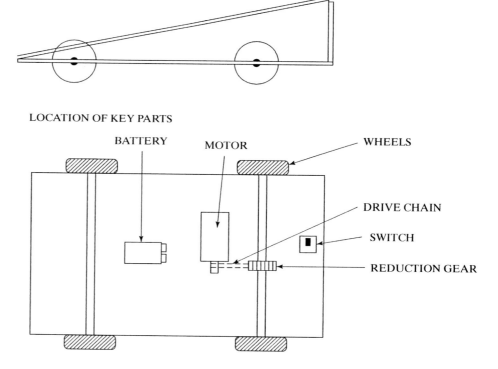

Figure 13.   Rough, preliminary sketch of a car for the Peak Performance Design Competition.

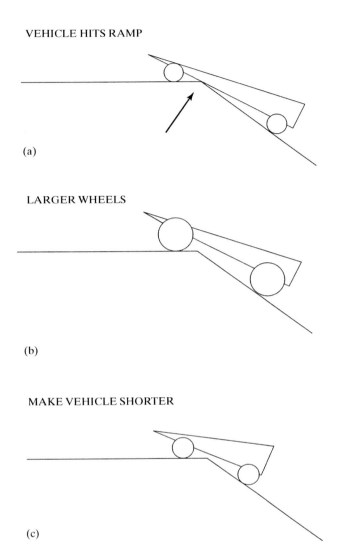

Figure 14. Vehicle at the top of the ramp. (a) Bottom of vehicle hits the ramp; (b) vehicle with larger wheels; (c) a shorter vehicle.

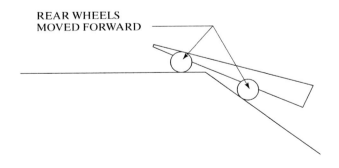

Figure 15. Moving the rear wheels forward.

gear box to preserve the net mechanical advantage between the motor and the wheels. This change will allow you to accommodate larger wheels. You buy some new wheels and try them with success. With the rear axle moved to its original location and the larger wheels in place, your car no longer bottoms out on the ramp.

You next consider the motor that will provide mechanical power to the drive shaft. Motors of all sizes and voltage ratings are available, including some alternating current (*ac*) motors, as well as direct current (*dc*) motors. Given that your car will be powered by batteries, your obvious choice is a dc motor. What voltage rating should you choose? You find no motors rated at 9 volts at the local hobby shop. "I don't think anyone makes 9-volt motors," says the salesperson behind the counter. You look up the Web pages of vendors,[2] scrutinize several catalogs, and find motors rated for 3, 6, 12, or 24 volts, but no 9-volt motors. Your professor explains that the rating of a motor specifies its operating voltage for continuous use. If a lower-than-rated voltage is used, the maximum torque available from the motor will be reduced. If the motor is connected to a higher-than-rated voltage, the excess current will heat the windings inside the motor and possibly damage it. During the competition, however, the motor will be energized only for about 15 seconds at a time. This interval may be short enough to allow a larger-than-rated voltage to be applied without damaging the motor. The feasibility of this intentional overloading must be verified by testing or by contacting the motor's manufacturer.

After hearing your professor's explanation, your team decides to purchase several different motors rated at 3 volts and 6 volts. You test each one by connecting it to a variable voltage supply and measure the current flow at several values of applied voltage.

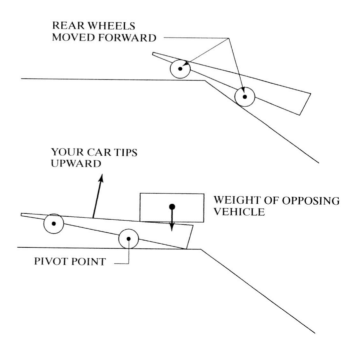

Figure 16.   Weight of opposing vehicle on top of rear end causes car to topple backwards.

[2] See, for example, *www.robotics.com* or *www.hobby-lobby.com*

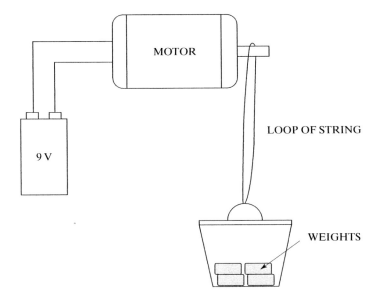

Figure 17.   Simple apparatus to measure motor torque.

You compute the power flow by multiplying the applied voltage by the current that actually flows to the motor. (Electrical power equals voltage times current.) You devise the apparatus shown in Figure 17 to measure the mechanical power delivered by the motor. Your contraption is a crude version of the industry-standard Prony brake used to measure motor torque.[3] The frictional rubbing of the weighted loop of string applies a mechanical load to the motor. You power each of your motors at the same voltage and add weights until the motor stalls. The motor that sustains the largest weight before stalling will have the highest torque. You check your mechanical loading measurements against your electrical measurements and use your data to determine which motor gives you the most mechanical torque when energized by a 9-volt power source.

As suggested by your professor, you and your teammate each keep a design notebook in which you record all your design decisions and the results of all your experiments and tests. Figure 18, for example, shows a page from your notebook in which you've recorded a list of the motors in your collection plus the results of the mechanical loading tests. You've also made a sketch of the loading apparatus of Figure 17 in your notebook. It's important to record the characteristics of the motors that you *don't* use, just in case your need to reconsider one of the rejected motors during a subsequent design revision. As your design proceeds, you record all calculations, specifications, and sketches pertinent to the drive train, including gear ratios, electrical power consumption, wheel diameters, weight of each part, and construction techniques. Your objective is to have a complete record of your design activities by the time you enter the vehicle competition.

---

[3] The Prony brake was invented in 1821 by Gaspard de Prony, a professor and examiner at the Ecole Polytechnique in France, as a way to measure the performance of machines and engines.

MOTOR A: TC-254			MOTOR B: RS-257-234		
# weights	V(volts)	I (amps)	# weights	V(volts)	I (amps)
0	9.0	0.02	0	9.0	0.05
1	8.9	0.05	1	8.8	0.1
2	8.9	0.07	2	8.7	0.17
3	8.8	0.1	3	8.5	0.23
4	8.7	0.2	4	8.0	0.3
5	8.0	0.5	5	7.6	0.7

MOTOR C: BOD-37A			MOTOR D: TOSH-7954		
# weights	V(volts)	I (amps)	# weights	V(volts)	I (amps)
0	9.0	0.01	0	9.0	0.01
1	8.9	0.04	1	8.9	0.11
2	8.9	0.05	2	8.9	0.21
3	8.8	0.1	3	8.8	0.31
4	8.7	0.25	4	8.7	0.41
5	8.0	0.52	5	8.7	0.51

Figure 18.   Page from lab notebook that documents mechanical loading tests on various motors.

PRACTICE!

1. Make a two-column list that outlines the advantages of the various power sources for the Design Competition.

2. Make a list of additional propulsion mechanisms not mentioned in this section that could be used to drive a Design Competition vehicle.

3. Make a two-column list that outlines the advantages of using gravity and friction versus an applied brake as a stopping mechanism for the Design Competition.

4. Determine the minimum energy needed to lift a vehicle of the maximum allowed weight (2 kilograms) from the bottom of the ramp to the top.

5. How much electrical energy (in joules) is needed to exert one newton of force over a distance of 1 meter (m)?

6. How much electrical power (in watts) is needed to exert one newton of force on a body over a distance of 1 m for 10 seconds?

7. Determine the number of turns per centimeter (cm) of wheel diameter that will be required to move a vehicle from the bottom of the ramp to the top of the ramp in the Design Competition.

8. Determine the diameter of the wheels needed to move a vehicle from the bottom of the ramp to the top in the Design Competition with 50 turns of the drive axle.

SUMMARY

The essential elements of the design process have been outlined at a very basic level. Design differs from analysis and reproduction because it involves multiple paths to solution, decision making, evaluation, revision, testing, and retesting. The *design cycle* is an important part of engineering problem solving, as are knowledge, experience, and intuition. *Documentation* is critical to the success of a product and should be an integral part of the design process.

The chapters that follow examine several aspects of design in more detail using the vehicle Design Competition as a continuing example. Some of the topics to be presented include teamwork, brainstorming, documentation, estimation, modeling, prototyping, and project organization. The use of computers is integrated into examples of these elements of engineering design.

KEY TERMS

Design	Analysis	Reproduction
Design cycle	Decision making	Testing
Evaluation	Iteration	Revision

PROBLEMS

The following problem statements can be used to practice problem-solving skills and idea generation. Some of them involve paper designs, while others are suitable for actual fabrication and testing.

1. Develop a design concept for a mechanism that will allow hands-free operation of a standard, wired telephone. Outline its basic form, key features, proposed method of construction, and prototyping plan. Consider size, weight, shape, safety factors, and ease of use.

2. Develop a concept for a device that will allow hands-free use of a cellular telephone without the addition of additional accessories such as an earphone or remote microphone. Your design should be based solely on a mechanical solution.

3. Design a device for carrying a cellular telephone on a bicycle. Your contraption should enable the rider to converse while holding on to the handlebars with both hands.

4. Design a device for securing a coffee cup near the driver's seat of an automobile. The device should prevent the cup from spilling and should not interfere with the proper operation of the car. It should be universally adaptable to a wide variety of vehicles. Address safety and liability issues as part of your design.

5. Develop at least three design concepts for a nonlethal mousetrap. Is your device cost-effective compared with an ordinary, spring-bale mousetrap? Is your trap more humane, and is it worth any added cost?

6. Devise a concept for a device that can dig holes in the ground for the installation of fence posts. Sketch a prototype and outline a test plan for your design concept.

7. Design a device that will allow the inside and outside surfaces of windows to be cleaned from the inside only. Compare projected cost with that of a simple, hand-held, squeegee-type window cleaner.

8. Design a system for feeding a pet lizard automatically when the owner is out of town.

9. Develop a design concept for a spill-free coffee cup.

10. Develop a design concept for a coffee-cup to be used by the driver of an automobile. The cup should enable fully hands-free operation.

11. Design a device for carrying bricks to the top of a house for chimney repair. (The alternative is to carry them up a ladder by hand.)

12. Design at least three different systems for measuring the height of a tall building.

13. Design a system that will enable a self-propelled lawn mower to cut the grass in a yard unattended.

14. Design a system for minimizing the number of red lights encountered by cars traveling east and west through a major city. The system should not unduly impede north-south traffic flow.

15. Devise a method for managing the flow of two-way railroad traffic on a one-track system. The single line of track has a parallel spur track located every five kilometers. These parallel sections of track allow one train to wait as another passes by in the opposite direction.

16. Develop a concept for a public transportation system in which every traveler can ride a private vehicle on demand from any one station to another.

17. Design a transportation system based on locating free-use bicycles at strategic points around a large city.

18. Design a transportation system based on locating one-time, fee-for-use automobiles at strategic points around a large city.

19. Most large airports provide carts for travelers to transport luggage from baggage claim areas to taxi stands, transit stations, and parking lots. Develop a system for locating and reclaiming carts that have been taken from a central terminal station.

20. Develop a design concept for a system to measure the speed of a passing train.

21. Design a system that will assist flight attendants in feeding passengers on a medium-size airplane without blocking the single central aisle with food and beverage carts.

22. Design a system for automatically turning off a small electric baking oven when a cake inside is done.

23. Design a system that will help a person locate misplaced eyeglasses.

24. Develop a concept that will assist individuals in finding keys that have been misplaced around the house.

25. Design an electric switch that will turn off lights if the room is vacated, but not sooner than some user-specified time interval.

26. Design a device that will enable a quadriplegic to change the channels on a television set.

27. Devise a system for turning on security lights at dusk and turning them off at dawn. These lights are to be installed throughout a large factory. Your system should have a single master override for all lights.

28. Design a warning system for your home freezer that will alert you to abrupt changes in temperature.

29. Design a method or concept for dispensing adhesive tape (e.g., "Scotch" tape) in small, precut lengths.

30. Design a system that will automatically water houseplants when they are in need of moisture.

31. Design a system that will selectively water sections of a garden based on the moisture content of the soil at the location of each plant.

32. Design an irrigation system that will bring water from a nearby pond to your vegetable garden.

33. Develop a design concept for a system that will automatically pick apples from the trees of a commercial apple orchard.

34. Design a system that can aerate the pond in a city park so that algae growth will not overtake other forms of wildlife.

35. Design a device that will allow a one-armed individual to properly use dental floss.

36. Design a system that will prevent the user of a battery charger from inserting the batteries the wrong way. The unit charges four AAA batteries simultaneously, but each battery must be inserted with its (+) end in the correct direction.

37. Design a method for counting the number of people who attend a football game.

38. Design a lamp post that will break away when struck by an errant automobile.

39. Design a system for automatically steering an oil tanker along a desired compass heading.

40. Design a weatherproof mail slot for a house that will keep cold air out but permit the insertion of mail from outside.

41. Most small sailboats have a tiller (steering stick) in lieu of a steering wheel. Design a system for automatically steering a tiller-controlled sailboat on a course that lies along a user-specified compass direction.

42. Design a system for automatically steering a tiller-controlled sailboat on a course that lies along a user-specified angle relative to the wind direction. Design for a simple boat that has no on-board electricity.

43. One of the problems with recycling of postconsumer waste is the sorting of materials. Consumers and homeowners cannot always be relied upon to sort correctly, yet one erroneously placed container can ruin a batch of recycled material. At the present time, most municipalities resort to manual labor to sort recyclable materials. Devise a concept that will sort metal cans, plastic bottles, and plastic containers at a recycling plant. Develop a plan for modeling and testing your system.

44. Design a kitchen device that will crush aluminum and steel cans in preparation for recycling. Such a device would be helpful for households that practice recycling but have limited storage space.

45. Devise a system for painting car bodies automatically by robot. You must include a method for training the robot for each painting task.

46. Devise a plan for a campus-wide information system that will allow any professor to access the grades of any student, while maintaining the privacy of the system to other users. A student also should be able to obtain his or her own grades, but not those of others.

47. Design an electric pencil sharpener that will turn off when the pencil has been properly sharpened.

48. Develop a design concept for a device that will turn on a car's windshield wipers automatically when rain falls. The wipers should come on only momentarily when rainfall is light but should be on all the time when the rainfall is moderate to heavy.

49. Design an apparatus that will keep a telescope pointed at a distant star despite the rotation of the earth.

50. Design a system for keeping a satellite's solar panels pointed at the sun.

51. Devise a system for transferring personnel in flight from one airplane to another.

52. Devise a system for automatically collecting tolls from cars traversing a major interstate highway. Note that many such systems exist throughout the United States. (See, for example, *www.mtafastlane.com or www.ezpass.com*.) This problem asks you to imagine (or find out) the details of how these systems work.

53. Laser communication, or "laser-com," is a system by which digital data is sent from one location to another via a modulated laser beam. (See, for example, *www.microlink.hr/omnibeam.html*, or *www.usa.canon.com/indtech/broadcasteq/canobeamdt50.html*.) Laser-com systems are used whenever hard connections via wires or fiber-optic cables are either too expensive or not possible. Laser-com links are much more difficult to tap for information than are other forms of wireless communication; hence, such systems are of obvious interest to the military for battlefield applications. One of the principal drawbacks of laser-com systems is the difficulty in maintaining beam alignment when the sender and receiver are moving. Design a system that will automatically direct the communication beams sent by two military vehicles to their respective receiving vehicles.

54. Design a concept for a voice-synthesized prompting system that can provide cues for an individual who must take medication on a strict regimen. The device need not be pocket sized, but should be portable and battery operated.

55. Design a system consisting of several panic buttons that will be installed at each of several workshop fabrication stations on a factory floor. Pressing any one of these buttons would activate a signal at a central control console and identify the location of the activated button. Ideally, voice communication over the system would be a desirable feature. One matter to consider is whether a wired or a wireless system is better.

56. An elementary school teacher needs a calendar-teaching system to help students learn about dates, appointments, and scheduling events. Your professor has asked you to develop a design concept. The basic system should be a large pad over which a monthly calendar can be placed. The underlying pad should have touch-sensitive sensors that can detect a finger placed on each day block in the calendar. The entire unit should interface with a desktop computer which will run a question-and-answer game or program. The typical types of questions to be asked might include, "You have scheduled a dentist appointment 2 weeks from today. Point to the day on the calendar on which you should go to the dentist," or "Sara's birthday is on February 11. Point to that day on the calendar." An appropriate reward, either visual, auditory, or both, should be issued by the computer for correct answers. A nonintimidating signal should be issued for incorrect answers. Outline the key features of your system and devise a development plan.

The following eight problems involve devices that will assist the professor running a Design Competition called "Peak Performance." In this competition, students are asked to build small, self-contained vehicles that travel up opposite sides of a trapezoidal ramp. The winner is the vehicle that lies closest to the top of the ramp after a 15-second time interval.

57. The rules of the Peak-Performance Design Competition state that each student-designed, autonomous vehicle be placed behind a starting line located 30 cm up the side of a 1.5-m. ramp. After the starting signal is given from the judge, contestants must release their vehicles, which then have 15 seconds to acquire and maintain a dominant position at the top of the ramp. Any vehicle that travels over the 30-cm starting line prior to the "go" signal loses the race. Currently, the starting sequence is initiated orally by the judge and timed by stopwatch. This system leads to great variability among judges, as many use different starting signals (e.g., "on your mark, get set, go!" or "one, two, three, go!"), and one may be lax in timing or checking for starting-line violations.

Design a system consisting of starting-line sensors, a start signal, a 15-second interval signal, and starting-line violation signals for each side of a double ramp.

The judge should have a button that initiates the start sequence. A series of periodic beeps that mimic the words, "ready, set, go!" should sound, with the final "go" being a loud and clearly distinguishable tone or buzzer. In addition, a green light or LED should illuminate when the "go" signal is sounded. The system should time for 15 seconds, then sound another tone or buzzer to indicate the end of the 15-second time interval. If a vehicle crosses the starting line prior to the "go" signal, a red light should go on for the violating vehicle's side of the ramp, and a special "violation" signal should be sounded to alert the judge.

58. Teams in the Peak Performance Design Competition are called to the floor when it is their turn to compete. After the initial call, each team has 3 minutes to arrive at its starting line. A team that does not arrive at the starting line after 3 minutes loses that run. Warnings are supposed to be given 2 minutes and 1 minute before the deadline. Traditionally, the announcer has called the teams and issued these warnings orally. With three races running simultaneously, all starting at different times, and with only some teams requiring the full 3 minutes to arrive, the proper issuing of these cues has been lax. The judges have asked that you design an automated system that will inform a given team how much of its 3-minute sequence has elapsed. The system must send an appropriate signal, oral, auditory, or visual, to only the affected team, and the timing sequence must be initiated from the judges' bench. As many as 80 teams may compete on a given day, and each is assigned one work table from a large array of 3 × 8-foot tables where the competition is held. Typically, the team being called is delayed, because it is repairing or modifying its vehicle.

    One of the key design issues is whether a wireless or wired system is better, given the logistic constraints of the competition environment. Because the event operates on a strict budget, final cost also is an important factor.

59. Vehicles entering the Peak Performance Design Competition must meet several requirements including a maximum battery-voltage limit. Each vehicle is checked once with a voltmeter at the start of the day by the head judge. Having a standardized voltage-checking device would shorten the time for voltage checking. Design a unit that has a rotary (or other type of) switch that can select a predetermined battery voltage. If the measured battery falls within the acceptable range, a green light should come on. If the voltage falls below or above the range, yellow and red lights, respectively, should come on.

60. Outline the design of a software tracking system for the Peak Performance Design Competition. Your system should enable the judges to automatically match up teams for matches, randomly at first, but by demonstrated ability thereafter (best teams against best teams; worst teams against worst teams). The program should display match sets before each round of the competition, and allow the recording judge to enter the result of each match after its winner has been determined. Assume a competition of up to 80 teams and six sets of matches between contenders.

61. Design a system for projecting matches on a display board so that the audience watching the Peak Performance Design Competition can keep track of who is racing who and the results of each match. Assume a competition of 20 teams with six sets of matches between contenders.

62. Design a system for detecting start-line violations for contenders in the Peak Performance Design Competition.

63. Design a system for determining the winner of each match in the Peak Performance Design Competition. Recall that the winner is the vehicle nearest the

center of the ramp after a 15-second time interval. Note that "nearest" can be an entirely subjective term; hence, your system for determining the winner must precisely define what "nearest" means.

64. Design a software system that will assist in registration for the Peak Performance Design Competition. Registration information includes name, address, and the school of the contenders. Registrants must pay a small fee, sign photograph permission and liability waiver forms, and receive an event T-shirt and assigned vehicle number. Several individuals work simultaneously on competition day to register participants as quickly as possible so that the event can begin on time.

65. A local company employs several workers who sort and package small (1 to 2 cm) parts in the 10 to 100-gram range. A typical operation might consist of putting 10 small parts in a polyethylene bag for subsequent packaging. As part of a course design project, your professor has asked you to design a mechanical sorting apparatus for dispensing these parts one at time so that the employees do not have to pick them up by hand. Develop an outline for how such a system might work, and draw a sketch of your proposed apparatus.

66. Ace Cleaning Services employs cognitively-challanged individuals performing a variety of cleaning tasks at four major buildings in the downtown area. Many of these workers have poor cognitive abilities and are unable to generalize the cleaning skills they have been taught. They cannot perform a supervisor-demonstrated office-cleaning task in a different office, even if a similar operation is involved. As a result, their cleaning job performance is often poor. Many of the employees rely on supervisor cues to repeatedly perform to acceptable standards the same task in different locations.

    A crew from Ace has been assigned to a 22-story office building with over 500,000 square feet of space that requires cleaning. Approximately 30 employees service this building between 6:00 a.m. and 10:00 a.m. with a staffing pattern of nine people. Workers are dispersed throughout the building to perform their daily cleaning routines. Supervisors are responsible for training and for checking that the work has been performed to acceptable standards. Many of the supervisors also perform direct labor, and hence cannot consistently provide prompting or cues to the rest of the employees all the time. A communication system is needed that can provide on-the-job cues to the cleaning staff. One system is needed for individuals who are literate and another for individuals who are not. Your task in this project is to design a modular system for either type of individual. The system must be designed so that additional units can be reproduced at low cost. As part of a project in your engineering design class, your professor has asked you to devise a system for providing recorded cues to Ace's employees. Develop a concept for the system, draw a sketch of one implementation, and outline how such a system might work.

67. A teacher at the nearby Carver School teaches a student who has severe developmental delays. This student is highly motivated by the Wheel of Fortune™ TV game show. The teacher currently has a 4-foot-diameter, wall-mounted, colorfully painted cardboard circle that spins and simulates the real game. Use of this wheel is supplemented by video clips of the game played on a VCR. The teacher would like a more elaborate, electronically-interfaced version of the game that enables the spinning dial to activate lights, voice, and the VCR clips. Despite the circuslike nature of this project, it is a top priority of the Carver school system. The customer is in need of an imaginative and creative response to this problem, and your engineering professor has asked you for ideas. Sketch several versions of the

system, highlighting the advantages and disadvantages of each approach. How would you test the success of your design?

68. A teacher wants a clock system that can help students to learn the relationship between time displayed by digital clocks and time displayed by analog clocks. The system should have a console that contains a large analog clock face, as well as a digital clock display with large digits. In operation, the teacher will set either clock, then ask the student to set the other clock to the same time. If the student sets the time correctly, the unit should signal the student appropriately. If the student fails to set the time correctly, the unit should also issue an appropriate response. Outline the salient features of such a system.

69. Your school has been asked by an individual confined to a wheelchair to build a small motorized flagpole that can be raised and lowered by pressing buttons. The person needs such a device to hold a bright orange flag to provide visibility outdoors while navigating busy city streets and sidewalks. The flag must be lowered when the individual enters buildings so that the pole does not interfere with doorways and low ceilings. Here is a copy of the letter received by your school:

East Crescent Residence Facility
Eleven Hastings Drive
West Walworth, MA 02100

Prof. Hugo Gomez
College of Engineering
Correll University
44 Hartford St.
Canton, MA 02215

May 18, 2001

RE: Retractable Flag for Wheelchair

Dear Professor Gomez,

I am the supervisor of a residence facility that services adults with special needs. One of our residents is confined to a wheelchair and spends a great deal of time traveling throughout the community, often on busy streets, in a motorized wheelchair. Although a flag on a long pole would increase her safety, she is reluctant to install one on her wheelchair, because it becomes a problem in restaurants, crowded stores, and on public buses. I was wondering if you might have some students who could design an electrically retractable flag, possibly with visual enhancement (e.g., a flashing light) that could be raised or lowered by the individual on demand. The flag deployment mechanism could operate from either the wheelchair's existing automobile-type storage battery or its own self-contained battery. If such a device is possible, could you give me a call? I would appreciate any assistance that you might be able to offer.

Sincerely yours,

Liz DeWalt
Director

Prof. Gomez has asked you to try to build such a device for Ms. DeWalt. How would you approach such a task? Such a seemingly simple device actually can be more complicated to design than you might think. Draw a sketch of the wheel-chair device, then devise a design plan for building and testing several designs. Include a list of possible safety hazards to bystanders and the user. How can you include the user in the design process, and why is it advisable to do so? Also write a report of your preliminary findings for Prof. Gomez. Your design strategy should begin with a conceptual drawing of the device that you can send to Ms. DeWalt for comments. Generate a specification list and general drawing of the apparatus as well as a cover letter to Ms. DeWalt.

Design Considerations: One goal of your design might be to make a flag device that can be mounted on any wheelchair, not just on that of Ms. DeWalt's client. Because many wheelchairs are custom designed for the user, your device must be easily adaptable for mounting on different wheelchair styles. Not all wheelchairs are motorized, hence your device must operate from its own batteries to accommodate hand-pushed wheelchairs. Another consideration in favor of separate battery power is that motorized wheelchair manufacturers usually specify that no other electrical or electronic equipment be connected to the primary motor battery for reasons of safety, reliability, and power integrity.

One last consideration concerns the placement of the switch needed to activate the flag. Like the flag itself, the activation switch must easily attach to structural features of the wheelchair and must be within easy reach of the user. At the same time, it must not be so obtrusive that it distracts the user when not in use and must not hurt anyone.

70. Develop a design concept for a computer-interfaced electronic display board that can be placed in the lobby of an office building to display messages of the day, announce upcoming seminars, or indicate the location of special events. The objective of the problem is to use a matrix of addressable light-emitting diodes (LEDs) rather than a video display. The system should accept messages by wire from a remote site. One approach might be to design your display board system so that it is capable of independently connecting to a local-area computer network. Alternatively, you could build a separate remote device that could be connected to a desktop computer and then brought down to the display board to load in the data. These examples are suggestions only. In general, any means for getting data to the board is acceptable, but a separate computer (PC) cannot become a dedicated part of the finished display.

71. An engineer is interested in measuring the small-valued ac magnetic fields generated by power lines and appliances. You have been asked to design a battery-powered, hand-held instrument capable of measuring the magnitude of ac magnetic fields in the range 0.1 to 10 μT (microtesla) at frequencies of 50-60 Hz. Magnetic fields of this magnitude are very small and are difficult to measure accurately. For comparison, the earth's dc magnetic field is on the order of 50 μT, and the magnetic field inside a typical electric motor is on the order of 1 T.

Using your knowledge of physics, summarize the important features that such a device should have. Outline a design plan for its development and construction. You have several options for the primary sensor. For example, it may consist of a flat coil of wire of appropriate diameter and number of turns, or, alternatively, you might consider using a commercially available semiconductor sensor. Note that dc fields, such as those produced by the earth or any nearby permanent magnets, are not of interest. Hence, any signal produced by dc fields in your instrument should be filtered out. Ideally, your unit should have a digital or analog display device and should accommodate a remote probe if possible.

72. A friend of yours runs a residence home for individuals who are mentally and physically challenged. She would like a medicine dispenser for dispensing pills at specific times. The unit is to be carried by an individual and must have sufficient capacity to hold medication for at least 1 day. The unit should open a cassette or compartment and should emit an audible or visual signal when it dispenses medication. The unit must be easy to load and should be easily programmable by a residence-home supervisor. Your friend has asked you to assess the feasibility of developing such a unit. Get together with one or more other students. Discuss the feasibility of the idea and develop several design concepts for further evaluation.

73. A friend of yours is an enthusiast of remote-control model airplanes. One perennial problem with radio-controlled airplanes concerns the lack of knowledge about the flight direction and orientation of the airplane when it is far from the ground-based operator. When the airplane is too far away to be seen clearly, the operator loses the ability to correctly control its motion. Develop a design concept for a roll-, pitch-, and compass-heading indicator system that can be mounted on the model airplane and used to send the information via radio back to the operator's control console. Your system should sense the pitch and roll of the airplane over the range +90 degrees to −90 degrees and be able to withstand a full 360-degree roll or loop-de-loop.

74. Your family has asked you to design a remote readout system for a vacation home to be interrogated by a remote computer over a modem and telephone line. The unit in the vacation home should answer the phone after 10 rings, provide means for an entry password, and then provide the following information: inside and outside temperatures, presence of any running water in the house, presence of any loud noises or unusual motion, and status of alarm switches installed on doors and windows. Discuss the design specifications for such a unit and develop a block diagram for its design and implementation.

3

Working in Teams

The engineer uses many technical skills when designing a device, product, or system. These skills represent the knowledge base acquired through years of study and on-the-job training. They are all but useless, however, if the engineer is unable to communicate and work with others. In addition to a strong set of technical skills, a good engineer must have nontechnical skills that include the ability to work in a team, generate new ideas, keep good documentation, and work within the framework of project management. Seldom does an engineer simply sit down and get right to work on the technical details of a project. Before beginning work in earnest, he or she spends much time planning, conducting feasibility studies, reviewing results of other projects, doing approximate calculations, interacting with other engineers, and defining the approach to the problem. This chapter introduces several teamwork skills that are essential elements of successful design.

SECTIONS

- Teamwork Skills
- Brainstorming
- Documentation: The Key to Project Success
- Project Management: Keeping the Team on Track

OBJECTIVES

In this chapter, you will learn about

- Teamwork as an essential element of engineering design.
- Brainstorming.
- Documentation and its vital role in the design process.
- Project management skills.

TEAMWORK SKILLS

The spirit of rugged individualism persists as a theme in books, movies, and television. The image of a lone hero striving for truth and justice against insurmountable odds appeals to our sense of adventure and daring. The dream of becoming the sole entrepreneur who endures economic and technical hardship to change the face of technology, to head a startup company of one that single-handedly takes on Microsoft or another large corporation, arouses our pioneering spirit. Yet, in the real world, engineers seldom work alone. Most engineering problems are interdisciplinary. True progress requires teamwork, cooperation, and the contributions of many individuals. This concept is easy to understand in the context of designing large structures, such as bridges, airports, or global computer networks. Teamwork is also critical to the design of complicated devices, such as automobiles, video players, medical implants, network routers, copy machines, or cellular telephones. These devices, and others like them, cannot be designed by one person alone. The great engineering accomplishments in space exploration, such as the Apollo moon landing, the International Space Station, and the Hubble space telescope, required hundreds (in some cases thousands) of engineers working with teams of physicists, chemists, astronomers, material scientists, medical specialists, mathematicians, and project managers. Teamwork is an important skill, and you must master it if you are to be a good engineer. Working in a team, as in Figure 1, requires that you speak clearly, write effectively, and have the ability to see another person's point of view. Each member of a team must understand how his or her task relates to the responsibilities of the team as a whole.

Many engineering firms offer team-building workshops as part of their employee training programs. Self-help books on the subject of teamwork abound. You'll have many opportunities to work as a team if you study engineering, and you should treat each one as a learning experience.

Effective Team Building

An effective team is one that works well together. It functions at its maximum potential when solving a design problem and thrives on the special capabilities of its individual members. One key characteristic of an effective team is a good supportive attitude among fellow teammates and team activities. Team morale and a sense of professionalism can be enhanced if team members agree upon some rules of behavior. The following set of guidelines illustrates one possible approach to building an effective design team.

1. Define Clear Roles

Each team member should understand how he or she is to function within the team. The responsibilities of each individual should be defined *before* work begins on the project. Roles need not be mutually exclusive, but they should be defined so that all aspects of the design problem fall within the jurisdiction of at least one person. In that way, no task will "fall between the cracks" during the design process.

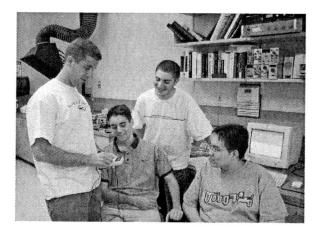

Figure 1.   Students working on a design project build strong team relationships.

2. Agree Upon Goals

Members of the team should agree upon the goals of the project. This consensus is not as easily achieved as you might think. One teammate may want to solve the problem using a traditional, time-tested approach, while another may want to attempt a far-out, esoteric path to success. Define a realistic set of goals at the outset. If the design process brings surprises, you can always redefine your goals midway through the project.

3. Define Procedures

Teammates should agree on a set of procedures for getting things done. Everything from documentation and the ordering of parts to communication with professors, clients, and customers should follow a predetermined procedure. In that way, misunderstandings about conduct can be greatly reduced.

4. Develop Effective Interpersonal Relationships

You must learn to work with everyone on your team, even with those individuals whom you may personally dislike. In the real world, a client will seldom care about any conflicts that occur behind the scenes. It's a sign of engineering professionalism to be able to rise above personality clashes as you concentrate on the job at hand. Be nice. Be professional. Forbid name calling, accusations, and assigning fault between team members.

5. Define Leadership Roles

Some teams work best when a single person emerges as a chosen leader. Other teams work better by consensus using distributed leadership or even no leadership at all. Regardless of your team's style, make sure that leadership roles are clearly defined and agreed upon at the start of a project.

PROFESSIONAL SUCCESS: YOU'RE THE TEAM LEADER, ONE TEAMMATE HAS DISAPPEARED, AND YOU'RE DOING ALL THE WORK

It's impossible to get along with all people all the time. When you work closely with other individuals, personal conflicts are inevitable. At times, these disagreements occur because one team member has failed to meet his or her responsibilities. At other times, the conflict arises from fundamental differences in personal outlook or priorities. However complicated your team relationships may become, remember that your customer does not care about them. Your customer is interested in receiving a well-designed product that reflects your best engineering abilities. It's up to you to resolve team conflicts internally. This resolution may mean that some team members will do more work than others, even if they will not be rewarded for their extra efforts. A good leader understands this trade-off and devises a plan to work around an errant teammate. Such situations may seem frustrating and unfair, but they happen in the real engineering world all the time. Learning how to deal with them as a student is part of your engineering education.

PRACTICE!

1. Define the roles, goals, and procedures that might apply to the design and construction of an eight-lane highway system under a major metropolitan city (*www.bigdig.com*).

2. Define the roles, goals, and procedures for a team of software engineers developing a Web site for the sales catalog of a national hardware store (*www.truevalue.com*).

3. Define the roles for a team of electrical and mechanical engineers developing a solar-powered car (*www.solarcar.arizona.edu*).

4. Define the roles, goals, and procedures that might apply to a team of biomedical engineers developing an artificial heart for mechanical implantation inside human subjects (*www.abiomed.com*).

5. Show how the five elements of effective team building might apply to the functioning of a soccer team (*www.fysa.com*).

6. Define the roles, goals, and procedures that might apply to the design and construction of an international space station (*www.boeing.com/defense-space/space/space station*).

BRAINSTORMING

One obvious area where teamwork plays an important role is the generation of new ideas for problem solving. When engineers gather to solve problems, they often resort to a creative process called brainstorming. Brainstorming requires a spontaneous mode of thinking that frees the mind from traditional boundaries. All too often, we limit our problem-solving approach to obvious solutions that have worked in the past. Responsible engineering sometimes requires that we consider other design alternatives, including those previously untried. A good engineer will never settle on a solution just because it's the first one to come to mind. When engineers brainstorm, creativity proceeds spontaneously unfettered by concerns that an idea is "way out" or impractical. When the constraints of traditional paradigms are removed, new solutions often emerge. Hearing the ideas of your teammates can tap the ideas buried deep inside your brain. Promising, but different, ideas are discarded as unfeasible only after study, analysis, and comparison with competing ideas. Brainstorming allows the engineer to consider as many options as possible before choosing the final design path.

Brainstorming can be done informally, or it can follow one of several time-tested formal methods These formal methods are appropriate for large group settings where organization is needed to avoid chaos. Less formal brainstorming methods are reserved for groups of one to three people who wish to generate ideas. Although they differ in execution, formal and informal brainstorming methods share the same set of core principles. The primary goal is to foster the uninhibited free exchange of ideas by creating a friendly, nonjudgmental environment. Brainstorming is an art. It requires practice, but anyone who has an open mind and some imagination learn this important skill.

Ground Rules for Brainstorming

The ground rules for brainstorming are designed to create a friendly, nonthreatening environment that encourages the free flow of ideas. Although the specific rules may vary, depending on the procedures followed, the following list can serve as a guideline:

1. No holding back. Any idea may be brought to the floor at any time.
2. No boundaries. An idea is never too outrageous or "way out" to mention.
3. No criticizing. An idea may not be criticized until the final discussion phase.
4. No dismissing. An idea may not be discounted until after group discussion.
5. No limit. There is no such thing as having too many ideas: the more the better.
6. No restrictions. Participants may generate ideas from any field of expertise.
7. No shame. A participant should never feel embarrassed about bringing up what seems like a stupid idea.

When a brainstorming session is in progress, one person should act as the facilitator, and another should record everyone's ideas. It's also possible to use video or audio tape in lieu of a human secretary.

Formal Brainstorming Method

When a large group gets together to brainstorm, formal structure is helpful. Without such a structure, a flood of competing ideas, all brought to the floor simultaneously, can create chaos. Instead of thinking creatively, participants become confrontational as they strive to be heard and gain a voice in the conversation. With so many randomly competing opinions, each person's creative process is inhibited, and the brainstorming session becomes unproductive. This effect is sometimes called "idea chaos." Adding formal structure to the brainstorming session restricts the flow of ideas to a manageable rate without restricting the number of ideas generated. In fact, the addition of a formal structure in large group settings can enhance the brain's creative process by preventing aggressive individuals from dominating the conversation and by providing time for people to think.

Of the many formal brainstorming techniques that exist, the *idea trigger* method has been well tested and is used often by brainstorming specialists in large group settings. The idea trigger method is based on the work of psychologists[1] and has been shown to enhance the brain's creative process. It relies on a process of alternating   tension and relaxation that taps the brain's creative potential. By listening to the ideas of others, receiving the foreign stimulus of other people's spoken ideas, and being forced to respond with counter ideas, a participant's behavioral patterns, personality constraints, and narrow modes of thinking can momentarily be broken, allowing ideas hidden in the recesses of the brain to come to the foreground. A shy participant who is reluctant to offer seemingly silly ideas, for example, will be more willing to do so under the alternating tension and relaxation of the purge-trigger sequence.

The idea trigger method requires a leader, at least four participants, and a printed form such as the one shown in Figure 2. The procedure has three phases, as follows.[2]

Phase 1: Idea Generation Phase   The problem or design issue is summarized by the leader. Each person is given a blank copy of the form shown in Figure 2. Without talking, each participant writes down in rapid succession as many ideas or solutions as possible. These entries are placed under Column 1. Key words suffice; whole sentences are not necessary. During the idea-generation phase, participants open their minds, consider many alternatives, and do not worry if ideas seem too trivial or ridiculous. "Pie in the sky" radical, or impossible ideas should be included. In short, participants write down anything that comes to mind that may be relevant to the problem. The fact that ideas are written down silently removes the element of intimidation from the idea-generation process.

After the first 2 minutes of the session, the group takes a break and then attempts to write down additional ideas under Column 1 for another 60 seconds. This *tension and relaxation* sequence has been shown to enhance creativity. It helps to extract all ideas from the brain's subconscious memory, much like squeezing and releasing a sponge several times to extract all the water.

Phase 2: Idea Trigger Phase   After the idea generation phase, the leader calls upon all members of the group. Each participant takes a turn reading his or her entries from Column 1. As each person recites Column-1 entries, others silently cross out the duplicates on their own lists. Hearing the ideas of others will trigger new ideas, which each person should enter under Column 2 as soon as they emerge. This process is called *idea triggering*. Hearing the remarks of others while pausing from the act of speaking causes the hidden thoughts stored in the subconscious to surface. The purpose of the idea trigger phase is not to discount the ideas from Column 1, but rather to amplify them, modify them, or generate new ideas.

After all members have read their Column-1 entries and have completed their Column-2 entries, the idea trigger process is repeated again. This time, entries from Column 2 are read, and any new ideas triggered are entered under Column 3. The process is repeated, with entries added to Columns 4, 5, etc., until all ideas are exhausted. Complex problems may require as many as five rounds of idea trigger phase.

---

[1] G. H. Muller, *The Idea Trigger Session Primer*, Ann Arbor, MI: A.I.R. Foundation, 197 S. F. Love, *Mastery and Management of Time*, Englewood Cliffs, NJ: Prentice-Hall, 1981.

[2] C. Lovas, *Integrating Design into the Engineering Curriculum*, Dallas, TX: Engineering Design Services Short Course and Workshop, October 1995.

IDEA TRIGGER SESSION

COLUMN 1	COLUMN 2	COLUMN 3	COLUMN 4
120 MINUTES			
60 SECONDS			

CONTRIBUTOR:

Figure 2.   Blank form for the idea trigger session.

The entries that appear under the second and third columns (and the fourth and fifth columns if the problem is complex) are usually the most creative. Such richness results from several factors. Often participants are secretly angered at having had their ideas stolen by another. This simple competitive pressure can propel a person toward new, unexplored territory. Conversely, seeing that one's ideas have not been duplicated by others can provide positive reinforcement, pushing the participant to come up with even better ideas. Some individuals may respond to their own unduplicated entries with a desire to produce more as a way of hoarding the good ideas. Yet others may subconsciously think that augmenting previously discussed ideas fosters group cooperation.

Phase 3: Compilation Phase   When the idea trigger phase has been completed, it's the job of the leader to compile everyone's sheets and make one master list of all the ideas that have been generated. The group then proceeds to discuss all ideas, discarding the ones that probably will not work, and deciding which of the remaining ideas are appropriate for further consideration and development.

EXAMPLE 1: A FORMAL BRAIN-STORMING SESSION

Let's illustrate the formal idea trigger method with an example. Four students, Tina, Juan, Paul, and Karin, are designing an entry for a design competition. The overall objective of the competition is to design a self-propelled vehicle that can climb a 1.5-meter ramp, stop at the top, and prevail over an opposing vehicle climbing up the ramp from the other side. The four students recently held a brainstorming session using the idea trigger method. They addressed all elements of the car design, including the issues of propulsion, offensive and defensive strategies, and a stopping mechanism. The following discussion chronicles their brainstorming session. Tina acted as the leader and timed the first 2 minutes, the break, and the subsequent 60-second idea generation phase. At the end of the phase, Juan's page looked like this:

JUAN	IDEA GENERATION PHASE COLUMN 1 (2 MINUTES):
	Support structure = wood (easy to make)
	Use angle irons from Mechano™
	Plastic body for lighter weight
	Zinc air batteries (lightweight)
	Wheels taken from my radio-controlled car
	Rubber band for chain drive
	Small car will be harder for opponent to deflect
	1 MINUTE:
	Ramming device
	Wedge-shaped body

Juan read his entries. As Paul listened he crossed out his own duplicate entries. When Juan was finished, Paul's first column, including crossouts, looked like this:

PAUL	IDEA GENERATION PHASE COLUMN 1 (2 MINUTES):
	~~No heavy batteries (use zinc air)~~
	Larger wheels for slower turning speed
	Gear box
	Higher torque (harder for opponent to push backwards)
	~~Use plastic for body~~
	Electronic timer for stopping mechanism
	Rechargeable batteries
	~~Wedge-shaped design~~
	1 MINUTE:
	~~Buy wheels from hobby shop for radio-controlled car~~
	Sense speed, determine distance traveled
	Aluminum frame

Next Karin read those of her entries that had not been duplicated by Juan. As Paul listened an idea flashed into his head. *A threaded rod*, he thought. *We can make the drive shaft from a threaded rod.* Paul reasoned that they could make the drive shaft from a threaded rod and have it screw a sliding nut toward a cutoff switch. The method would not be foolproof, because slipping wheels could ruin the system's ability to track distance. It seemed worth discussing, though, so Paul wrote down "threaded rod" under his Column 2 entries.

When Karin heard Juan read his "ramming device" entry, it had made her think about using an ejected object as part of an offensive strategy. She wrote the words "ejected device" under her Column 2 entries. Tina reacted similarly to Juan's idea and wrote the words, "lob something on the track ahead of opposing car" under her Column 2 entries. The spoken trigger phase made its way around the group. When everyone had finished, Tina acting as leader, started the process again. This time, everyone read their Column 2 entries and wrote down new ideas under Column 3. As Karin read her entry about ejected devices from Column 2, Tina got another idea. The idea of an ejected object brought to her a fleeting image from the Herman Melville novel *Moby Dick*. She imagined a flying spear with a barbed tip shot ahead of the vehicle over the top of the hill. *After hitting the carpet in front of the opposing vehicle,* she thought, *the barbed tip will dig into the carpet, blocking the other car. This spear will be very difficult to dislodge.* Tina wrote down "harpoon" under her Column 3 entries.

The second idea-trigger round progressed, and Tina started a third. After about 45 minutes, the entire Phase 2 session was finished. Tina suggested a break so that she could compile everyone's lists of ideas. Her combined list of entries from everyone's three columns looked like this:

COMPLETE LIST OF IDEAS FROM EVERYONE'S SHEETS

SHAPE:

Small car = harder for opponent to deflect

Wedge-shaped vehicle having same width as track

Rolling can design

Snow-plow shaped wedge

STRUCTURE:

Support structure = wood (easy to make)

Aluminum frame

Plastic body for light weight.

Use angle irons from Mechano™

Hot-melt glue balsa wood

POWER:

Zinc air batteries (lightweight)

Rechargeable batteries

Change batteries after every run

Electronic timer for stopping mechanism

Microprocessor-controlled car with onboard sensors

Sense speed, determine distance traveled from microprocessor software

PROPULSION:

Wheels from radio-controlled car purchased at hobby shop

Large wheels

COMPLETE LIST OF IDEAS FROM EVERYONE'S SHEETS

PROPULSION:

Rubber band for chain drive

Plastic-linked chain from junked radio-controlled car chassis

Single large mousetrap with mechanical links

Wind-up large rubber band

STRATEGIES:

Ramming device

Flying barbed harpoon

Pickup arm

Throw jacks in front of oncoming opponent

Roll over opponent with large roller

After the break, Tina reconvened the team to discuss the list of ideas. They weeded out the ones that did not seem feasible and compared ideas that looked promising. They combined multiple ideas and converged on a slow-moving, wedge-shaped vehicle concept for the prototype stage. They also decided to try out Tina's offensive strategy of a flying harpoon designed to dig into the carpet and block the path of the opposing vehicle.

Informal Brainstorming

The formal brainstorming method discussed in the previous section requires organization and planning. In contrast, informal brainstorming can be done anywhere. As a technique for engineering design, informal brainstorming in a round table format is appropriate for small groups of people. Ideas are contributed in random order by any participant. The flow of ideas need not be logical, and new proposals can be offered whenever they come to mind. The previously introduced ground rules should still be enforced during an informal brainstorming session.

EXAMPLE 2: INFORMAL BRAIN-STORMING

The following example of an informal brainstorming session describes a conversation that might have taken place between two team members working on a design competition in which the objective is to design a battery-powered vehicle capable of climbing a ramp and stopping at the top. In this case, Tina and Juan discuss the problem of how to stop the vehicle when it arrives at the top of the ramp. Note the ebb and flow of ideas between the two students. They do not immediately fixate on the first idea that comes to mind, but instead allow the flow of ideas to lead them to the solution most likely to succeed.

Tina: "Let's use a switch to turn off the electric motor when the car gets to the top of the ramp."

Juan: "OK, we could." *He thought for a while.* "We could also modify the switch so that it trails behind and is springloaded into the closed position. Putting the car on a flat surface will press the lever arm, close the switch, and connect the battery to the motor. When the car reaches the top, the switch arm will stay on the slope, allowing the switch arm to spring downward. The switch will open, disconnect the battery from the motor, and stop the car." (Juan drew the sketch shown in Figure 3.)

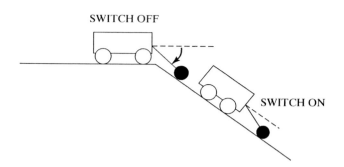

Figure 3.   Juan's idea for a stopping switch.

Tina: "That *might* work, but maybe the switch will open before the car clears the top of the ramp. If we don't construct everything *exactly* right, the switch may open before the car goes past the transition from the sloping ramp to the top of the hill." (She drew the sketch shown in Figure 4.)

Juan: "Yes, early switch opening might be a problem. But, we can try my idea and just see if it works."

Tina: "Before we do that, though, how about this idea: We can connect a long screw thread to the drive shaft of the car and put a sliding nut of some kind (one that doesn't turn) along the shaft. As the shaft turns, it will thread through the nut and move it toward a normally-closed switch on the car body, opening it just after the right amount of distance is traveled. It might look something like this:" (She drew the sketch shown in Figure 5 and showed it to Juan.)

Juan: "Yeah! We could let it self-calibrate before each run by placing the car on the top of the hill with the nut just forcing the switch into the 'off' position, then manually roll the car backwards down to the starting point. As the nut travels back along the threaded rod, it will be placed in just the right starting position so that it trips the switch to off when the car gets to the top of the ramp." *He thought a moment more.* "How about a butterfly wing nut on the rotating shaft? We could buy one at the hardware store instead of having to make our own. One wing of the nut could ride against the car frame and prevent the nut from turning as the shaft turns. That way, the nut would be screwed down along the threaded shaft. The other wing of the nut could be used to press the switch." (Juan drew the sketch shown in Figure 6.)

Tina: "Yes. We can use one of those switches that has three terminals: normally open (NO), normally closed (NC), and common (COM)." Tina was describing a switch of the type shown in Figure 7. "The switch stays in the closed position, with COM connected to NC, and with NO connected to nothing, until the switch is pressed. When that happens, COM becomes connected to the NO terminal and NC is left unconnected."

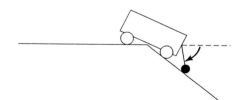

Figure 4.   Premature opening of the switch.

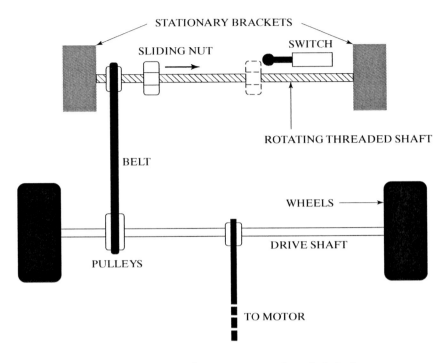

Figure 5.   Nonturning nut moves along a rotating, threaded shaft.

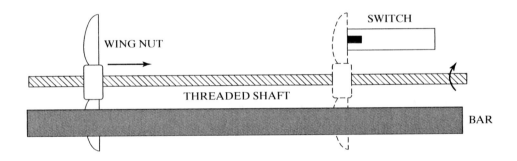

Figure 6.   The wing nut concept.

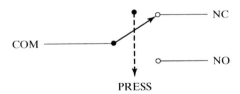

Figure 7.   Switch showing normally open (NO) and normally closed (NC) contacts. The normal state of the switch refers to the condition where no force is applied to its pushbutton or lever arm.

After some thought, Tina continued. "You know, we don't have to run a separate threaded rod from the drive shaft. We can make the drive shaft *be* a threaded rod, like this." (Tina drew the sketch shown in Figure 8 and presented it to Juan.)

"That way, we'll have a simpler design, less friction, and an easy way to attach the wheels to the drive shaft with locking nuts."

Juan: "I like this idea much better than the switch idea. It seems more foolproof."

Tina: "On the other hand, if we use the threaded-rod idea and the wheels slip at all, the wing nut will still thread itself down the turning shaft, but the car won't be moving, so it will stop before it reaches the top of the hill."

Juan: "We could go back to our separate shaft idea and grease the shaft very well to reduce friction."

Tina: "No, that still won't solve the problem of the slipping wheels."

Juan: "Well, then, I have another idea. We could use a threaded shaft that is separate from the drive shaft and have it be turned by two idler wheels, rather than by the motor. The idler wheels will run along the track and turn the wing nut shaft but will be much less likely to slip because they won't be driven by the motor and will experience a much smaller torque." (Juan drew the sketch shown in Figure 9.)

"The idler wheels won't be connected in any way to the drive shaft or driven wheels. Even if the drive wheels slip, the only way that the idler wheels can turn is if the car is moving. If the idlers themselves get stuck, they'll drag along the track and *not* move the nut by the correct amount. But if the mechanism is well lubricated, sticking idler wheels should not be a problem."

Tina: "OK. Do you think we should consider an electronic timer that keeps the motor turned on for a fixed amount of time? We could experiment with the car and find out the exact amount of time needed for it to get to the top."

Juan: "Or how about an altimeter that measures the height of the car off the floor?"

Tina: "Or maybe a string that hooks to the base of the ramp, unwinds as the car goes up, and pulls a switch to the off position when the car gets to the top?"

Juan: "That's not allowed by the rules. All parts of the car have to lie inside the 1-meter marks at the end of 15 seconds."

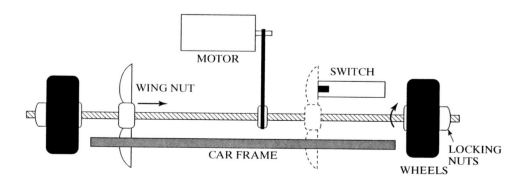

Figure 8.   Threaded rod also serves the function of a drive shaft.

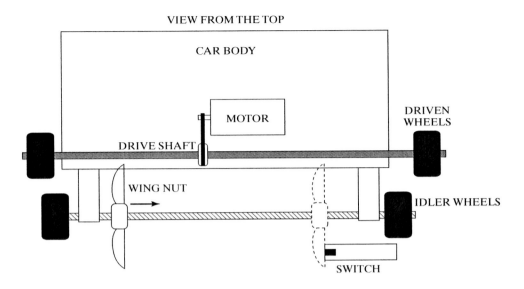

VIEW FROM THE TOP

CAR BODY

MOTOR

DRIVEN WHEELS

DRIVE SHAFT

WING NUT

IDLER WHEELS

SWITCH

Figure 9.   Idler wheels turn the threaded rod, which is not driven by the motor.

Tina checked the rules and confirmed that Juan was right. They both considered the altimeter idea and decided that it was not feasible. *If* they could find one at all, an altimeter with a resolution in the 1-meter range would be an expensive (and heavy) instrument indeed. Neither student wanted to design an altimeter from scratch. Their primary desire was to focus on the design of the vehicle itself. They also decided against the electronic timer idea for now. They were afraid that the car might travel at increasingly slower speeds from run to run as the battery ran down, and they remembered from their electronics class that the speed of the typical electronic timer is independent of its power supply voltage.

With their preliminary design concepts prioritized, they focused their attention on the two mechanical solutions: the trip switch and the concept of the sliding nut. They decided to build a few prototypes and try out the two basic ideas.

The foregoing conversation between Tina and Juan illustrates the principles of informal brainstorming. As each person stated a new idea, the other amplified upon it and came up with new ones, without prejudging each other. In the end, the two students condensed their list of ideas into one or two concepts that seemed feasible and they agreed to try them out in test experiments. The flow of conversation between Tina and Juan was appropriate for two people and even would have worked for three or four. Had their design team been larger, a formal brainstorming method, such as the idea trigger method discussed in the previous section, would have been more appropriate.

PROFESSIONAL SUCCESS: WHAT TO DO WHEN ONE INDIVIDUAL DOMINATES A BRAINSTORMING SESSION

Suppose that you are the leader of a brainstorming session, and one member of your team dominates the conversation. That person may criticize participants, dismiss unconventional ideas, cut off speakers, or otherwise break the rules. When this situation occurs, it's your responsibility to keep the offender in line. Say to the group, "Hey, we need to stick to the formal rules of brainstorming. Let's institute a don't-speak-until-called-upon rule." This approach will tactfully short-circuit the behavior of the dominant person and maintain harmony among team members.

PRACTICE!

1. Conduct a one-person mini-brainstorming session and add as many ideas as you can to the final list of ideas compiled by Tina, Juan, Paul, and Karin during their idea trigger session. Allow yourself 4 minutes of brainstorm time to compile your ideas.

2. A nonengineering friend complains about a pair of eyeglasses that keeps falling off. Give yourself 5 minutes of brainstorming time, and compile a list of as many ideas as you can for solving your friend's problem. After the 5 minutes are over, take a short break, then sort out your list, categorizing each idea with a "feasibility" rating of 1 to 5, with 5 the most feasible.

3. Over a time span of 2 minutes, write down as many ways as you can for safely confining a dog to your backyard.

4. Write down as many ideas as you can for designing a hands-free water faucet.

5. As a way to save energy, you'd like to devise a method for reminding people to turn off lights. In a time span of 2 minutes, devise as many methods as you can to achieve this objective.

6. Can brainstorming be used to solve math problems? Why or why not?

7. Develop as many concepts as you can for a system that will automatically feed pellets to a pet hamster. Allow yourself 3 minutes of brainstorming time. If possible, work with a group of up to four people.

DOCUMENTATION: THE KEY TO PROJECT SUCCESS

Engineering design is never performed in isolation. Even the simplest of projects involves a designer and those who will benefit from the finished product. More often, a design effort involves considerably more individuals who worry about many facets of the product. The design of an automobile, for example, encompasses the work of mechanical, electrical, industrial, biomedical, and safety engineers. A consumer products company involved in the production of, say, cellular telephones, will bring together computer, electrical, mechanical, and manufacturing engineers in a multidisciplinary team that may include people from sales and marketing. Complex engineering projects are successful only if everyone on the design team communicates with everyone else at all phases of the design effort.

One way in which engineers communicate with each other is through careful record keeping. Good documentation is essential when engineers work in teams. When you work as a member of a design team, it's your responsibility to maintain a comprehensive collection of design concepts, sketches, detailed drawings, test results, redesigns, reports, and schematics. This *documentation trail* serves as a tool for passing information on to team members who may need to repeat or verify your work, manufacture your product from a prototype, apply for patents based on your inventions, or even take over your job should you be promoted or move to another company. Written records are also a good way to communicate with yourself. Many an engineer has been unable to reproduce design accomplishments or confirm test results due to sloppy record keeping. Indeed, one of the marks of a professional engineer is the discipline needed to keep accurate, neat, up-to-date records. Documentation should never be performed as an afterthought. If a project is dropped by one team member, the state of documentation should *always* be such that another team member can resume the project without delay. As a student of engineering, you should learn the art of record keeping and develop good documentation habits early in your career. Most companies, laboratories, and other technical institutions require their employees to keep records that document the results of their engineering efforts.

Paper Versus Electronic Documentation

Today, just about every piece of engineering documentation, with the exception of the engineer's notebook described in the next section, is produced on a computer. Examples of documents destined for preservation include word processed text, spreadsheets, schematics, drawings, design layouts, and simulated test results. Some engineers prefer to store information on disk so that it can be viewed on screen and printed out only as needed. Others prefer the older method of preserving documentation by printing everything on paper and storing the documents in a physical file cabinet. Whichever method you choose, you should follow the following important guidelines:

- *Organize your information:* It's important to store documentation in an organized and logical manner. If the project is small, its documentation should be stored in a single folder (paper or electronic). Larger projects may require a group of folders, each relating to different aspects of the project. The folders should be labeled and dated with informative titles such as "Propulsion System for XYZ Project" and kept in a place that will be easy to find should another team member need to use it.

- *Back up your information:* It's equally important to store a duplicate copy of all documentation. This guideline applies to written as well as electronic information. Fire, flood, theft, misplacement, and the all-too-common disk crash can lead to the loss of a project's documentation trail. Archival storage of records in a different physical location will help to keep a project on track should one of these catastrophes occur.

The Engineers' Logbook

One important vehicle for record keeping is the *engineer's logbook,* sometimes called the *engineer's notebook.* A well-maintained logbook serves as a permanent record that includes all ideas, calculations, innovations, and test results that emerge from the design process. When engineers work in a team, each team member keeps a logbook. When the project is brought to completion, all logbooks of all team members are placed in an archive and remain the property of the company. An engineering notebook thus serves as an archival record of new ideas and engineering research achievements *whether or not they lead to commercial use.* A complete logbook serves as evidence of inventorship and establishes the date of conception and "reduction to practice" of a new idea. It shows that the inventor (you!) has used diligence in advancing the invention to completion. In this respect, the engineer's logbook is more than just a simple lab notebook. It serves as a valuable document that has legal implications. When you work as an engineer, you have a professional responsibility to your employer, your colleagues, and to the integrity of your job to keep a good logbook.

The notebook shown in Figure 10 is typical of many used in industry, government labs, and research institutions. It has permanently bound and numbered pages, a cardboard cover, and quadrille lines that form a coarse grid pattern. A label fixed to the front cover uniquely identifies the notebook and its contents. The company, laboratory, or project name is printed at the top, and the notebook is assigned a unique number by the user. In some companies and large research labs, a central office assigns notebook numbers to its employees when the notebook is signed out.

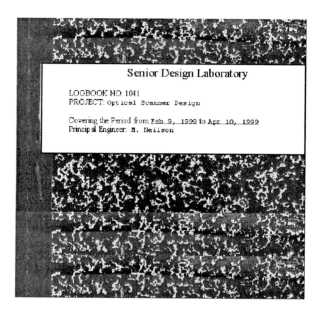

Figure 10.   Cover label of a typical engineer's logbook.

The techniques for logbook use differ from those used in some science and introductory engineering classes where instructors encourage students to write things down first on loose scratch paper and then recopy relevant items into a neat notebook. This procedure is bad practice for a design engineer. Although notebooks prepared in this way are easier for instructors to grade, the finished notebook seldom resembles a running record of what actually occurred in the laboratory and is not especially useful for engineering design projects. Design is as much a *process* as it is a final product, and the act of writing down ideas as they emerge and of recording (and commenting on) events as they happen helps engineers to think and be creative. Also, keeping a record of what did *not* work is just as important as recording what did, so that mistakes will not be repeated in the future.

Logbook Format

An engineering logbook should be used as a design tool. Enter everything into your logbook, no matter how seemingly irrelevant. Write down ideas as you think of them, even if you have no immediate plans to pursue them. Keep an ongoing record of successes and failures. Record the results of every test—mechanical, structural, electrical, system, flight, or performance—even if the results may not be used in the final design. Stop to write things down. This habit will require discipline but will always be worth the trouble. Important information, including some you might otherwise have forgotten, will be in your logbook and will be at your fingertips when you need it.

Any logbook format that meets your needs and those of your team is suitable, as long as it forms a permanent record of your contributions to the design process. Ban loose paper from the laboratory. It is easily lost, misfiled, or spilled upon. Resist the temptation to reach for loose paper when you need to do a calculation. Instead of grabbing that pad to record information, draw a sketch, or discuss an idea, take the time to open your logbook. You'll be glad you did when those numbers and sketches you need are readily available. Unbound paper used for anything other than doodling has no place in an engineering laboratory.

Using Your Engineer's Logbook

As chief author of your logbook, you have the freedom to set your own objectives for its use. The following guidelines, however, are typical of those used by many engineers and design teams:

1. Each person working on a project should keep a separate logbook specifically for that project. All relevant data should be entered. When the logbook is full, it should be stored in a safe place specifically designated for logbook storage. In that way, everyone will know where to find the logbook when it's needed.

2. All ideas, calculations, experiments, tests, mechanical sketches, flowcharts, circuit diagrams, etc, related to the project should be entered into the logbook. Entries should be dated and written in ink. Pencil has a nasty habit of smudging when pages rub against each other. Relevant computer-generated plots, graphics, schematics, or photos printed on loose paper should be pasted or taped onto bound logbook pages. This procedure will help prevent loss of important data.

3. Logbook entries should outline the problem addressed, tests performed, calculations made, and so forth, but subjective conclusions about the success of the tests (e.g., "I believe...") should be avoided. The facts should speak for themselves. Logbook entries should not be a tape recording of your opinions.

4. The voice of the logbook should speak to a third-party reader. Assume that your logbook will be read by teammates, your boss, or perhaps someone from marketing.

5. In settings where intellectual property is at stake, the concluding page of each session should be dated and, where appropriate, signed. This practice eliminates all ambiguity with regard to dates of invention and disclosure. Important entries that signify key events in the design process should be periodically and routinely witnessed by at least one other person, and preferably two. Witnesses should endorse and date the relevant pages with the words, "witnessed and understood."

6. Logbook pages should not be left blank. If a portion of a page must be left blank, a vertical or slanted line should be drawn through it. Pages should be numbered consecutively and not be torn out. These measures are necessary should your logbook ever become part of a legal proceeding where the integrity of the information comes into question. Do not make changes using correction fluid. Cross out instead, This precaution will prevent you from creating obscure or questionable entries should your logbook be entered as legal evidence in patent or liability actions. Although this precaution probably won't be relevant to logbooks you keep for college design courses, it's a good idea to begin now so that the procedure becomes a career habit.

EXAMPLE 3: AN ENGINEER'S LOGBOOK

The following example illustrates proper use of an engineering logbook. Imagine that the logbook pages shown describe a self-propelled vehicle that you are designing for a student design competition called "Peak Performance." The first page, Figure 11, shows your preliminary sketch of a basic concept based on a vehicle that has the shape of a moving wedge. The second page, Figure 12, contains some calculations that estimate the battery drain as the vehicle moves up the contest ramp. The entries on the third page,

Figure 13, show a list of parts and materials to be purchased at the hardware store. These parts will enable you to build a prototype and test your vehicle's ability to climb the ramp.

DESIGN CONCEPT FOR DEFENSIVE STRATEGY.

Opposing vehicle

DRIVE CHAIN

BATTERY   MOTOR   WHEELS

Figure 11.   Logbook entry: Moving wedge concept for competition vehicle.

BATTERY POWER REQUIREMENTS

Estimate the weight of the vehicle:
$$0.9 \text{ kg} \times 10 \text{ N/kg} = 9 \text{ Newtons}$$

Compute the stored energy as the vehicle arrives at the top of the ramp:
$$9 \text{ N} \times 3 \text{ ft} \times 12 \text{ in/ft} \times 0.25 \text{ m/in} = 8 \text{ J}$$

Estimate the mechanical power. Assume vehicle takes about 7 sec to travel up the ramp:
$$8 \text{ J/7 sec} = 1.1 \text{ Watts}$$

Estimate the current drain on a 9-V battery (assume $P_{elec} = P_{mech}$ -- neglect losses for now):
$$I = P/V = 1.1 \text{ W/9V} = 0.12 \text{ A}$$

Figure 12.   Logbook entry: Power consumption calculations.

PEAK PERFORMANCE DESIGN COMPETITION   2/7/99

PARTS LIST (to be purchased at hardware store)

Nuts and bolts (#8 × 1/2" with washers)
Wood screws (#6 × 3/4" long)
L-brackets (4):
Super Glue
Electrical tape
Solder (small cheap soldering iron? Or borrow?)
Switch (may have to go to electronic parts store)
Long threaded rod #10 thread size (will they have one?)
#10 thread wing nut

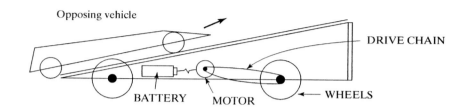

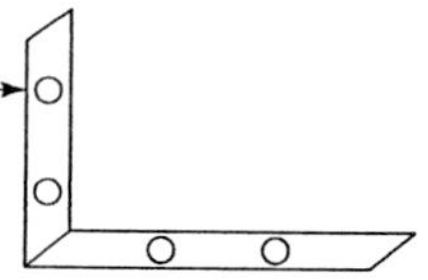

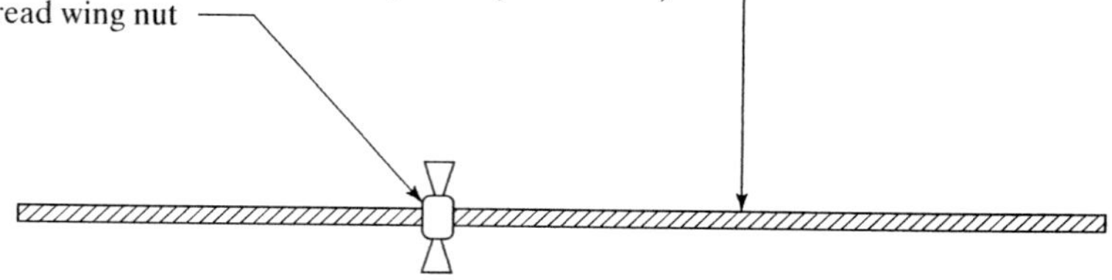

Figure 13.   Logbook entry: List of parts to be purchased at the hardware store.

Technical Reports and Memoranda

Logbooks provide but one method by which a team keeps a good documentation trail. Engineers also communicate by writing technical reports at the significant milestones of a design project. A technical report describes a particular accomplishment and perhaps provides some project history or background material before explaining the details of what was achieved. The report may contain theory, data, test results, calculations, design parameters, or fabrication dimensions. Technical reports form the backbone of a company's or laboratory's technical database. Reports are typically stored in archival format, each with its own title and catalog number. Information for technical reports is easily gathered from logbooks that are accurate and up to date. When the time comes to write a journal paper, patent application, or product application note, the technical report becomes an indispensable reference tool. It is wise for engineering students to study techniques for writing technical reports in a clear and concise manner.

A technical report is also an appropriate way to explain why a particular idea did not work or was not attempted. Taking the time to write a technical report about a negative result or design failure can save considerable time should a design concept be revisited by engineers who were not present when the original project was undertaken.

Schematics and Drawings

Documentation does not always appear in the form of text. Graphical records, such as drawings, circuit schematics, photographs, and plots, also become part of the documentation trail. These items typically are created with the help of computer software tools. If the documents are to be stored electronically, then all files related to a particular project should be organized in a logical hierarchy. Some engineers choose to keep all files for a project in a single file folder on the computer. Others prefer to sort files by the applications that produce them (e.g., CAD drawings in one folder, spreadsheet files in another). Other engineers like to transfer all the computer files related to a given project to a single removable disk that can be stored in a physical file cabinet folder. If paper is chosen as the storage medium, then graphical output should be printed on paper and kept in a folder along with other written records. Regardless of which storage method is chosen, the information related to a particular project should be carefully preserved in a format that will prevent loss.

Software Documentation and the Role of the Engineering Notebook

Of all design endeavors, the writing of software is the one most prone to poor documentation. The revision loop of a software design cycle can be extremely rapid, because the typical software development tool enables a programmer to make small changes and test their effects immediately. This rapid-fire method of development invites poor documentation habits. Seldom does the software engineer find a good time to stop and document the flow of a program, because most pauses are short and change is frequent. As a result, the documentation for many software programs is added after the fact, if at all.

If you find yourself writing software, get into the habit of including documentation in your program as you go along. All software development tools provide a means for adding comment lines right inside the program code. Add them frequently to explain why you've taken a certain approach or written a particular section of program code. Explain the meaning of object names and program variables. Your in-program documentation should enable other engineers on your team to completely understand and take over the writing of your sections of the program simply by reading the comment lines. Good in-program documentation also will be invaluable to you should you need to modify your program at a later time. It's amazing how quickly a programmer can forget the internal logic of a program after setting it aside for only a short time.

If your program is destined for commercial sale, then good internal documentation and truly helpful "help" files are essential. Documentation included inside the program on a regular basis will easily translate into help files and an instruction manual when the need arises. One trick used by top-notch software developers is to write the help and instruction files as the program code is developed, rather than as an afterthought. Changes to the instruction manual can be made at the same time that changes are made in the program code. The abundance of commercial software packages with pathetic or poorly written help files or instruction manuals is testimony to generations of software engineers who have perpetuated a tendency toward poor documentation habits. If you master the skill of documenting software, your software products will be better utilized and more successful than those with poor documentation.

Although the keeping of engineering logbooks is less relevant to software development than to other types of engineering, logbooks still can play a special role. On the pages of your notebook, you can outline the overall flow of the program and the interconnections between its various modules. You can try out sketches for graphical user interfaces without first having to write actual computer code. You can draw plots of relational databases and make lists of the variables to be used in the software.

PROFESSIONAL SUCCESS: HOW TO KEEP GOOD RECORDS ALL THE TIME

If you want to keep a good documentation trail, get into the habit of carrying your logbook with you wherever you go. In that way, it will be available whenever you have a thought or idea that needs recording. Buy a medium-size notebook that can fit easily into your backpack. Clip a pen right inside the front cover. Be sure to write your name and contact information on the front cover in case you misplace your logbook! A tiny, 3" ∞ 5" bound notebook will do nicely. Although writing space will be limited because of the smaller size, you'll be more likely to carry it if it's not overly large.

PRACTICE!

1. Refer to the logbook calculations of Figure 12. Revise the estimate of the current drain on the battery if the vehicle weight is 2.1 kg.

2. Refer to the logbook calculations of Figure 12. Convert all quantities to metric units and rewrite the logbook page.

3. Refer to the logbook calculations of Figure 12. Revise the estimate of the current drain on the battery if the ramp height is 1.4 m and its length is 3.3 m.

The Importance of Logbooks: A Case Study

This case involved a small, Massachusetts-based biomedical engineering company called Abiomed (pronounced ab-ee-oh-med). Among its other heart-related projects, Abiomed is a leading contender for the development of an artificial human heart that will become a permanent replacement for individuals that could otherwise stay alive only with a human heart transplant. As noted on the company Website (*www.abiomed.com*), heart disease is the leading cause of death in the United States. Hundreds of thousands of people in the United States alone could be saved each year if transplants were available, yet only about 2,000 transplantable hearts become available in any given year. Hence, the need for a permanent artificial heart is real and widespread. Doctors at Jewish Hospital in Louisville, Kentucky installed the first Abiocor artificial heart in a human patient in July 2001.

Abiomed began its total artificial heart project in earnest in the early 1990s. The major components of the heart system, depicted in Figure 14, include the central pump, interconnecting tubes that connect to the subject's principle blood vessels, and a system for transferring power through the skin from a battery pack worn outside the body. One key feature of the power transfer process, the lack of wires piercing the skin, is essential for the long-term efficacy of the artificial heart, because skin perforations are prime entry points for infection and require constant medical supervision in a skilled-care facility. The Abiomed artificial heart is being designed to enable the patient some semblance of a normal, mobile, home life. The system for transferring electrical power, called the transcutaneous energy transfer device, or "TET," is essentially a pair of concentric, high-frequency magnetic coils—one implanted under the skin, and one worn outside the skin. (Transcutaneous means "through the skin.") Abiomed wished to have its engineers fully focus on the daunting task of developing the heart pump itself, and so it hired another biomedical engineering company, World Heart Corporation of Ottawa, Canada, to design the energy transfer module.

After about 4 years of effort, World Heart was still unable to produce a TET that met Abiomed's stringent technical specifications. Although World Heart claimed to be converging on a solution, Abiomed was not convinced that a satisfactory TET device was imminent. Faced with an impending critical animal test that would determine future funding of its entire heart project from the National Institutes of Health, Abiomed decided to sever its reliance on the World Heart TET. The Abiomed CEO instructed one of his engineers, Dr. Z, to develop a home-grown TET device as quickly as possible. Dr. Z is a very capable fellow, and after only 4 months of effort, he succeeded in designing and testing a fully-working version of a TET device that met all the requirements of Abiomed's impending heart-pump test.

This development led to a lawsuit by World Heart, who claimed that Abiomed could not have developed its own TET device in the mere time span of 4 months without having stolen secrets and technology from World Heart. After all, World Heart claimed, its engineers had worked on the project for 4 years and were only just beginning to converge on a successful solution. How could the Abiomed engineer have designed a superior TET in only 4 months? Abiomed countered with a claim that its short path to success was due solely to the high competency of its engineer, and that, in fact, it had taken special precautions to ensure that nothing would be stolen from the previous World Heart design effort. The suit went to court and, in the end,

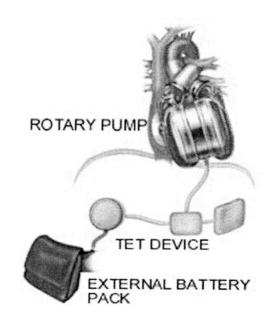

ROTARY PUMP

TET DEVICE

EXTERNAL BATTERY
PACK

Figure 14.   Total artificial heart system. (*Graphic courtesy of Abiomed, Inc.*)

Abiomed prevailed. The jury recognized that Abiomed's TET design, while performing the same basic transcutaneous energy-transfer function as the World Heart device, was completely different with regard to all details of implementation. The Abiomed device, the jury concluded, used different circuits, materials, magnetic construction, and semiconductor components.

During the trial, a key component of Abiomed's defense was the logbook kept by the engineer who designed the TET. This logbook was used to prove that Abiomed had designed its own, independent version of the TET. Following the company's customary logbook policy, as well as sound engineering practice, Dr. Z had kept careful records of his TET design, having entered every design concept, schematic, circuit layout, and test result that emerged during the design process. He had even noted the various circuit configurations that had blown up on the test bench before his first working model emerged. Each page of his logbook had been dated, and each lab session involving successful tests had been signed and countersigned by another Abiomed engineer. During trial, entire pages of Dr. Z's logbook were reproduced and projected on a large screen for the jury to see. Dr. Z's logbook played a crucial role in the success of Abiomed's legal defense.

The presentation of Dr. Z's logbook in court, while critical to the outcome of the trial, did not proceed flawlessly, however. Several pages of the logbook involving work done in mid January 1996, had been incorrectly dated with the year 1995. Following a common mistake that many individuals make when the year changes, Dr. Z had, without thinking, hastily written the year from the previous month of December. The lawyers for World Heart were quick to seize upon this error as prima fascia evidence that something was "fishy." They claimed Dr. Z had forged portions of his logbook in an attempt to present a false picture of his accomplishments. In the end, the jury was not convinced and realized that Dr. Z's error was nothing more than a common calendar mistake. Nevertheless, this seemingly small lack of attention to detail in logbook procedure put the case against Abiomed in jeopardy for a time.

PROFESSIONAL SUCCESS: DEVELOPING GOOD LOGBOOK HABITS

Most of us follow routines without thinking. When we wake up in the morning, we brush our teeth. When we eat, we instinctively reach for a clean plate. When we get into a car, we (hopefully) buckle our seatbelts automatically. An as engineer, the urge to write things down in your logbook should become as instinctive as these other common tasks. In contrast to these personal health procedures, however, we engineers are not trained from childhood to record our experiences in a notebook. Developing this instinct requires practice, but it can become part of your routine over time. When personal computers and the Internet first came into being, most people did not think very much about the novelty of e-mail. Now checking one's mail has become a daily routine for most. You developed this unnatural skill by practicing it over time. It should be the same with your engineer's logbook. Force yourself to get into the habit of using your logbook whenever you practice design. Over time, it will become as natural a gesture as brushing your teeth.

PROJECT MANAGEMENT: KEEPING THE TEAM ON TRACK

Even the simplest of design project must be properly managed if it is to be successful. A systematic approach to design is always preferable to a random, hit-or-miss approach. While the subject of project management could (and does) occupy the contents of entire books and the curricula of programs in business administration, three project management tools—the *organizational chart*, the *time line*, and the *Gantt chart*—form a basic set that should be understood by all engineers.

Organizational Chart

When engineers work on a team-oriented design project, some hierarchy among individuals is necessary. It would be nice if an engineering team could always function as a simple group of colleagues, but inevitably some team members will be burdened more than others, and some tasks will fall between the cracks, unless everyone's responsibilities are clearly spelled out. One vehicle for specifying the management structure of a design team is the *organizational chart*. An organizational chart indicates who is responsible for each aspect of a design project. It also describes the hierarchy and reporting structure of the team. Figure 15 illustrates a simple organizational chart that might be used by students in a vehicle design competition. In this particular case, Tina acts as the team leader, but she, in turn, reports to the course teaching assistant for leadership and guidance. In the corporate world, where the structuring of workers and bosses can become complex, organizational charts are essential because each employee must understand to whom he or she reports and must know the responsibility chain from upper management on downward. Note that organizational charts are used by all sorts of companies, not just engineering firms. Figure 16, for example, outlines the organization of the transportation department of a large American city. The features of this chart are identical to those found in the charts of large engineering companies.

Time Line

Time management is critical to the success of any design project. In a perfect world, engineers would have as much time as needed to work on all aspects of a design project, but in the real world, deadlines have a nasty habit of creating pressure to "get the product out the door." Demands for demonstrations of progress, prototype tests, something for "sales and marketing to show," and the pressures of corporate life require that an engineer develop a sense of how much time will be needed for each aspect of product development. A *time line* is a valuable tool for an engineer who wants to keep a project on schedule. A time line is simply a linear plot on which each of the various phases of a design project is assigned a milestone date. If a given task is in danger of not being completed before its designated milestone date, it is the job of the engineer to allocate more time, and overtime if necessary, to the task so that it can be completed on schedule. A typical time line, in this case one prepared by students designing a vehicle for a class design competition, is shown in Figure 17.

Gantt Chart

When a project becomes complex and involves many people, a simple time line may be inadequate for managing all aspects of the project. Similarly, if the project's various parts are interdependent, so that the completion of one phase depends on the success of others, the *Gantt Chart* of Figure 18 is a more appropriate time-management

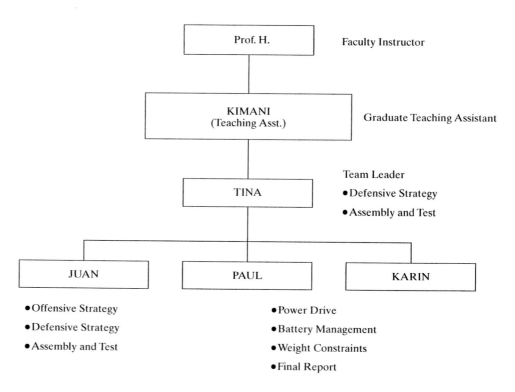

Figure 15.　Organizational chart showing responsibilities of a Peak Performance vehicle design team.

tool. The Gantt chart is simply a two-dimensional plot in which the horizontal axis is time measured in blocks of days, weeks, or months, and the vertical axis represents either the tasks to be completed or the individuals responsible for those tasks. Unlike the simple one-dimensional time line, which displays only the milestone dates for each phase of the project, the Gantt chart shows how much time is allotted to each task. It also shows the time overlap periods that are indicative of the interdependency between the various aspects of the project. When a particular task has been completed, it can be shaded in on the Gantt chart, so that the status of the project can be determined at a glance.

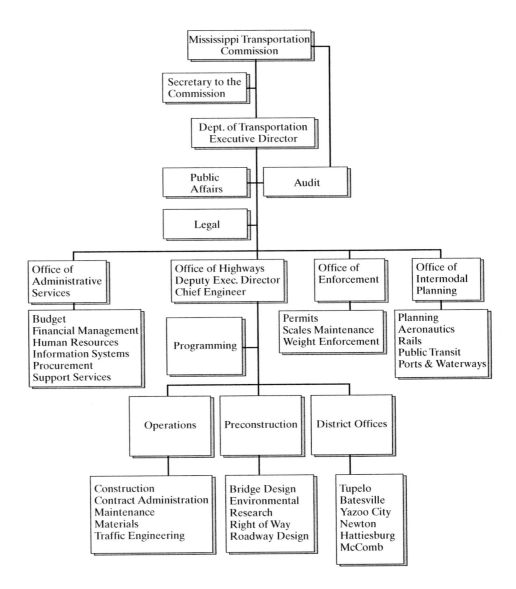

Figure 16.   Organizational chart of the Mississippi Department of Transportation. (*Chart courtesy of MDOT.*)

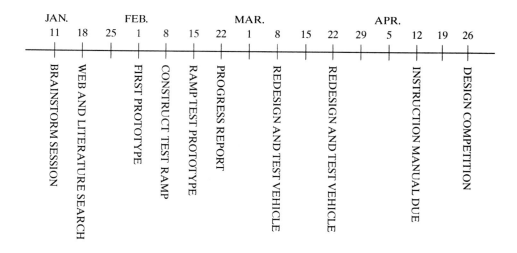

Figure 17.   Time line for scheduling tasks for the Peak Performance vehicle design team.

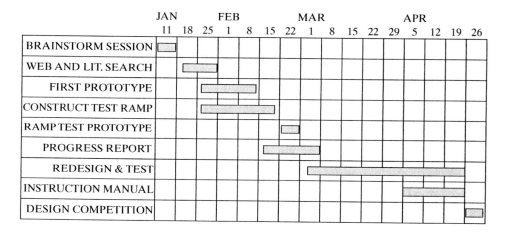

Figure 18.   Gantt chart provides a more comprehensive, two-dimensional method of scheduling the tasks for the Peak Performance vehicle design team.

PROFESSIONAL SUCCESS: THE LAWS OF TIME ESTIMATION

How long will it take to perform a particular design task? How much time should I allot to each segment of the design cycle? The following three Laws of Time Estimation will help you to determine the time required for elements of the design process:

1.   Everything takes longer than expected.

2.   If you've worked on something similar before, estimate the amount of time required to finish the task. The actual amount of time required will be about four times longer.

3.   If you've *never* worked on something similar before, estimate the amount of time required to finish the task. The actual amount of time required will be equal to the next highest time unit: Something estimated to take an hour will really take a day; something estimated to take a day will take a week, etc.

PRACTICE!

1.   Devise an organizational chart and time line for building a float for the homecoming parade at your college or university.

2.   Develop a time line for completing your course requirements over the time span of 4 academic years.

3.   Develop a Gantt chart for hosting an educational conference on engineering design. Consider all needed arrangements, including food, transportation, lodging, and meeting facilities.

4.   A large nonprofit organization is planning a walkathon in which about 3,000 people will walk a total of 60 miles in 3 days and will sleep in tent camps each night. Develop an organizational chart for all persons involved in planning and implementing this event.

5.   A student organization is planning to enter an international solar car competition (see, for example, *www.winstonsolar.org*). Develop a Gantt chart that will guide the team in the design and construction of a competition vehicle.

KEY TERMS

Teamwork	Brainstorming	Documentation
Project Management	Time Line	Organizational Chart
Gantt Chart		

PROBLEMS

Brainstorming: Use brainstorming methods to generate solutions to the following problems:

1.   You are given a barometer, a stop watch, and a tape measure. In how many different ways can you determine the height of the Sears Tower in Chicago?

2.   Design a sensing mechanism that can measure the speed of a bicycle.

3.   Many international airline flights still allow smoking in the rear seats of the aircraft. Design a system that will remove or deflect smoke from the front seats of the aircraft.

4.   You are given an egg, some tape, and several drinking straws. Using only these materials, design a system that will prevent the egg from being broken when dropped from a height of 6 ft (2 m).

5.   Devise as many different methods as you can for using your desktop computer to tell time.

6.   Design a system for washing the inside surfaces of the windows of a large aquarium (the kind the public visits to see large sea creatures) from the outside.

7.   Design a system to be used by a quadriplegic to turn the pages of a book.

8.   Devise a system for automatically raising and lowering the flag at dawn and dusk each day.

9.   Design a system that will automatically turn on a car's windshield wipers when needed.

10. Develop a device that can alert a blind person to the fact that water in a pot has boiled.

11. Devise a system for lining up screws on an assembly-line conveyor belt so that they are all pointing in the same direction.

12. Develop a method for detecting leaks in latex surgical gloves during the manufacturing process.

13. Devise a method for deriving an electrical signal from a magnetic compass so that it can be interfaced with a computer running navigational software.

14. Given a coil of rope and eight poles, devise a method to build a temporary emergency shelter in the wilderness.

15. Devise an alarm system to prevent an office thief from stealing the memory chips from inside a personal computer.

16. Imagine custodial workers who are in the habit of yanking on the electric cords of vacuum cleaners to unplug them from the wall. Devise a system or device to prevent damage to the plugs on the ends of the cords.

17. Develop a system for automatically dispensing medication to an elderly person who has difficulty keeping track of schedules.

18. Develop a system for reminding a business executive about meetings and appointments and changes in schedule that originate from the home office. The executive is always on the go, but can carry a variety of portable devices and gadgets. Feel free to use your knowledge of existing communications systems and technology, if necessary.

19. Devise a system that will agitate and circulate the water in an outdoor swimming pool so that a chlorine additive will be evenly distributed. Assume that an electrical outlet is available at the site of the pool.

20. Devise a system that will allow a truck driver to check tire air pressure without getting out of the vehicle.

Documentation:

21. Begin to keep a logbook of your class activities. Enter sketches and records of design assignments, inventions, and ideas.

22. Pretend that you are Alexander Graham Bell, the inventor of the telephone. Prepare several logbook pages that describe your invention.

23. Pretend that you are Marie Curie, the discoverer of the radioactive element radium. Prepare several logbook pages that describe the activities leading to your discovery.

24. Pretend that you are Dr. Zephram Cockrane, the inventor of plasma warp drive on the television and movie series *Star Trek*. Prepare several logbook pages that describe your invention. (*Star Trek, First Contact*: *www.startrek.com/library/ movies/viii_main.html*)

25. Imagine that you are Elias Howe, the first inventor to perfect the sewing machine by putting the eye of the needle in its tip. This innovation made possible the bobbin system still in use in sewing machines today. Prepare several logbook pages that describe your invention and its initial tests.

26. Reconstruct logbook pages as they might have appeared for the person inventing the common paper clip.

27. Imagine that you are Dr. Z, the engineer involved in the Abiomed case described in Section 3. Sketch the logbook pages that outline the basic operating concept of your transcutaneous energy transfer device.

28. The invention of the incandescent light bulb is largely attributed to the famous American inventor, Thomas Edison. Reconstruct the logbook pages that Edison may have kept describing his classic design efforts.

29. The cotton gin was developed by an American inventor, Eli Whitney, around 1800. This invention had a profound effect on the economics and history of the early United States. Reconstruct logbook pages in which Whitney outlines the basic features and development of his invention. Note that patent law in America was in its infancy around the time that Whitney did his work on the cotton gin.

30. Samuel F.B. Morse, inventor of the telegraph in the 1830s and the pioneer who launched the world's first "information age," was actually an artist by profession when he developed his classic invention. During a long voyage home from study in France, he passed his time thinking about conversations he had heard concerning ongoing experiments in Europe on electricity and magnetism. He developed his ideas for the telegraph while returning to the United States. Sketch out the logbook pages that Morse may have kept during his long sea voyage.

31. The first calculator was designed by Jack Kilby, an engineer for Texas Instruments. Look up the history of this inventor on the Web, and see if you can reconstruct the probable appearance of one or more pages from his logbook.

32. Sketch out a logbook page that describes a design concept for a recumbent bicycle.

33. Prepare a logbook page that describes the inner workings of a common CD player.

Project Management:

34. Suppose that you've been given the assignment to write a research paper on the history of human air flight. Develop a time line for completing this comprehensive research assignment.

35. Create a Gantt chart for your own hypothetical entry into a national solar-powered vehicle design competition.

36. Imagine that you work for a company that is designing an electric car for commercial sale. Create an organizational chart for the company and a Gantt chart for designing the vehicle's drive train.

37. Choose an engineering company with which you are familiar or in which you have an interest. Develop an organizational chart for the company. Information about a company's structure and personnel often can be found on the company's Web site.

38. Imagine that you wish to start your own company to write software tools for doing business on the Web. Create an organizational chart that outlines the positions you'll need to fill to get the company started.

39. Develop a time line for the completion of the prototype of an automobile powered from fuel cells rather than an internal combustion engine.

4

Introduction

Objectives

After reading this chapter, you will be able to

- Know why it is important to study engineering ethics
- Understand the distinction between business and personal ethics, and
- See how ethical problem solving and engineering design are similar.

On August 10, 1978, a Ford Pinto was hit from behind on a highway in Indiana. The impact of the collision caused the Pinto's fuel tank to rupture and burst into flames, leading to the deaths of three teenage girls riding in the car. This was not the first time that a Pinto had caught on fire as the result of a rear-end collision. In the seven years since the introduction of the Pinto, there had been some 50 lawsuits related to rear-end collisions. However, this time Ford was charged in a criminal court for the deaths of the passengers.

This case was a significant departure from the norm and had important implications for the Ford engineers and managers. A civil lawsuit could only result in Ford being required to pay damages to the victim's estates. A criminal proceeding, on the other hand, would indicate that Ford was grossly negligent in the deaths of the passengers and could result in jail terms for the Ford engineers or managers who worked on the Pinto.

The case against Ford hinged on charges that it was known that the gas-tank design was flawed and was not in line with accepted engineering standards, even though it did meet applicable federal safety standards at the time. During the trial, it was determined that Ford engineers were aware of the dangers of this design, but management, concerned with getting the Pinto to market rapidly at a price competitive with subcompact cars already introduced or planned by other manufacturers, had constrained the engineers to use this design.

The dilemma faced by the design engineers who worked on the Pinto was to balance the safety of the people who would be riding in the car against the need to produce the Pinto at a price that would be competitive in the market. They had to attempt to balance their duty to the public against their duty to their employer. Ultimately, the attempt by Ford to save a few dollars in manufacturing costs led to the expenditure of millions of dollars in defending lawsuits and payments to victims. Of course, there were also uncountable costs in lost sales due to bad publicity and a public perception that Ford did not engineer its products to be safe.

1 BACKGROUND IDEAS

The Pinto case is just one example of the ethical problems faced by engineers in the course of their professional practice. Ethical cases can go far beyond issues of public safety and may involve bribery, fraud, environmental protection, fairness, honesty in research and testing, and conflicts of interest. During their undergraduate education, engineers receive training in basic and engineering sciences, problem-solving methodology, and engineering design, but generally receive little training in business practices, safety, and ethics.

This problem has been partially corrected, as many engineering education programs now have courses in what's called engineering ethics. Indeed, the Accreditation Board for Engineering and Technology (ABET), the body responsible for accrediting undergraduate engineering programs in the United States, has mandated that ethics topics be incorporated into undergraduate engineering curricula. The purpose of this book is to provide a text and a resource for the study of engineering ethics and to help future engineers be prepared for confronting and resolving ethical dilemmas, such as the design of an unsafe product like the Pinto, that they might encounter during their professional careers.

A good place to start a discussion of ethics in engineering is with definitions of ethics and engineering ethics. Ethics is the study of the characteristics of morals. Ethics also deals with the moral choices that are made by each person in his or her relationship with other persons. As engineers, we are concerned with ethics because these definitions apply to all of the choices an individual makes in life, including those made while practicing engineering.

For our purposes, the definition of ethics can be narrowed a little. Engineering ethics is the rules and standards governing the conduct of engineers in their role as professionals. Engineering ethics encompasses the more general definition of ethics, but applies it more specifically to situations involving engineers in their professional lives. Thus, engineering ethics is a body of philosophy indicating the ways that engineers should conduct themselves in their professional capacity.

2 WHY STUDY ENGINEERING ETHICS?

Why is it important for engineering students to study engineering ethics? Several notorious cases that have received a great deal of media attention in the past few years have led engineers to gain an increased sense of their professional responsibilities. These cases have led to an awareness of the importance of ethics within the engineering profession as engineers realize how their technical work has far-reaching impacts on society. The work of engineers can affect public health and safety and can influence business practices and even politics.

One result of this increase in awareness is that nearly every major corporation now has an ethics office that has the responsibility to ensure that employees have the ability to express their concerns about issues such as safety and corporate business practices in a way that will yield results and won't result in retaliation against the employee. Ethics offices also try to foster an ethical culture that will help to head off ethical problems in a corporation before they start.

The goal of this book and courses in engineering ethics is to sensitize you to important ethical issues before you have to confront them. You will study important cases from the past so that you will know what situations other engineers have faced and will know what to do when similar situations arise in your professional career. Finally, you will learn techniques for analyzing and resolving ethical problems when they arise.

Our goal is frequently summed up using the term "moral autonomy." Moral autonomy is the ability to think critically and independently about moral issues and to apply this moral thinking to situations that arise in the course of professional engineering practice. The goal of this book, then, is to foster the moral autonomy of future engineers.

The question asked at the beginning of this section can also be asked in a slightly different way. Why should a future engineer bother studying ethics at all? After all, at this point in your life, you're already either a good person or a bad person. Good people already know the right thing to do, and bad people aren't going to do the right thing no matter how much ethical training they receive. The answer to this question lies in the nature of the ethical problems that are often encountered by an engineer. In most situations, the correct response is very obvious. For example, it is clear that to knowingly equip the Pinto with wheel lugs made from substandard, weak steel that is susceptible to breaking is unethical and wrong. This action could lead to the loss of a wheel while driving and could cause numerous accidents and put many lives at risk. Of course, such a design decision would also be a commercial disaster for Ford.

However, many times, the ethical problems encountered in engineering practice are very complex and involve conflicting ethical principles. For example, the engineers working on the Pinto were presented with a very clear dilemma. Trade-offs were made so that the Pinto could be successfully marketed at a reasonable price. One of these trade-offs involved the placement of the gas tank, which led to the accident in Indiana. So, for the Ford engineers and managers, the question became the following: Where does an engineering team strike the balance between safety and affordability and, simultaneously, between the ability of the company to sell the car and make a profit.

These are the types of situations that we will discuss in this book. The goal, then, is not to train you to do the right thing when the ethical choice is obvious and you already know the right thing to do. Rather, the goal is to train you to analyze complex problems and learn to resolve these problems in the most ethical manner.

3 ENGINEERING IS MANAGING THE UNKNOWN

One source of the ethical issues encountered in the course of engineering practice is a lack of knowledge. This is by no means an unusual situation in engineering. Engineers often encounter situations in which they don't have all of the information that is needed. By its nature, engineering design is about creating new devices and products. When something is new, many questions need to be answered. How well does it work? How will it affect people? What changes will this lead to in society? How well will this work under all of the conditions that it will be exposed to? Is it safe? If there are some safety concerns, how bad are they? What are the effects of doing nothing?

So, to a large extent, an engineer's job is about managing the unknown. How does an engineer accomplish this? Really, as an engineer you can never be absolutely certain that your design will never harm anyone or cause detrimental changes to society. But you must test your design as thoroughly as time and resources permit to ensure that it operates safely and as planned. Also, you must use your creativity to attempt to foresee the possible consequences of your work.

4 PERSONAL VS. BUSINESS ETHICS

In discussing engineering ethics, it is important to make a distinction between personal ethics and professional, or business, ethics, although there isn't always a clear boundary between the two. Personal ethics deals with how we treat others in our day-to-day lives. Many of these principles are applicable to ethical situations that occur in business and engineering. However, professional ethics often involves choices on an organizational level rather than a personal level. Many of the problems will seem different because they involve relationships between two corporations, between a corporation and the government, or between corporations and groups of individuals. Frequently, these types of relationships pose problems that are not encountered in personal ethics.

5 THE ORIGINS OF ETHICAL THOUGHT

Before proceeding, it is important to acknowledge in a general way the origins of the ethical philosophies that we will be discussing in this book. The Western ethical thought that is discussed here originated in the philosophy of the ancient Greeks and their predecessors. It has been developed through subsequent centuries by many thinkers in the Judeo–Christian tradition. Interestingly, non-Western cultures have independently developed similar ethical principles.

Although for many individuals, personal ethics are rooted in religious beliefs, this is not true for everyone. Certainly, there are many ethical people who are not religious, and there are numerous examples of nominally religious people who are not ethical. So while the ethical principles that we will discuss come to us filtered through a religious tradition, these principles are now cultural norms in the West, and as such, they are widely accepted regardless of their origin. We won't need to refer explicitly to religion in order to discuss ethics in the engineering profession.

6 ETHICS AND THE LAW

We should also mention the role of law in engineering ethics. The practice of engineering is governed by many laws on the international, federal, state, and local levels. Many of these laws are based on ethical principles, although many are purely of a practical, rather than a philosophical, nature. There is also a distinction between what is legal and what is ethical. Many things that are legal could be considered unethical. For example, designing a process that releases a known toxic, but unregulated, substance into the environment is probably unethical, although it is legal.

Conversely, just because something is illegal doesn't mean that it is unethical. For example, there might be substances that were once thought to be harmful, but have now been shown to be safe, that you wish to incorporate into a product. If the law has not caught up with the latest scientific findings, it might be illegal to release these substances into the environment, even though there is no ethical problem in doing so.

As an engineer, you are always minimally safe if you follow the requirements of the applicable laws. But in engineering ethics, we seek to go beyond the dictates of the law. Our interest is in areas where ethical principles conflict *and* there is no legal guidance for how to resolve the conflict.

7 ETHICS PROBLEMS ARE LIKE DESIGN PROBLEMS

At first, many engineering students find the types of problems and discussions that take place in an engineering ethics class a little alien. The problems are more open ended and are not as susceptible to formulaic answers as are problems typically assigned in other engineering classes. Ethics problems rarely have a correct answer that will be arrived at by everyone in the class. Surprisingly, however, the types of problem-solving techniques that we will use in this book and the nature of the answers that result bear a striking resemblance to the most fundamental engineering activity: engineering design.

The essence of engineering practice is the design of products, structures, and processes. The design problem is stated in terms of specifications: A device must be designed that meets criteria for performance, aesthetics, and price. Within the limits of these specifications, there are many correct solutions. There will, of course, be some solutions that are better than others in terms of higher performance or lower cost. Frequently, there will be two (or more) designs that are very different, yet perform identically. For example, competing automobile manufacturers may design a car to meet the same market niche, yet each manufacturer's solution to the problem will be somewhat different. In fact, we will see later that although the Pinto was susceptible to explosion after rear-end impact, other similar subcompact automobiles were not. In engineering design, there is no unique correct answer!

Ethical problem solving shares these attributes with engineering design. Although there will be no unique correct solution to most of the problems we will examine, there will be a range of solutions that are clearly right, some of which are better than others. There will also be a range of solutions that are clearly wrong. There are other similarities between engineering ethics and engineering design. Both apply a large body of knowledge to the solution of a problem, and both involve the use of analytical skills. So although the nature of the solutions to the problems in ethics will be different from those in most engineering classes, approaches to the problems and the ultimate solution will be very similar to those in engineering practice.

8 CASE STUDIES

Before starting to learn the theoretical ideas regarding engineering ethics and before looking at some interesting real-life cases that will illustrate these ideas, let's begin by looking at a very well-known engineering ethics case: the space shuttle *Challenger* accident. This case is presented in depth at the end of this chapter, but at this point we will look at a brief synopsis of the case to further illustrate the types of ethical issues and questions that arise in the course of engineering practice.

Many readers are already familiar with some aspects of this case. The space shuttle *Challenger* was launched in extremely cold weather. During the launch, an O-ring on one of the solid-propellant boosters, made more brittle by the cold, failed. This failure led to the explosion during liftoff. Engineers who had designed this booster had concerns about launching under these cold conditions and recommended that the launch be delayed, but they were overruled by their management (some of whom were trained as engineers), who didn't feel that there were enough data to support a delay in the launch. The shuttle was launched, resulting in the well-documented accident.

On the surface, there appear to be no engineering ethical issues here to discuss. Rather, it seems to simply be an accident. The engineers properly recommended that there be no launch, but they were overruled by management. In the strictest sense this can be considered an accident—no one wanted the *Challenger* to explode—but there are still many interesting questions that should be asked. When there are safety concerns, what is the engineer's responsibility before the launch decision is made? After the launch decision is made, but before the actual launch, what duty does the engineer have? If the decision doesn't go the engineer's way, should she complain to upper management? Or should she bring the problem to the attention of the press? After the accident has occurred, what are the duties and responsibilities of the engineers? If the launch were successful, but the *post mortem* showed that the O-ring had failed and an accident had very nearly occurred, what would be the engineer's responsibility? Even if an engineer moves into management, should he separate engineering from management decisions?

These types of questions will be the subject of this book. As an engineer, you will need to be familiar with ideas about the nature of the engineering profession, ethical theories, and the application of these theories to situations that are likely to occur in professional practice. Looking at other real-life cases taken from newspaper accounts and books will help you examine what engineers should do when confronted with ethically troubling situations. Many cases will be *post mortem* examinations of disasters, while others may involve an analysis of situations in which disaster was averted when many of the individuals involved made ethically sound choices and cooperated to solve a problem.

A word of warning is necessary: The cliché "Hind-sight is 20/20" will seem very true. When studying a case several years after the fact and knowing the ultimate outcome, it is easy to see what the right decision should have been. Obviously, had NASA owned a crystal ball and been able to predict the future, the *Challenger* would never have been launched. Had Ford known the number of people who would be killed as a result of gas-tank failures in the Pinto and the subsequent financial losses in lawsuits and criminal cases, it would have found a better solution to the problem of gas-tank placement. However, we rarely have such clear predictive abilities and must base decisions on our best guess of what the outcome will be. It will be important in studying the cases presented here to try to look at them from the point of view of the individuals who were involved at the time, using their best judgment about how to proceed, and not to judge the cases solely based on the outcome.

APPLICATION

The Space Shuttle *Challenger* and *Columbia* Accidents

The NASA Space Shuttle Disasters

The space shuttle is one of the most complex engineered systems ever built. The challenge of lifting a space vehicle from earth into orbit and have it safely return to earth presents many engineering problems. Not surprisingly, there have been several accidents in the U.S. space program since its inception, including two failures of the space shuttle. The disasters involving the space shuttles *Challenger* and *Columbia* illustrate many of the issues related to engineering ethics as shown in the following discussion.

The Space Shuttle *Challenger* Disaster

The explosion of the space shuttle *Challenger* is perhaps the most widely written about case in engineering ethics because of the extensive media coverage at the time of the accident and also because of the many available government reports and transcripts of congressional hearings regarding the explosion. The case illustrates many important ethical issues that engineers face: What is the proper role of the engineer when safety issues are a concern? Who should have the ultimate decision-making authority to order a launch? Should the ordering of a launch be an engineering or a managerial decision? This case has already been presented briefly, and we will now take a more in-depth look.

Background

The space shuttle was designed to be a reusable launch vehicle. The vehicle consists of an orbiter, which looks much like a medium-sized airliner (minus the engines!), two solid-propellant boosters, and a single liquid-propellant booster. At takeoff, all of the boosters are ignited and lift the orbiter out of the earth's atmosphere. The solid rocket boosters are only used early in the flight and are jettisoned soon after takeoff, parachute back to earth, and are recovered from the ocean. They are subsequently repacked with fuel and are reused. The liquid-propellant booster is used to finish lifting the shuttle into orbit, at which point the booster is jettisoned and burns up during reentry. The liquid booster is the only part of the shuttle vehicle that is not reusable. After completion of the mission, the orbiter uses its limited thrust capabilities to reenter the atmosphere and glides to a landing.

The accident on January 28, 1986 was blamed on a failure of one of the solid rocket boosters. Solid rocket boosters have the advantage that they deliver far more thrust per pound of fuel than do their liquid-fueled counterparts, but have the disadvantage that once the fuel is lit, there is no way to turn the booster off or even to control the amount of thrust produced. In contrast, a liquid-fuel rocket can be controlled by throttling the supply of fuel to the combustion chamber or can be shut off by stopping the flow of fuel entirely.

In 1974, the National Aeronautics and Space Administration (NASA) awarded the contract to design and build the solid rocket boosters for the shuttle to Morton Thiokol. The design that was submitted by Thiokol was a scaled-up version of the Titan missile, which had been used successfully for many years to launch satellites. This design was accepted by NASA in 1976. The solid rocket consists of several cylindrical pieces that are filled with solid propellant and stacked one on top of the other to form the completed booster. The assembly of the propellant-filled cylinders was performed at Thiokol's plant in Utah. The cylinders were then shipped to the Kennedy Space Center in Florida for assembly into a completed booster.

A key aspect of the booster design are the joints where the individual cylinders come together, known as the field joints, illustrated schematically in Figure 1a. These are tang and clevis joints, fastened with 177 clevis pins. The joints are sealed by two O-rings, a primary and a secondary. The O-rings are designed to prevent hot gases from the combustion of the solid propellant from escaping. The O-rings are made from a type of synthetic rubber and so are not particularly heat resistant. To prevent the hot gases from damaging the O-rings, a heat-resistant putty is placed in the joint. The Titan booster had only one O-ring in the field joint. The second O-ring was added to the booster for the shuttle to provide an extra margin of safety since, unlike the Titan, this booster would be used for a manned space craft.

Early Problems with the Solid Rocket Boosters

Problems with the field-joint design had been recognized long before the launch of the *Challenger*. When the rocket is ignited, the internal pressure causes the booster wall to expand outward, putting pressure on the field joint. This pressure causes the joint to open slightly, a process called "joint rotation," illustrated in Figure 1b. The joint was designed so that the internal pressure pushes on the putty, displacing the primary O-ring into this gap, helping to seal it. During testing of the boosters in 1977, Thiokol became aware that this joint-rotation problem was more severe than on the Titan and discussed it with NASA. Design changes were made, including an increase in the thickness of the O-ring, to try to control this problem.

Further testing revealed problems with the secondary seal, and more changes were initiated to correct that problem. In November of 1981, after the second shuttle flight, a postlaunch examination of the booster field joints indicated that the O-rings were being eroded by hot gases during the launch. Although there was no failure of the joint, there was some concern about this situation, and Thiokol looked into the use of different types of putty and alternative methods for applying it to solve the problem. Despite these efforts, approximately half of the shuttle flights before the *Challenger* accident had experienced some degree of O-ring erosion. Of course, this type of testing and redesign is not unusual in engineering. Seldom do things work correctly the first time, and modifications to the original design are often required.

It should be pointed out that erosion of the O-rings is not necessarily a bad thing. Since the solid rocket boosters are only used for the first few minutes of the flight, it might be perfectly acceptable to design a joint in which O-rings erode in a controlled manner. As long as the O-rings don't completely burn through before the solid boosters run out of fuel and are jettisoned, this design should be fine. However, this was not the way the space shuttle was designed, and O-ring erosion was one of the problems that the Thiokol engineers were addressing.

Figure 1
(a) A schematic drawing of a tang and clevis joint like the one on the *Challenger* solid rocket boosters.
(b) The same joint as in Figure 1a, but with the effects of joint rotation exaggerated. Note that the O-rings no longer seal the joint.

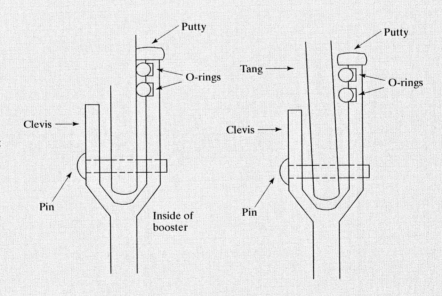

The first documented joint failure came after the launch on January 24, 1985, which occurred during very cold weather. The postflight examination of the boosters revealed black soot and grease on the outside of the booster, which indicated that hot gases from the booster had blown by the O-ring seals. This observation gave rise to concern about the resiliency of the O-ring materials at reduced temperatures. Thiokol performed tests of the ability of the O-rings to compress to fill the joints and found that they were inadequate. In July of 1985, Thiokol engineers redesigned the field joints without O-rings. Instead, they used steel billets, which should have been better able to withstand the hot gases. Unfortunately, the new design was not ready in time for the *Challenger* flight in early 1986 [Elliot, 1991].

The Political Climate

To fully understand and analyze the decision making that took place leading to the fatal launch, it is important also to discuss the political environment under which NASA was operating at the time. NASA's budget was determined by Congress, which was becoming increasingly unhappy with delays in the shuttle project and shuttle performance. NASA had billed the shuttle as a reliable, inexpensive launch vehicle for a variety of scientific and commercial purposes, including the launching of commercial and military satellites. It had been promised that the shuttle would be capable of frequent flights (several per year) and quick turnarounds and would be competitively priced with more traditional nonreusable launch vehicles. NASA was feeling some urgency in the program because the European Space Agency was developing what seemed to be a cheaper alternative to the shuttle, which could potentially put the shuttle out of business.

These pressures led NASA to schedule a record number of missions for 1986 to prove to Congress that the program was on track. Launching a mission was especially important in January 1986, since the previous mission had been delayed numerous times by both weather and mechanical failures. NASA also felt pressure to get the *Challenger* launched on time so that the next shuttle launch, which was to carry a probe to examine Halley's comet, would be launched before a Russian probe designed to do the same thing. There was additional political pressure to launch the Challenger before the upcoming state-of-the-union address, in which President Reagan hoped to mention the shuttle and a special astronaut—the first teacher in space, Christa McAuliffe—in the context of his comments on education.

The Days Before the Launch

Even before the accident, the *Challenger* launch didn't go off without a hitch, as NASA had hoped. The first launch date had to be abandoned due to a cold front expected to move through the area. The front stalled, and the launch could have taken place on schedule. But the launch had already been postponed in deference to Vice President George Bush, who was to attend. NASA didn't want to antagonize Bush, a strong NASA supporter, by postponing the launch due to inclement weather after he had arrived. The launch of the shuttle was further delayed by a defective microswitch in the hatch-locking mechanism. When this problem was resolved, the front had changed course and was now moving through the area. The front was expected to bring extremely cold weather to the launch site, with temperatures predicted to be in the low 20's (°F) by the new launch time.

Given the expected cold temperatures, NASA checked with all of the shuttle contractors to determine if they foresaw any problems with launching the shuttle in cold temperatures. Alan McDonald, the director of Thiokol's Solid Rocket Motor Project, was concerned about the cold weather problems that had been experienced with the solid rocket boosters. The evening before the rescheduled launch, a teleconference was arranged between engineers and management from the Kennedy Space Center, NASA's Marshall Space Flight Center in Huntsville, Alabama, and Thiokol in Utah to discuss the possible effects of cold temperatures on the performance of the solid rocket boosters. During this teleconference, Roger Boisjoly and Arnie Thompson, two Thiokol engineers who had worked on the solid-propellant booster design, gave an hour-long presentation on how the cold weather would increase the problems of joint rotation and sealing of the joint by the O-rings.

Table 1 Space Shuttle *Challenger* Accident: Who's Who

Organizations	
NASA	The National Aeronautics and Space Administration, responsible for space exploration. The space shuttle is one of NASA's programs.
Marshall Space Flight Center	A NASA facility that was in charge of the solid rocket booster development for the shuttle.
Morton Thiokol	A private company that won the contract from NASA for building the solid rocket boosters for the shuttle.

People	
NASA	
Larry Mulloy	Solid Rocket Booster Project manager at Marshall
Morton Thiokol	
Roger Boisjoly / Arnie Johnson	Engineers who worked on the Solid Rocket Booster Development Program.
Joe Kilminster	Engineering manager on the Solid Rocket Booster Development Program.
Alan McDonald	Director of the Solid Rocket Booster Project.
Bob Lund	Vice president for engineering.
Jerald Mason	General manager.

The engineers' point was that the lowest temperature at which the shuttle had previously been launched was 53°F, on January 24, 1985, when there was blow-by of the O-rings. The O-ring temperature at *Challenger's* expected launch time the following morning was predicted to be 29°F, far below the temperature at which NASA had previous experience. After the engineers' presentation, Bob Lund, the vice president for engineering at Morton Thiokol, presented his recommendations. He reasoned that since there had previously been severe O-ring erosion at 53°F and the launch would take place at significantly below this temperature where no data and no experience were available, NASA should delay the launch until the O-ring temperature could be at least 53°F. Interestingly, in the original design, it was specified that the booster should operate properly down to an outside temperature of 31°F.

Larry Mulloy, the Solid Rocket Booster project manager at Marshall and a NASA employee, correctly pointed out that the data were inconclusive and disagreed with the Thiokol engineers. After some discussion, Mulloy asked Joe Kilminster, an engineering manager working on the project, for his opinion. Kilminster backed up the recommendation of his fellow engineers. Others from Marshall expressed their disagreement with the Thiokol engineers' recommendation, which prompted Kilminster to ask to take the discussion off line for a few minutes. Boisjoly and other engineers reiterated to their management that the original decision not to launch was the correct one.

A key fact that ultimately swayed the decision was that in the available data, there seemed to be no correlation between temperature and the degree to which blow-by gasses had eroded the O-rings in previous launches. Thus, it could be concluded that there was really no trend in the data indicating that a launch at the expected temperature would necessarily be unsafe. After much discussion, Jerald Mason, a senior manager with Thiokol, turned to Lund and said, "Take off your engineering hat and put on your management hat," a phrase that has become famous in engineering ethics discussions. Lund reversed his previous decision and recommended that the launch proceed. The new recommendation included an indication that there was a safety concern due to the cold weather, but that the data were inconclusive and the launch was recommended. McDonald, who was in Florida, was surprised by this recommendation and attempted to convince NASA to delay the launch, but to no avail.

The Launch

Contrary to the weather predictions, the overnight temperature was 8°F, colder than the shuttle had ever experienced before. In fact, there was a significant accumulation of ice on the launchpad from safety showers and fire hoses that had been left on to prevent the pipes from freezing. It has been estimated that the aft field joint of the right-hand booster was at 28°F.

NASA routinely documents as many aspects of launches as possible. One part of this monitoring is the extensive use of cameras focused on critical areas of the launch vehicle. One of these cameras, looking at the right booster, recorded puffs of smoke coming from the aft field joint immediately after the boosters were ignited. This smoke is thought to have been caused by the steel cylinder of this segment of the booster expanding outward and causing the field joint to rotate. But, due to the extremely cold temperature, the O-ring didn't seat properly. The heat-resistant putty was also so cold that it didn't protect the O-rings, and hot gases burned past both O-rings. It was later determined that this blow-by occurred over 70° of arc around the O-rings.

Very quickly, the field joint was sealed again by byproducts of the solid rocket-propellant combustion, which formed a glassy oxide on the joint. This oxide formation might have averted the disaster had it not been for a very strong wind shear that the shuttle encountered almost one minute into the flight. The oxides that were temporarily sealing the field joint were shattered by the stresses caused by the wind shear. The joint was now opened again, and hot gases escaped from the solid booster. Since the booster was attached to the large liquid-fuel booster, the flames from the solid-fuel booster blow-by quickly burned through the external tank. The liquid propellant was ignited and the shuttle exploded.

The Aftermath

As a result of the explosion, the shuttle program was grounded as a thorough review of shuttle safety was conducted. Thiokol formed a failure-investigation team on January 31, 1986, which included Roger Boisjoly. There were also many investigations into the cause of the accident, both by the contractors involved (including Thiokol) and by various government bodies. As part of the governmental investigation, President Reagan appointed a blue-ribbon commission, known as the Rogers commission, after its chair. The commission consisted of distinguished scientists and engineers who were asked to look into the cause of the accident and to recommend changes in the shuttle program.

One of the commission members was Richard Feynman, a Nobel prize winner in physics, who ably demonstrated to the country what had gone wrong. In a demonstration that was repeatedly shown on national news programs, he demonstrated the problem with the O-rings by taking a sample of the O-ring material and bending it.

Explosion of the space shuttle *Challenger* soon after lift-off in January 1986. NASA/Johnson Space Center

The flexibility of the material at room temperature was evident. He then immersed it in ice water. When Feynman again bent the O-ring, it was obvious that the resiliency of the material was severely reduced, a very clear demonstration of what happened to the O-rings on the cold launch date in Florida.

As part of the commission hearings, Boisjoly and other Thiokol engineers were asked to testify. Boisjoly handed over to the commission copies of internal Thiokol memos and reports detailing the design process and the problems that had already been encountered. Naturally, Thiokol was trying to put the best possible spin on the situation, and Boisjoly's actions hurt this effort. According to Boisjoly, after this action he was isolated within the company, his responsibilities for the redesign of the joint were taken away, and he was subtly harassed by Thiokol management [Boisjoly, 1991, and Boisjoly, Curtis, and Mellicam, 1989].

Eventually, the atmosphere became intolerable for Boisjoly, and he took extended sick leave from his position at Thiokol. The joint was redesigned, and the shuttle has since flown numerous successful missions. However, the ambitious launch schedule originally intended by NASA has never been met. It was reported in 2001 that NASA has spent $5 million to study the possibility of installing some type of escape system to protect the shuttle crew in the event of an accident. No decision has yet been made. Possibilities include ejection seats or an escape capsule that would work during the first three minutes of flight. These features were incorporated into earlier manned space vehicles and in fact were in place on the shuttle until 1982. Whether such a system would have saved the astronauts aboard the *Challenger* is unknown.

The Space Shuttle *Columbia* Failure

During the early morning hours of February 1, 2003, many people across the United States awoke to a loud noise, sounding like the boom associated with supersonic aircraft. This was the space shuttle *Columbia* breaking up during reentry to the earth's atmosphere. This accident was the second loss of a space shuttle in 113 flights—all seven astronauts aboard the *Columbia* were killed—and pieces of the shuttle were scattered over a wide area of eastern Texas and western Louisiana. Over 84,000 individual pieces were eventually recovered, comprising only about 38% of the shuttle.

This was the 28th mission flown by the *Columbia,* a 16-day mission involving many tasks. The first indication of trouble during reentry came when temperature sensors near the left wheel well indicated a rise in temperature. Soon, hydraulic lines on the left side of the craft began to fail, making it difficult to keep control of the vehicle. Finally, it was impossible for the pilots to maintain the proper positioning of the shuttle during reentry—the *Columbia* went out of control and broke up.

The bottom of the space shuttle is covered with ceramic tiles designed to dissipate the intense heat generated during reentry from space. The destruction of the *Columbia* was attributed to damage to tiles on the leading edge of the left wing. During liftoff, a piece of insulating foam on the external fuel tank dislodged and struck the shuttle. It was estimated that this foam struck the shuttle wing at over 500 miles per hour, causing significant damage to the tiles on the wing over an area of approximately 650 cm^2. With the integrity of these tiles compromised, the wing structure was susceptible to extreme heating during reentry and ultimately failed.

Interestingly, shuttle launches are closely observed by numerous video cameras. During this launch, the foam separation and strike had been observed. Much thought was given during *Columbia*'s mission to attempting to determine whether significant damage had occurred. For example, there was some discussion of trying to use ground-based telescopes to look at the bottom of the shuttle while in orbit. Unfortunately, even if it had been possible to observe the damage, there would have been no way to repair the damage in space. The only alternatives would have been to attempt to launch another shuttle on a dangerous rescue mission, or attempt to get the astronauts to the space station in the hopes of launching a later rescue mission to bring them back to earth. In the end, NASA decided that the damage from the foam strike had probably not been significant and decided to continue with the mission and reentry as planned.

This was not the first time that foam had detached from the fuel tank during launch, and it was not the first time that foam had struck the shuttle. Apparently numerous small pieces of foam hit the shuttle during every launch, and on at least seven occasions previous to the *Columbia* launch, large pieces of foam had detached and hit the shuttle. Various solutions to the problem had been proposed over the years, but none had been implemented. Although NASA engineers initially identified foam strikes as a major safety concern for the shuttle, after many launches with no safety problems due to the foam, NASA management became complacent and overlooked the potential for foam to cause major problems. In essence, the prevailing attitude suggested that if there had been numerous launches with foam strikes before, with none leading to major accidents, then it must be safe to continue launches without fixing the problem.

In the aftermath of this mishap, an investigative panel was formed to determine the cause of the accident and to make recommendations for the future of the shuttle program. The report of this panel contained information on their findings regarding the physical causes of the accident: the detachment of the foam, the damage to the tiles, and the subsequent failure of critical components of the shuttle. More significantly, the report also went into great depth on the cultural issues within NASA that led to the accident. The report cited a "broken safety culture" within NASA. Perhaps most damning was the assessment that many of the problems that existed within NASA that led to the *Challenger* accident sixteen years earlier had not been fixed. Especially worrisome was the finding that schedule pressures had been allowed to supercede good engineering judgment. An accident such as the *Challenger* explosion should have led to a major change in the safety and ethics culture within NASA. But sadly for the crew of the *Columbia,* it had not.

After the *Columbia* accident, the space shuttle was once again grounded until safety concerns related to foam strikes could be addressed. By 2005, NASA was confident that steps had been taken to make the launch of the shuttle safe and once again restarted the launch program. In July of 2005, *Discovery* was launched. During this launch, another foam strike occurred. This time, NASA was prepared and had planned for means to photographically assess potential damage to the heat shield, and also planned to allow astronauts to make a space walk to assess damage to the tiles and to make repairs as necessary. The damage from this strike was repaired in space and the shuttle returned to earth safely. Despite the success of the in-orbit repairs, NASA again grounded the shuttle fleet until a redesign of the foam could be implemented. The redesign called for removal of foam from areas where foam detachment could have the greatest impact on tiles. The shuttle has once again resumed flight, with a successful launch in September of 2006.

SUMMARY

Engineering ethics is the study of moral decisions that must be made by engineers in the course of engineering practice. It is important for engineering students to study ethics so that they will be prepared to respond appropriately to ethical challenges during their careers. Often, the correct answer to an ethical problem will not be obvious and will require some analysis using ethical theories. The types of problems that we will encounter in studying engineering ethics are very similar to the design problems that engineers work on every day. As in design, there will not be a single correct answer. Rather, engineering ethics problems will have multiple correct solutions, with some solutions being better than others.

REFERENCES

ROGER BOISJOLY, "The Challenger Disaster: Moral Responsibility and the Working Engineer," in Deborah G. Johnson, *Ethical Issues in Engineering,* Prentice Hall, Upper Saddle River, NJ, 1991, pp. 6–14.

NORBERT ELLIOT, ERIC KATZ, AND ROBERT LYNCH, "The Challenger Tragedy: A Case Study in Organizational Communication and Professional Ethics," *Business and Professional Ethics Journal,* vol. 12, 1990, pp. 91–108.

JOSEPH R. HERKERT, "Management's Hat Trick: Misuse of 'Engineering Judgment' in the Challenger Incident," *Journal of Business Ethics,* vol. 10, 1991, pp. 617–620.

PATRICIA H. WERHANE, "Engineers and Management: The Challenge of the Challenger Incident," *Journal of Business Ethics,* vol. 10, 1991, pp. 605–16.

RUSSELL BOISJOLY, Ellen Foster Curtis, and Eugene Mellican, "Roger Boisjoly and the Challenger Disaster: The Ethical Dimensions," *Journal of Business Ethics,* vol. 8, 1989, pp. 217–230.

SANGER, DAVID E., "Loss of the Shuttle: The Overview; Shuttle Breaks Up, Seven Dead," Feb. 2, 2003, sect. 1, p. 1. Numerous other articles can be found in *The New York Times* on February 2, 2003 and subsequent days or in any local U.S. newspaper.

COLUMBIA ACCIDENT INVESTIGATION BOARD, Information on the investigation including links to the final report can be found at the board's web site, www.caib.gov.

PROBLEMS

1   How different are personal ethics and business ethics? Is this difference true for you personally?

2   What are the roots of your personal ethics?

3   Engineering design generally involves five steps: developing a statement of the problem and/or a set of specifications, gathering information pertinent to the problem, designing several alternatives that meet the specifications, analyzing the alternatives and selecting the best one, and testing and implementing the best design. How is ethical problem solving like this?

Space Shuttle *Challenger*

4   The astronauts on the *Challenger* mission were aware of the dangerous nature of riding a complex machine such as the space shuttle, so they can be thought of as having given informed consent to participating in a dangerous enterprise. What role did informed consent play in this case? Do you think that the astronauts had enough information to give informed consent to launch the shuttle that day?

5   Can an engineer who has become a manager truly ever take off her engineer's hat? Should she?

6   Some say that the shuttle was really designed by Congress rather than NASA. What does this statement mean? What are the ramifications if this is true?

7   Aboard the shuttle for this flight was the first teacher in space. Should civilians be allowed on what is basically an experimental launch vehicle? At the time, many felt that the placement of a teacher on the shuttle was for purely political purposes. President Reagan was widely seen as doing nothing while the American educational system decayed. Cynics felt that the teacher-in-space idea was cooked up as a method of diverting attention from this problem and was to be seen as Reagan's doing something for education while he really wasn't doing anything. What are the ethical implications if this scenario is true?

8   Should a launch have been allowed when there were no test data for the expected conditions? Keep in mind that it is probably impossible to test for all possible operating conditions. More generally, should a product be released for use even when it hasn't been tested over all expected operational conditions? When the data is inconclusive, which way should the decision go?

9   During the aftermath of the accident, Thiokol and NASA investigated possible causes of the explosion. Boisjoly accused Thiokol and NASA of intentionally downplaying the problems with the O-rings while looking for other causes of the accident. If true, what are the ethical implications of this type of investigation?

10 It might be assumed that the management decision to launch was prompted in part by concerns for the health of the company and the space program as a whole. Given the political climate at the time of the launch, if problems and delays continued, ultimately Thiokol might have lost NASA contracts, or NASA budgets might have been severely reduced. Clearly, this scenario could have led to the loss of many jobs at Thiokol and NASA. How might these considerations ethically be factored into the decision?

11 Engineering codes of ethics require engineers to protect the safety and health of the public in the course of their duties. Do the astronauts count as "the public" in this context?

12 What should NASA management have done differently? What should Thiokol management have done differently?

13 What else could Boisjoly and the other engineers at Thiokol have done to prevent the launch from occurring?

Space Shuttle *Columbia*

14 The *Columbia* tragedy was attributed to a foam strike on the shuttle wing. This sort of strike had occurred often in previous flights. What role do you think complacency of NASA engineers and managers played in this story?

15 Some people believe that the shuttle should have been better engineered for crew safety, including provisions for repair of the shuttle during the mission, escape of the crew when problems occur during launch, or having a backup shuttle ready to launch for rescue missions. What are some reasons why NASA would not have planned this when the shuttle was designed?

16 The space shuttle is an extremely complex engineered system. The more complex a system, the harder it is to make safe especially in a harsh environment such as outer space. Do you think that two accidents in 113 flights is an acceptable level of risk for an experimental system such as the shuttle?

5

Professionalism and Codes of Ethics

Objectives

After reading this chapter, you will be able to

- Determine whether engineering is a profession
- Understand what codes of ethics are, and
- Examine some codes of ethics of professional engineering societies.

Late in 1994, reports began to appear in the news media that the latest generation of Pentium® microprocessors, the heart and soul of personal computers, was flawed. These reports appeared not only in trade journals and magazines aimed at computer specialists, but also in *The New York Times* and other daily newspapers. The stories reported that computers equipped with these chips were unable to correctly perform some relatively simple multiplication and division operations.

At first, Intel, the manufacturer of the Pentium microprocessor, denied that there was a problem. Later, it argued that although there was a problem, the error would be significant only in sophisticated applications, and most people wouldn't even notice that an error had occurred. It was also reported that Intel had been aware of the problem and already was working to fix it. As a result of this publicity, many people who had purchased Pentium-based computers asked to have the defective chip replaced. Until the public outcry had reached huge proportions, Intel refused to replace the chips. Finally, when it was clear that this situation was a public relations disaster for them, Intel agreed to replace the defective chips when customers requested it.

Did Intel do anything unethical? To answer this question, we will need to develop a framework for understanding ethical problems. One part of this framework will be the codes of ethics that have been established by professional engineering organizations. These codes help guide engineers in the course of their professional duties and give them insight into ethical problems such as the one just described. The engineering codes of ethics hold that engineers should not make false claims or represent a product to be something that it is not. In some ways, the Pentium case might seem to simply be a public-relations problem. But, looking at the problem with a code of ethics will indicate that there is more to this situation than simple PR, especially since the chip did not operate in the way that Intel claimed it did.

In this chapter, the nature of professions will be examined with the goal of determining whether engineering is a profession. Two representative engineering codes of ethics will be looked at in detail. At the end of this chapter,

From *Engineering Ethics*, Third Edition, Charles B. Fledderman. Copyright © 2008 by Pearson Education. Published by Prentice Hall, Inc. All rights reserved.

the Pentium case is presented in more detail along with two other cases, and codes of ethics are applied to analyze what the engineers in these cases should have done.

1 INTRODUCTION

When confronted by an ethical problem, what resources are available to an engineer to help find a solution? One of the hallmarks of modern professions are codes of ethics promulgated by various professional societies. These codes serve to guide practitioners of the profession in making decisions about how to conduct themselves and how to resolve ethical issues that might confront them. Are codes of ethics applicable to engineering? To answer this question, we must first consider what professions are and how they function and then decide if this definition applies to engineering. Then we will examine codes of ethics in general and look specifically at some of the codes of engineering professional societies.

2 IS ENGINEERING A PROFESSION?

In order to determine whether engineering is a profession, the nature of professions must first be examined. As a starting point, it will be valuable to distinguish the word "profession" from other words that are sometimes used synonymously with "profession": "job" and " occupation." Any work for hire can be considered a job, regardless of the skill level involved and the responsibility granted. Engineering is certainly a job—engineers are paid for their services—but the skills and responsibilities involved in engineering make it more than just a job.

Similarly, the word "occupation" implies employment through which someone makes a living. Engineering, then, is also an occupation. How do the words "job" and "occupation" differ from "profession?"

The words "profession" and "professional" have many uses in modern society that go beyond the definition of a job or occupation. One often hears about "professional athletes" or someone referring to himself as a "professional carpenter," for example. In the first case, the word "professional" is being used to distinguish the practitioner from an unpaid amateur. In the second case, it is used to indicate some degree of skill acquired through many years of experience, with an implication that this practitioner will provide quality services.

Neither of these senses of the word "professional" is applicable to engineers. There are no amateur engineers who perform engineering work without being paid while they train to become professional, paid engineers. Likewise, the length of time one works at an engineering-related job, such as an engineering aide or engineering technician, does not confer professional status no matter how skilled a technician one might become. To see what is meant by the term "professional engineer," we will first examine the nature of professions.

2.1 What Is a Profession?

What are the attributes of a profession? There have been many studies of this question, and some consensus as to the nature of *professions* has been achieved. Attributes of a profession include

1. Work that requires sophisticated skills, the use of judgment, and the exercise of discretion. Also, the work is not routine and is not capable of being mechanized;
2. Membership in the profession requires extensive formal education, not simply practical training or apprenticeship;

3. The public allows special societies or organizations that are controlled by members of the profession to set standards for admission to the profession, to set standards of conduct for members, and to enforce these standards; and,
4. Significant public good results from the practice of the profession [Martin and Schinzinger, 2000].

The terms "judgment" and "discretion" used in the first part of this definition require a little amplification. Many occupations require judgment every day. A secretary must decide what work to tackle first. An auto mechanic must decide if a part is sufficiently worn to require complete replacement, or if rebuilding will do. This is not the type of judgment implied in this definition. In a profession, "judgment" refers to making significant decisions based on formal training and experience. In general, the decisions will have serious impacts on people's lives and will often have important implications regarding the spending of large amounts of money.

"Discretion" can have two different meanings. The first definition involves being discrete in the performance of one's duties by keeping information about customers, clients, and patients confidential. This confidentiality is essential for engendering a trusting relationship and is a hallmark of professions. While many jobs might involve some discretion, this definition implies a high level of significance to the information that must be kept private by a professional. The other definition of discretion involves the ability to make decisions autonomously. When making a decision, one is often told, "Use your discretion." This definition is similar in many ways to that of the term "judgment" described previously. Many people are allowed to use their discretion in making choices while performing their jobs. However, the significance of the decision marks the difference between a job and a profession.

One thing not mentioned in the definition of a profession is the compensation received by a professional for his services. Although most professionals tend to be relatively well compensated, high pay is not a sufficient condition for professional status. Entertainers and athletes are among the most highly paid members of our society, and yet few would describe them as professionals in the sense described previously. Although professional status often helps one to get better pay and better working conditions, these are more often determined by economic forces.

Earlier, reference was made to "professional" athletes and carpenters. Let's examine these occupations in light of the foregoing definition of professions and see if athletics and carpentry qualify as professions. An athlete who is paid for her appearances is referred to as a professional athlete. Clearly, being a paid athlete does involve sophisticated skills that most people do not possess, and these skills are not capable of mechanization. However, substantial judgment and discretion are not called for on the part of athletes in their "professional" lives, so athletics fails the first part of the definition of "professional." Interestingly, though, professional athletes are frequently viewed as role models and are often disciplined for a lack of discretion in their personal lives.

Athletics requires extensive training, not of a formal nature, but more of a practical nature acquired through practice and coaching. No special societies (as opposed to unions, which will be discussed in more detail later) are required by athletes, and athletics does not meet an important public need; although entertainment is a public need, it certainly doesn't rank highly compared to the needs met by professions such as medicine. So, although they are highly trained and very well compensated, athletes are not professionals.

Similarly, carpenters require special skills to perform their jobs, but many aspects of their work can be mechanized, and little judgment or discretion is required. Training in carpentry is not formal, but rather is practical by way of apprenticeships. No organizations or societies are required. However, carpentry certainly does meet an aspect of the public good—providing shelter is fundamental to society—although perhaps not to the same extent as do professions such as medicine. So, carpentry also doesn't meet the basic requirements to be a profession. We can see, then, that many jobs or occupations whose practitioners might be referred to as professionals don't really meet the basic definition of a profession. Although they may be highly paid or important jobs, they are not professions.

Before continuing with an examination of whether engineering is a profession, let's look at two occupations that are definitely regarded by society as professions: medicine and law. Medicine certainly fits the definition of a profession given previously. It requires very sophisticated skills that can't be mechanized, it requires judgment as to appropriate treatment plans for individual patients, and it requires discretion. (Physicians have even been granted physician–patient privilege, the duty not to divulge information given in confidence by the patient to the physician.) Although medicine requires extensive practical training learned through an apprenticeship called a residency, it also requires much formal training (four years of undergraduate school, three to four years of medical school, and extensive hands-on practice in patient care). Medicine has a special society, the American Medical Association (AMA), to which a large fraction of practicing physicians belong and that participates in the regulation of medical schools, sets standards for practice of the profession, and enforces codes of ethical behavior for its members. Finally, healing the sick and helping to prevent disease clearly involve the public good. By the definition presented previously, medicine clearly qualifies as a profession.

Similarly, law is a profession. It involves sophisticated skills acquired through extensive formal training; has a professional society, the American Bar Association (ABA); and serves an important aspect of the public good. (Although this last point is increasingly becoming a point of debate within American society!) The difference between athletics and carpentry on one hand and law and medicine on the other is clear. The first two really cannot be considered professions, and the latter two most certainly are.

2.2 Engineering as a Profession

Using medicine and law as our examples of professions, it is now time to consider whether engineering is a profession. Certainly, engineering requires extensive and sophisticated skills. Otherwise, why spend four years in college just to get a start in engineering? The essence of engineering design is judgment: how to use the available materials, components and devices, to reach a specified objective. Discretion is required in engineering: Engineers are required to keep their employers' or clients' intellectual-property and business information confidential. Also, a primary concern of any engineer is the safety of the public that will use the products and devices he designs. There is always a trade-off between safety and other engineering issues in a design, requiring discretion on the part of the engineer to ensure that the design serves its purpose and fills its market niche safely.

The point about mechanization needs to be addressed a little more carefully with respect to engineering. Certainly, once a design has been performed, it can easily be replicated without the intervention of an engineer. However, each new situation that requires a new design or a modification of an existing design requires an engineer. Industry commonly uses many computer-based tools for generating designs, such as computer-aided design (CAD) software. This shouldn't be mistaken for mechanization of engineering. CAD is simply a tool used by engineers, not a replacement for the skills of an actual engineer. A wrench can't fix an automobile without a mechanic. Likewise, a computer with CAD software can't design an antilock braking system for an automobile without an engineer.

Engineering requires extensive formal training. Four years of undergraduate training leading to a bachelor's degree in an engineering program is essential, followed by work under the supervision of an experienced engineer. Many engineering jobs even require advanced degrees beyond the bachelor's degree. The work of engineers serves the public good by providing communication systems, transportation, energy resources, and medical diagnostic and treatment equipment, to name only a few.

Before passing final judgment on the professional status of engineering, the nature of engineering societies requires a little consideration. Each discipline within engineering has a professional society, such as the Institute of Electrical and Electronics Engineers (IEEE) for electrical engineers and the American Society of Mechanical Engineers (ASME) for mechanical engineers. These societies serve to set professional standards and frequently work with schools of engineering to set standards for admission and curricula. However, these societies differ significantly from the AMA and the ABA. Unlike law and medicine, each specialty of engineering has its own society. There is no overall engineering society that most engineers identify with, although the National Society of Professional Engineers (NSPE) tries to function in this way. In addition, relatively few practicing engineers belong to their professional societies. Thus, the engineering societies are weak compared to the AMA and the ABA.

It is clear that engineering meets all of the definitions of a profession. In addition, it is clear that engineering practice has much in common with medicine and law. Interestingly, although they are professionals, engineers do not yet hold the same status within society that physicians and lawyers do.

2.3 Differences between Engineering and Other Professions

Although we have determined that engineering is a profession, it should be noted that there are significant differences between how engineering is practiced and how law and medicine are practiced. Lawyers are typically self-employed in private practice, essentially an independent business, or in larger group practices with other lawyers. Relatively few are employed by large organizations such as corporations. Until recently, this was also the case for most physicians, although with the accelerating trend toward managed care and HMOs in the past decade, many more physicians work for large corporations rather than in private practice. However, even physicians who are employed by large HMOs are members of organizations in which they retain much of the decision-making power—often, the head of an HMO is a physician—and make up a substantial fraction of the total number of employees.

In contrast, engineers generally practice their profession very differently from physicians and lawyers. Most engineers are not self-employed, but more often are a small part of larger companies involving many different occupations, including accountants, marketing specialists, and extensive numbers of less skilled manufacturing employees. The exception to this rule is civil engineers, who generally practice as independent consultants either on their own or in engineering firms similar in many ways to law firms. When employed by large corporations, engineers are rarely in significant managerial positions, except with regard to managing other engineers. Although engineers are paid well compared to the rest of society, they are generally less well compensated than physicians and lawyers.

Training for engineers is different than for physicians and lawyers. One can be employed as an engineer after four years of undergraduate education, unlike law and medicine, for which training in the profession doesn't begin until after the undergraduate program has been completed. As mentioned previously, the engineering societies are not as powerful as the AMA and the ABA, perhaps because of the number of different professional engineering societies. Also, both law and medicine require licenses granted by the state in order to practice. Many engineers, especially those employed by large industrial companies, do not have engineering licenses. It can be debated whether someone who is unlicensed is truly an engineer or whether he is practicing engineering illegally, but the reality is that many of those who are employed as engineers are not licensed. Finally, engineering doesn't have the social stature that law and medicine have (a fact that is reflected in the lower pay that engineers receive as compared to that of lawyers and doctors). Despite these differences, on balance, engineering is still clearly a profession, albeit one that is not as mature as medicine and law. However, it should be striving to emulate some of the aspects of these professions.

2.4 Other Aspects of Professional Societies

We should briefly note that professional societies also serve other, perhaps less noble, purposes than those mentioned previously. Sociologists who study the nature of professional societies describe two different models of professions, sometimes referred to as the social-contract and the business models. The social-contract model views professional societies as being set up primarily to further the public good, as described in the definition of a profession given previously. There is an implicit social contract involved with professions, according to this model. Society grants the professions' perks such as high pay, a high status in society, and the ability to self-regulate. In return for these perks, society gets the services provided by the profession.

A perhaps more cynical view of professions is provided by the business model. According to this model, professions function as a means for furthering the economic advantage of the members. Put another way, professional organizations are labor unions for the elite, strictly limiting the number of practitioners of the profession, controlling the working conditions for professionals, and artificially inflating the salaries of its members. An analysis of both models in terms of law and medicine would show that there are ways in which these professions exhibit aspects of both of these models.

Where does engineering fit into this picture? Engineering is certainly a service-oriented profession and thus fits into the social-contract model quite nicely. Although some engineers might wish to see engineering professional societies function more according to the business model, they currently don't function that way. The engineering societies have virtually no clout with major engineering employers to set wages and working conditions or to help engineers resolve ethical disputes with their employers.

Moreover, there is very little prospect that the engineering societies will function this way in the near future.

2.5 If Engineering Were Practiced More Like Medicine

It is perhaps instructive to speculate a little on how engineering might change in the future if our model of the engineering profession were closer to that of law or medicine. One major change would be in the way engineers are educated. Rather than the current system, in which students study engineering as undergraduates and then pursue advanced degrees as appropriate, prospective engineers would probably get a four-year "preengineering" degree in mathematics, physics, chemistry, computer science, or some combination of these fields. After the four-year undergraduate program, students would enter a three- or four-year engineering professional program culminating in a "doctor of engineering" degree (or other appropriately named degree). This program would include extensive study of engineering fundamentals, specialization in a field of study, and perhaps "clinical" training under a practicing engineer.

How would such engineers be employed? The pattern of employment would certainly be different. Engineers in all fields might work for engineering firms similar to the way in which civil engineers work now, consulting on projects for government agencies or large corporations. The corporate employers who now have numerous engineers on their staff would probably have far fewer engineers on the payroll, opting instead for a few professional engineers who would supervise the work of several less highly trained "engineering technicians." Adoption of this model would probably reduce the number of engineers in the work force, leading to higher earnings for those who remain. Those relegated to the ranks of engineering technicians would probably earn less than those currently employed as engineers.

3 CODES OF ETHICS

An aspect of professional societies that has not been mentioned yet is the codes of ethics that engineering societies have adopted. These codes express the rights, duties, and obligations of the members of the profession. In this section, we will examine the codes of ethics of professional engineering societies.

It should be noted that although most of the discussion thus far has focused on professionalism and professional societies, codes of ethics are not limited to professional organizations. They can also be found, for example, in corporations and universities as well. We start with some general ideas about what codes of ethics are and what purpose they serve and then examine two professional engineering codes in more detail.

3.1 What Is a Code of Ethics?

Primarily, a code of ethics provides a framework for ethical judgment for a professional. The key word here is "framework." No code can be totally comprehensive and cover all possible ethical situations that a professional engineer is likely to encounter. Rather, codes serve as a starting point for ethical decision making. A code can also express the commitment to ethical conduct shared by members of a profession. It is important to note that ethical codes do not establish new ethical principles. They simply reiterate principles and standards that are already accepted as responsible engineering practice. A code expresses these principles in a coherent, comprehensive, and accessible manner. Finally, a code defines the roles and responsibilities of professionals [Harris, Pritchard, and Rabins, 2000].

It is important also to look at what a code of ethics is not. It is not a recipe for ethical behavior; as previously stated, it is only a framework for arriving at good ethical choices. A code of ethics is never a substitute for sound judgment. A code of ethics is not a legal document. One can't be arrested for violating its provisions, although expulsion from the professional society might result from code violations. As mentioned in the previous section, with the current state of engineering societies, expulsion from an engineering society generally will not result in an inability to practice engineering, so there are not necessarily any direct consequences of violating engineering ethical codes. Finally, a code of ethics doesn't create new moral or ethical principles. As described in the previous chapter, these principles are well established in society, and foundations of our ethical and moral principles go back many centuries. Rather, a code of ethics spells out the ways in which moral and ethical principles apply to professional practice. Put another way, a code helps the engineer to apply moral principles to the unique situations encountered in professional practice.

How does a code of ethics achieve these goals? First, a code of ethics helps create an environment within a profession where ethical behavior is the norm. It also serves as a guide or reminder of how to act in specific situations. A code of ethics can also be used to bolster an individual's position with regard to a certain activity: The code provides a little backup for an individual who is being pressured by a superior to behave unethically. A code of ethics can also bolster the individual's position by indicating that there is a collective sense of correct behavior; there is strength in numbers. Finally, a code of ethics can indicate to others that the profession is seriously concerned about responsible, professional conduct [Harris, Pritchard, and Rabins, 2000]. A code of ethics, however, should not be used as "window dressing," an attempt by an organization to appear to be committed to ethical behavior when it really is not.

3.2 Objections to Codes

Although codes of ethics are widely used by many organizations, including engineering societies, there are many objections to codes of ethics, specifically as they apply to engineering practice. First, as mentioned previously, relatively few practicing engineers are members of professional societies and so don't necessarily feel compelled to abide by their codes. Many engineers who are members of professional societies are not aware of the existence of the society's code, or if they are aware of it, they have never read it. Even among engineers who know about their society's code, consultation of the code is rare. There are also objections that the engineering codes often have internal conflicts, but don't give a method for resolving the conflict. Finally, codes can be coercive: They foster ethical behavior with a stick rather than with a carrot [Harris, Pritchard, and Rabins, 2000]. Despite these objections, codes are in very widespread use today and are generally thought to serve a useful function.

3.3 Codes of the Engineering Societies

Before examining professional codes in more detail, it might be instructive to look briefly at the history of the engineering codes of ethics. Professional engineering societies in the United States began to be organized in the late 19th century, with new societies created as new engineering fields have developed in this century. As these societies matured, many of them created codes of ethics to guide practicing engineers.

Early in the current century, these codes were mostly concerned with issues of how to conduct business. For example, many early codes had clauses forbidding advertising of services or prohibiting competitive bidding by engineers for design projects. Codes also spelled out the duties that engineers had toward their employers. Relatively less emphasis than today was given to issues of service to the public and safety. This imbalance has changed greatly in recent decades as public perceptions and concerns about the safety of engineered products and devices have changed. Now, most codes emphasize commitments to safety, public health, and even environmental protection as the most important duties of the engineer.

3.4 A Closer Look at Two Codes of Ethics

Having looked at some ideas about what codes of ethics are and how they function, let's look more closely at two codes of ethics: the codes of the IEEE and the NSPE. Although these codes have some common content, the structures of the codes are very different.

The IEEE code is short and deals in generalities, whereas the NSPE code is much longer and more detailed. An explanation of these differences is rooted in the philosophy of the authors of these codes. A short code that is lacking in detail is more likely to be read by members of the society than is a longer code. A short code is also more understandable. It articulates general principles and truly functions as a framework for ethical decision making, as described previously.

A longer code, such as the NSPE code, has the advantage of being more explicit and is thus able to cover more ground. It leaves less to the imagination of the individual and therefore is more useful for application to specific cases. The length of the code, however, makes it less likely to be read and thoroughly understood by most engineers.

There are some specifics of these two codes that are worth noting here. The IEEE code doesn't mention a duty to one's employer. However, the IEEE code does mention a duty to protect the environment, a clause added relatively recently, which is somewhat unique among engineering codes. The NSPE code has a preamble that succinctly presents the duties of the engineer before going on to the more explicit discussions of the rest of the code. Like most codes of ethics, the NSPE code does mention the engineer's duty to his or her employer in Section I.4, where it states that engineers shall "[a]ct ... for each employer ... as faithful agents or trustees."

3.5 Resolving Internal Conflicts in Codes

One objection to codes of ethics is the internal conflicts that can exist within them, with no instructions on how to resolve these conflicts. An example of this problem would be a situation in which an employer asks or even orders an engineer to implement a design that the engineer feels will be unsafe. It is made clear that the engineer's job is at stake if he doesn't do as instructed. What does the NSPE code tell us about this situation?

In clause I.4, the NSPE code indicates that engineers have a duty to their employers, which implies that the engineer should go ahead with the unsafe design favored by his employer. However, clause I.1 and the preamble make it clear that the safety of the public is also an important concern of an engineer. In fact, it says that the safety of the public is paramount. How can this conflict be resolved?

There is no implication in this or any other code that all clauses are equally important. Rather, there is a hierarchy within the code. Some clauses take precedence over others, although there is generally no explicit indication in the code of what the hierarchy is. The preceding dilemma is easily resolved within the context of this hierarchy. The duty to protect the safety of the public is paramount and takes precedence over the duty to the employer. In this case, the code provides very clear support to the engineer, who must convince his supervisor that the product can't be designed as requested. Unfortunately, not all internal conflicts in codes of ethics are so easily resolved.

3.6 Can Codes and Professional Societies Protect Employees?

One important area where professional societies can and should function is as protectors of the rights of employees who are being pressured by their employer to do something unethical or who are accusing their employers or the government of unethical conduct. The codes of the professional societies are of some use in this since they can be used by employees as ammunition against an employer who is sanctioning them for pointing out unethical behavior or who are being asked to engage in unethical acts.

An example of this situation is the action of the IEEE on behalf of three electrical engineers who were fired from their jobs at the Bay Area Rapid Transit (BART) organization when they pointed out deficiencies in the way the control systems for the BART trains were being designed and tested. After being fired, the engineers sued BART, citing the IEEE code of ethics which impelled them to hold as their primary concern the safety of the public who would be using the BART system. The IEEE intervened on their behalf in court, although ultimately the engineers lost the case.

If the codes of ethics of professional societies are to have any meaning, this type of intervention is essential when ethical violations are pointed out. However, since not all engineers are members of professional societies and the engineering societies are relatively weak, the pressure that can be exerted by these organizations is limited.

3.7 Other Types of Codes of Ethics

Professional societies aren't the only organizations that have codified their ethical standards. Many other organizations have also developed codes of ethics for various purposes similar to those of the professional engineering organizations. For example, codes for the ethical use of computers have been developed, and student organizations in universities have framed student codes of ethics. In this section, we will examine how codes of ethics function in corporations.

Many of the important ethical questions faced by engineers come up in the context of their work for corporations. Since most practicing engineers are not members of professional organizations, it seems that for many engineers, there is little ethical guidance in the course of their daily work. This problem has led to the adoption of codes of ethics by many corporations.

Even if the professional codes were widely adopted and recognized by practicing engineers, there would still be some value to the corporate codes, since a corporation can tailor its code to the individual circumstances and unique mission of the company. As such, these codes tend to be relatively long and very detailed, incorporating many rules specific to the practices of the company. For example, corporate codes frequently spell out in detail the company policies on business practices, relationships with suppliers, relationships with government agencies, compliance with government regulations, health and safety issues, issues related to environmental protection, equal employment opportunity and affirmative action, sexual harassment, and diversity and racial/ethnic tolerance. Since corporate codes are coercive in nature—your continued employment by the company depends on your compliance with the company code—these codes tend to be longer and more detailed in order to provide very clear and specific guidelines to the employees.

Codes of professional societies, by their nature, can't be this explicit, since there is no means for a professional society to reasonably enforce its code. Due to the typically long lengths of these codes, no example of a corporate *code of ethics* can be included here. However, codes for companies can sometimes be found via the Internet at corporate websites.

Some of the heightened awareness of ethics in corporations stems from the increasing public scrutiny that has accompanied well-publicized disasters, such as the cases presented in this book, as well as from cases of fraud and cost overruns, particularly in the defense industry, that have been exposed in the media. Many large corporations have developed corporate codes of ethics in response to these problems, to help heighten employee's awareness of ethical issues, and to help establish a strong corporate ethics culture. These codes give employees ready access to guidelines and policies of the corporations. But, as with professional codes, it is important to remember that these codes cannot cover all possible situations that an employee might encounter; there is no substitute for good judgment. A code also doesn't substitute for good lines of communications between employees and upper management and for workable methods for fixing ethical problems when they occur.

APPLICATION

Cases

Codes of ethics can be used as a tool for analyzing cases and for gaining some insight into the proper course of action. Before reading these cases, it would be helpful to read a couple of the codes in Appendix A, especially the code most closely related to your field of study, to become familiar with the types of issues that codes deal with. Then, put yourself in the position of an engineer working for these companies—Intel, Paradyne computers, and 3Bs construction—to see what you would have done in each case.

The Intel Pentium® Chip

In late 1994, the media began to report that there was a flaw in the new Pentium microprocessor produced by Intel. The microprocessor is the heart of a personal computer and controls all of the operations and calculations that take place. A flaw in the Pentium was especially significant, since it was the microprocessor used in 80% of the personal computers produced in the world at that time.

Apparently, flaws in a complicated integrated circuit such as the Pentium, which at the time contained over one million transistors, are common. However, most of the flaws are undetectable by the user and don't affect the operation of the computer. Many of these flaws are easily compensated for through software. The flaw that came to light in 1994 was different: It was detectable by the user. This particular flaw was in the floating-point unit (FPU) and caused a wrong answer when double-precision arithmetic, a very common operation, was performed.

A standard test was widely published to determine whether a user's microprocessor was flawed. Using spreadsheet software, the user was to take the number 4,195,835, multiply it by 3,145,727, and then divide that result by 3,145,727. As we all know from elementary math, when a number is multiplied and then divided by the same number, the result should be the original number. In this example, the result should be 4,195,835. However, with the flawed FPU, the result of this calculation was 4,195,579 [Infoworld, 1994]. Depending on the application, this six-thousandths-of-a-percent error might be very significant.

At first, Intel's response to these reports was to deny that there was any problem with the chip. When it became clear that this assertion was not accurate, Intel switched its policy and stated that although there was indeed a defect in the chip, it was insignificant and the vast majority of users would never even notice it. The chip would be replaced for free only for users who could demonstrate that they needed an unflawed version of the chip [Infoworld, 1994]. There is some logic to this policy from Intel's point of view, since over two million computers had already been sold with the defective chip.

Of course, this approach didn't satisfy most Pentium owners. After all, how can you predict whether you might have a future application where this flaw might be significant? IBM, a major Pentium user, canceled the sales of all IBM computers containing the flawed chip. Finally, after much negative publicity in the popular personal computer literature and an outcry from Pentium users, Intel agreed to replace the flawed chip with an unflawed version for any customer who asked to have it replaced.

It should be noted that long before news of the flaw surfaced in the popular press, Intel was aware of the problem and had already corrected it on subsequent versions. It did, however, continue to sell the flawed version and, based on its early insistence that the flaw did not present a significant problem to users, seemingly planned to do so until the new version was available and the stocks of the flawed one were exhausted. Eventually, the damage caused by this case was fixed as the media reports of the problem died down and as customers were able to get un-flawed chips into their computers. Ultimately, Intel had a write-off of 475 million dollars to solve this problem.

What did Intel learn from this experience? The early designs for new chips continue to have flaws, and sometimes these flaws are not detected until the product is already in use by consumers. However, Intel's approach to these problems has changed. It now seems to feel that problems need to be fixed immediately. In addition, the decision is now based on the consumer's perception of the significance of the flaw, rather than on Intel's opinion of its significance.

Indeed, similar flaws were found in 1997 in the early versions of the Pentium II and Pentium Pro processors. This time, Intel immediately confirmed that the flaw existed and offered customers software that would correct it. Other companies also seem to have benefited from Intel's experience. For example, Intuit, a leading man-ufacturer of tax preparation and financial software, called a news conference in March of 1995 to apologize for flaws in its TurboTax software that had become ap-parent earlier in that year. In addition to the apology, they offered consumers re-placements for the defective software.

Runway Concrete at the Denver International Airport

In the early 1990s, the city of Denver, Colorado, embarked on one of the largest public works projects in history: the construction of a new airport to replace the aging Stapleton International Airport. The new Denver International Airport (DIA) would be the first new airport constructed in the United States since the Dallas–Fort Worth Airport was completed in the early 1970s. Of course, the size and complexity of this type of project lends itself to many problems, including cost over-runs, worker safety and health issues, and controversies over the need for the pro-ject. The construction of DIA was no exception.

Perhaps the most widely known problem with the airport was the malfunc-tioning of a new computer-controlled high-tech baggage handling system, which in preliminary tests consistently mangled and misrouted baggage and frequently jammed, leading to the shutdown of the entire system. Problems with the baggage handling system delayed the opening of the airport for over a year and cost the city millions of dollars in expenses for replacement of the system and lost revenues while the airport was unable to open. In addition, the baggage system made the air-port the butt of many jokes, especially on late-night television.

More interesting from the perspective of engineering ethics are problems dur-ing the construction of DIA involving the concrete used for the runways, taxiways, and aprons at the airport. The story of concrete problems at DIA was first reported by the *Denver Post* in early August of 1993 as the airport neared completion. Two subcontractors filed lawsuits against the runway paving contractor, California con-struction company Ball, Ball, & Brosamer (known as 3Bs), claiming that 3Bs owed them money. Parts of these suits were allegations that 3Bs had altered the recipe for the concrete used in the runway and apron construction, deliberately diluting the concrete with more gravel, water, and sand (and thus less cement), thereby weakening it. 3Bs motivation for doing so would be to save money and thus to increase their profits. One of the subcontractors, CSI Trucking, whose job was to haul the sand and gravel used in the concrete, claimed that 3Bs hadn't paid them for materials that had been delivered. They claimed that these materials had been used to dilute the mixture, but hadn't been paid for, since the payment would leave a record of the improper recipe.

At first, Denver officials downplayed the reports of defective concrete, relying on the results of independent tests of the concrete. In addition, the city of Denver ordered core samples to be taken from the runways. Tests on these cores showed that the runway concrete had the correct strength. The subcontractors claimed that the improperly mixed concrete could have the proper test strength, but would lead to a severely shortened runway lifetime. The FBI also became involved in investigating this case, since federal transportation grants were used by Denver to help finance the construction of the runways.

The controversy seemed to settle down for a while, but a year later, in August of 1994, the Denver district attorney's office announced that it was investigating allegations that inspection reports on the runways were falsified during the construction. This announcement was followed on November 13, 1994 by a lengthy story in the *Denver Post* detailing a large number of allegations of illegal activities and unethical practices with regard to the runway construction.

The November 13 story revolved around an admission by a Fort Collins, Colorado, company, Empire Laboratories, that test reports on the concrete had been falsified to hide results which showed that some of the concrete did not meet the specifications. Attorneys for Empire said that this falsification had happened five or six times in the course of this work, but four employees of Empire claimed that the altering of test data was standard operating procedure at Empire.

The nature of the test modifications and the rationale behind them illustrate many of the important problems we will discuss in this book, including the need for objectivity and honesty in reporting results of tests and experiments. One Empire employee said that if a test result was inconsistent with other tests, then the results would be changed to mask the difference. This practice was justified by Empire as being "based upon engineering judgment" [*Denver Post*, Nov. 13, 1994]. The concrete was tested by pouring test samples when the actual runways were poured. These samples were subjected to flexural tests, which consist of subjecting the concrete to an increasing force until it fails. The tests were performed at 7 days after pouring and also at 28 days. Many of the test results showed that the concrete was weaker at 28 days than at 7 days. However, the results should have been the opposite, since concrete normally increases in strength as it cures. Empire employees indicated that this apparent anomaly was because many of the 7-day tests had been altered to make the concrete seem stronger than it was.

Other problems with the concrete also surfaced. Some of the concrete used in the runways contained clay balls up to 10 inches in diameter. While not uncommon in concrete batching, the presence of this clay can lead to runways that are significantly weaker than planned.

Questions about the short cement content in 3Bs concrete mixture also resurfaced in the November *Denver Post* article. The main question was "given that the concrete batching operation was routinely monitored, how did 3Bs get away with shorting the cement content of the concrete?" One of the batch plant operators for

3Bs explained that they were tipped off about upcoming inspections. When an inspector was due, they used the correct recipe so that concrete would appear to be correctly formulated. The shorting of the concrete mixture could also be detected by looking at the records of materials delivered to the batch plants. However, DIA administrators found that this documentation was missing, and it was unclear whether it had ever existed.

A batch plant operator also gave a sworn statement that he had been directed to fool the computer that operated the batch plant. The computer was fooled by tampering with the scale used to weigh materials and by inputting false numbers for the moisture content of the sand. In some cases, the water content of the sand that was input into the computer was a negative number! This tampering forced the computer to alter the mixture to use less cement, but the records printed by the computer would show that the mix was properly constituted. In his statement, the batch plant operator also swore that this practice was known to some of the highest officials in 3Bs.

Despite the problems with the batching of the concrete used in the runways, DIA officials insisted that the runways built by 3Bs met the specifications. This assertion was based on the test results, which showed that although some parts of the runway were below standard, all of the runways met FAA specifications. 3Bs was paid for those areas that were below standard at a lower rate than for the stronger parts of the runway. Further investigations about misdeeds in the construction of DIA were performed by several groups, including a Denver grand jury, a federal grand jury, the FBI, and committees of Congress.

On October 19, 1995, the *Denver Post* reported the results of a lawsuit brought by 3Bs against the city of Denver. 3Bs contended that the city still owed them $2.3 million (in addition to the $193 million that 3Bs had already been paid) for the work they did. The city claimed that this money was not owed. The reduction was a penalty due to low test results on some of the concrete. 3Bs claimed that those tests were flawed and that the concrete was fine. A hearing officer sided with the city, deciding that Denver didn't owe 3Bs any more money. 3Bs said that they would take their suit to the next higher level.

As of the summer of 2003, DIA has been in operation for many years and no problems have surfaced regarding the strength of the runways. Unfortunately, problems with runway durability might not surface until after several more years of use. In the meantime, there is still plenty of litigation and investigation of this and other unethical acts surrounding the construction of this airport.

Competitive Bidding and the Paradyne Case

Although competitive bidding is a well-established practice in purchasing, it can lead to many ethical problems associated with deception on the part of the vendor or with unfairness on the part of the buyer in choosing a vendor. The idea behind competitive bidding is that the buyer can get a product at the best price by setting up competition between the various suppliers. Especially with large contracts, the temptation to cheat on the bidding is great. Newspapers frequently report stories of deliberate underbidding to win contracts, followed by cost overruns that are unavoidable; theft of information on others' bids in order to be able to underbid them, etc. Problems also exist with buyers who make purchase decisions based on elements other than the advertised bid criteria, who leak information to a preferred bidder, or who give advance notice or detailed knowledge of evaluation procedures to preferred bidders. The Paradyne computer case is useful in illustrating some of the hazards associated with competitive bidding.

The Paradyne case began on June 10, 1980, when the Social Security Administration (SSA) published a request for proposals (RFP) for computer systems to replace the older equipment in its field offices. Its requirement was for computers that provide access to a central database. This database was used by field offices in the processing of benefit claims and in issuing new social security numbers. SSA intended to purchase an off-the-shelf system already in the vendor's product line, rather than a customized system. This requirement was intended to minimize the field testing and bugs associated with customized systems. In March of 1981, SSA let a contract for $115 million for 1,800 computer systems to Paradyne.

Problems occurred immediately upon award of the contract, when the Paradyne computers failed the acceptance testing. The requirements were finally relaxed so that the computers would pass. After delivery, many SSA field offices reported frequent malfunctions, sometimes multiple times per day, requiring manual rebooting of the system. One of the contract requirements was that the computers function 98% of the time. This requirement wasn't met until after 21 months of operation. After nearly two years of headaches and much wasted time and money, the system finally worked as planned [Davis, 1988].

Subsequent investigation by SSA indicated that the product supplied by Paradyne was not an off-the-shelf system, but rather was a system that incorporated new technology that had yet to be built and was still under development. Paradyne had proposed selling SSA their P8400 model with the PIOS operating system. The bid was written as if this system currently existed. However, at the time that the bid was prepared, the 8400 system did not exist and had not been developed, prototyped, or manufactured [Head, 1986].

There were other problems associated with Paradyne's performance during the bidding. The RFP stated that there was to be a preaward demonstration of the product, not a demonstration of a prototype. Paradyne demonstrated to SSA a different computer, a modified PDP 11/23 computer manufactured by Digital Equipment Corporation (DEC) placed in a cabinet that was labeled P8400. Apparently, many of the DEC labels on the equipment that was demonstrated to SSA had Paradyne labels pasted over them. Paradyne disingenuously claimed that since the DEC equipment was based on a 16-bit processor, as was the P8400 they proposed, it was irrelevant whether the machine demonstrated was the DEC or the actual P8400. Of course, computer users recognize that this statement is nonsense. Even modern "PC-compatible" computers with the same microprocessor chip and operating system can have widely different operating characteristics in terms of speed and the software that can be run.

There were also questions about the operating system. Apparently, at the time of Paradyne's bid, the PIOS system was under development as well and hadn't been tested on a prototype of the proposed system. Even a functioning hardware system will not operate correctly without the correct operating system. No software has ever worked correctly the first time, but rather requires extensive debugging to make it operate properly with a new system. Significantly, the DEC system with the P8400 label that was actually tested by SSA was not running with the proposed PIOS system.

Some of the blame for this fiasco can also be laid at the feet of the SSA. There were six bidders for this contract. Each of the bidders was to have an on-site visit from SSA inspectors to determine whether it was capable of doing the work that it included in its bid. Paradyne's capabilities were not assessed using an on-site visit. Moreover, Paradyne was judged based on its ability to manufacture modems, which was then its main business. Apparently, its ability to produce complete computer systems wasn't assessed. As part of its attempt to gain this contract, Paradyne hired a former SSA official who, while still working for SSA, had participated in preparing the RFP and had helped with setting up the team that would evaluate the bids. Paradyne had notified SSA of the hiring of this person, and SSA decided that there were no ethical problems with this. However, when the Paradyne machine failed the initial acceptance test, this Paradyne official was directly involved in negotiating the relaxed standards with his former boss at SSA.

This situation was resolved when the Paradyne computers were finally brought to the point of functioning as required. However, as a result of these problems, there were many investigations by government agencies, including the Securities and Exchange Commission, the General Accounting Office, the House of Representatives' Government Operations Committee, the Health and Human Services Department (of which SSA is part), and the Justice Department.

KEY TERMS

Code of ethics	Professions	Professional societies

REFERENCES

Charles E. Harris, Jr., Michael S. Pritchard, and Michael J. Rabins, *Engineering Ethics, Concepts and Cases,* Wadsworth Publishing Company, Belmont CA., 2000.
Roland Schinzinger and Mike W. Martin, *Introduction to Engineering Ethics,* McGraw-Hill, New York, 2000.

Intel Pentium Chip Case
"When the Chips Are Down," *Time,* Dec. 26–Jan. 2 1995, p. 126.
"The Fallout from Intel's Pentium Bug," *Fortune,* Jan. 16, 1995, p. 15.
"Pentium Woes Continue," *Infoworld,* Nov. 18, 1994, vol. 16, issue 48, p. 1.
"Flawed Chips Still Shipping," *Infoworld,* Dec. 5, 1994, vol. 16, issue 49, p. 1.
Numerous other accounts from late 1994 and early 1995 in The *Wall Street Journal, The New York Times,* etc.

DIA Runaway Concrete
Lou Kilzer, Robert Kowalski, and Steven Wilmsen, "Concrete Tests Faked at Airport," *Denver Post,* Nov. 13, 1994, Section A, p. 1.

Paradyne Computers
J. Steve Davis, "Ethical Problems in Competitive Bidding: The Paradyne Case," *Business and Professional Ethics Journal,* vol. 7, 1988, p. 3.
Robert V. Head, "Paradyne Dispute: A Matter of Using a Proper Tense," *Government Computer News,* February 14, 1986, p. 23.

PROBLEMS

1   What changes would have to be made for engineering to be a profession more like medicine or law?

2   In which ways do law, medicine, and engineering fit the social-contract and the business models of a profession?

3   The first part of the definition of a profession presented previously said that professions involve the use of sophisticated skills. Do you think that these skills are primarily physical or intellectual skills? Give examples from professions such as law, medicine, and engineering, as well as from nonprofessions.

4   Read about the space shuttle *Challenger* accident in 1986. (You can find information on this in magazines, newspapers, or on the internet.) Apply an engineering code of ethics to this case. What guidance might one of the engineering society codes of ethics have given the Thiokol engineers when faced with a decision to launch? Which specific parts of the code are applicable to this situation? Does a manager who is trained as an engineer still have to adhere to an engineering code of ethics?

5   Write a code of ethics for students in your college or department. Start by deciding what type of code you want: short, long, detailed, etc. Then, list the important ethical issues you think students face. Finally, organize these ideas into a coherent structure.

6   Imagine that you are the president of a small high-technology firm. Your company has grown over the last few years to the point where you feel that it is important that your employees have some guidelines regarding ethics. Define the type of company you are running; then develop an appropriate code of ethics. As in Question 2, start by deciding what type of code is appropriate for your company. Then, list specific points that are important—for example, relationships with vendors, treatment of fellow employees, etc. Finally, write a code that incorporates these features.

Intel Pentium Chip

7   Was this case simply a customer-relations and PR problem, or are there ethical issues to be considered as well?

8   Use an engineering code of ethics to analyze this case. Especially, pay attention to issues of accurate representation of engineered products and to safety issues.

9   When a product is sold, is there an implication that it will work as advertised?

10   Should you reveal defects in a product to a consumer? Is the answer to this question different if the defect is a safety issue rather than simply a flaw? (It might be useful to note in this discussion that although there is no apparent safety concern for someone using a computer with this flaw, PCs are often used to control a variety of instruments, such as medical equipment. For such equipment, a flaw might have a very real safety implication.) Is the answer to this question different if the customer is a bank that uses the computer to calculate interest paid, loan payments, etc., for customers?

11   Should you replace defective products even if customers won't recognize the defect?

12   How thorough should testing be? Is it ever possible to say that no defect exists in a product or structure?

13   Do flaws that Intel found previously in the 386 and 486 chips have any bearing on these questions? In other words, if Intel got away with selling flawed chips before without informing consumers, does that fact have any bearing on this case?

14   G. Richard Thoman, an IBM senior vice president, was quoted as saying, "Nobody should have to worry about the integrity of data calculated on an IBM machine." How does this statement by a major Intel customer change the answers to the previous questions?

15   Just prior to when this problem surfaced, Intel had begun a major advertising campaign to make Intel a household name. They had gotten computer manufacturers to place "Intel Inside" labels on their computers and had spent money on television advertising seeking to increase the public demand for computers with Intel processors, with the unstated message that Intel chips

were of significantly higher quality than other manufacturers' chips. How might this campaign have affected what happened in this case?

16 What responsibilities did the engineers who were aware of the flaw have before the chip was sold? After the chips began to be sold? After the flaw became apparent?

DIA Runaway Concrete

17 Using a code of ethics, analyze the actions of the batch plant operators and Empire Laboratories.

18 Is altering data a proper use of "engineering judgment"? What alternative might have existed to altering the test data on the concrete?

19 Who is responsible for ensuring that the materials used in a project meet the specifications, the supplier or the purchaser?

Paradyne Computers

20 Choose an engineering code of ethics and use it to analyze this case. Were the engineers and managers of Paradyne operating ethically?

21 In preparing their bid, Paradyne wrote in the present tense, as if the computer they proposed currently existed, rather than in the future tense, which would have indicated that the product was still under development. Paradyne claimed that the use of the present tense in its bid (which led SSA to believe that the P8400 actually existed) was acceptable, since it is common business practice to advertise products under development this way. Was this a new product announcement with a specified availability date? Is there a distinction between a response to a bid and company advertising? Is it acceptable to respond to a bid with a planned system if there is no indication when that system is expected to be available?

22 Paradyne also claimed that it was acting as a system integrator (which was allowed by the RFP), using components from other manufacturers to form the Paradyne system. These other components were mostly off the shelf, but they had never been integrated into a system before. Does this meet the SSA requirement for an existing system?

23 Once the Paradyne machine failed the initial test, should the requirements have been relaxed to help the machine qualify? If the requirements were going to be modified, should the bidding process have been reopened to the other bidders and others who might now be able to bid? Should bidding be reopened even if it causes a delay in delivery, increased work for the SSA, etc.?

24 Was it acceptable for Paradyne to submit another manufacturer's system for testing with a Paradyne label on it?

25 Was it acceptable to represent a proposed system as existing, if indeed that is what Paradyne did?

26 Is it ethical for a former SSA employee to take a job negotiating contracts with the SSA for a private company? Did this relationship give Paradyne an unfair advantage over its competition?

6

Understanding Ethical Problems

Objectives

After reading this chapter, you will be able to

- Discuss several ethical theories and
- See how these theories can be applied to engineering situations.

In late 1984, a pressure-relief valve on a tank used to store methyl isocyanate (MIC) at a Union Carbide plant in Bhopal, India, accidentally opened. MIC is a poisonous compound used in the manufacture of pesticides. When the valve opened, MIC was released from the tank and a cloud of toxic gas formed over the area surrounding the plant. Unfortunately, this neighborhood was very densely populated. Some two thousand people were killed and thousands more injured as a result of the accident. Many of the injured have remained permanently disabled.

The causes of the accident are not completely clear, but there appear to have been many contributing factors. Pipes in the plant were misconnected, and essential safety systems were either broken or had been taken off-line for maintenance. The effects of the leak were intensified by the presence of so many people living in close proximity to the plant.

Among the many important issues this case brings up are questions of balancing risk to the local community with the economic benefits to the larger community of the state or nation. Undoubtedly, the presence of this chemical plant brought significant local economic benefit. However, the accident at the plant also brought disaster to the local community at an enormous cost in human lives and suffering. How can we decide if on balance the economic benefit brought by this plant outweighed the potential safety hazards?

In order to answer this question and analyze other engineering ethics cases, we need a framework for analyzing ethical problems. Codes of ethics can be used as an aid in analyzing ethical issues. In this chapter, we will examine moral theories and see how they can also be used as a means for analyzing ethical cases such as the Bhopal disaster.

1 INTRODUCTION

In this chapter, we will develop moral theories that can be applied to the ethical problems confronted by engineers. Unfortunately, a thorough and in-depth discussion of all possible ethical theories is beyond the scope of this text.

Rather, some important theories will be developed in sufficient detail for use in analyzing cases.

Our approach to ethical problem solving will be similar to that taken in other engineering classes. To learn how to build a bridge, you must first learn the basics of physics and apply this physics to engineering statics and dynamics. Only when the basic theory and understanding of these topics has been acquired can problems in structures be solved and bridges built. Similarly, in ethical problem solving, we will need some knowledge of ethical theory to provide a framework for understanding and reaching solutions in ethical problems. In this chapter, we will develop this theoretical framework and apply it to an engineering case. We will begin by looking at the origins of Western ethical thinking.

2 A BRIEF HISTORY OF ETHICAL THOUGHT

It is impossible in this text to give a complete history of ethical thinking. Many books, some of them quite lengthy, have already been written on this subject. However, it is instructive to give a brief outline of the origins and development of the ethical principles that will be applied to engineering practice.

The moral and ethical theories that we will be applying in engineering ethics are derived from a Western cultural tradition. In other words, these ideas originated in the Middle East and Europe. Western moral thought has not come down to us from just a single source. Rather, it is derived both from the thinking of the ancient Greeks as well as from ancient religious thinking and writing, starting with Judaism and its foundations.

Although it is easy to think of these two sources as separate, there was a great deal of influence on ancient religious thought by the Greek philosophers. The written sources of the Jewish moral traditions are the Torah and the Old Testament of the Bible and their enumeration of moral laws, including the Ten Commandments. Greek ethical thought originated with the famous Greek philosophers that are commonly studied in freshman philosophy classes, principally Socrates and Aristotle, who discussed ethics at great length in his *Nichomachean Ethics*. Greek philosophic ideas were melded together with early Christian and Jewish thought and were spread throughout Europe and the Middle East during the height of the Roman Empire.

Ethical ideas were continually refined during the course of history. Many great thinkers have turned their attention to ethics and morals and have tried to provide insight into these issues through their writings. For example, philosophers such as Locke, Kant, and Mill wrote about moral and ethical issues. The thinking of these philosophers is especially important for our study of engineering ethics, since they did not rely on religion to underpin their moral thinking. Rather, they acknowledged that moral principles are universal, regardless of their origin, and are applicable even in secular settings.

Many of the moral principles that we will discuss have also been codified and handed down through the law. So, in discussing engineering ethics, there is a large body of thinking—philosophical, legal, and religious—to draw from. However, even though there are religious and legal origins of many of the moral principles that we will encounter in our study of engineering ethics, it is important to acknowledge that ethical conduct is fundamentally grounded in a concern for other people. It is not just about law or religion.

3 ETHICAL THEORIES

In order to develop workable ethical problem-solving techniques, we must first look at several theories of ethics in order to have a framework for decision making. Ethical problem solving is not as cut and dried as problem solving in most engineering classes. In most engineering classes, there is generally just one theory to consider when tackling a problem. In studying engineering ethics, there are several theories that will be considered. The relatively large number of theories doesn't indicate a weakness in theoretical understanding of ethics or a "fuzziness" of ethical thinking. Rather, it reflects the complexity of ethical problems and the diversity of approaches to ethical problem solving that have been developed over the centuries.

Having multiple theories to apply actually enriches the problem-solving process, allowing problems to be looked at from different angles, since each theory stresses different aspects of a problem. Even though we will use multiple theories to examine ethical problems, each theory applied to a problem will not necessarily lead to a different solution. Frequently, different theories yield the same solution. Our basic ethical problem-solving technique will utilize different theories and approaches to analyze the problem and then try to determine the best solution.

3.1 What Is a Moral Theory?

Before looking more closely at individual moral theories, we should start with a definition of what a moral theory is and how it functions. A moral theory defines terms in uniform ways and links ideas and problems together in consistent ways [Harris, Pritchard and Rabins, 1985]. This is exactly how the scientific theories used in other engineering classes function. Scientific theories also organize ideas, define terms, and facilitate problem solving. So, we will use moral theories in exactly the same way that engineering theories are used in other classes.

There are four ethical theories that will be considered here, each differing according to what is held to be the most important moral concept. *Utilitarianism* seeks to produce the most utility, defined as a balance between good and bad consequences of an action, taking into account the consequences for everyone affected. A different approach is provided by *duty ethics.* Duty ethics contends that there are duties that should be performed (for example, the duty to treat others fairly or the duty not to injure others) regardless of whether these acts lead to the most good. *Rights ethics* emphasizes that we all have moral rights, and any action that violates these rights is ethically unacceptable. Like duty ethics, the ultimate overall good of the actions is not taken into account. Finally, *virtue ethics* regards actions as right that manifest good character traits (virtues) and regards actions as bad that display bad character traits (vices); this ethical theory focuses on the type of person we should strive to be.

3.2 Utilitarianism

The first of the moral theories that will be considered is utilitarianism. Utilitarianism holds that those actions are good that serve to maximize human well-being. The emphasis in utilitarianism is not on maximizing the well-being of the individual, but rather on maximizing the well-being of society as a whole, and as such it is somewhat of a collectivist approach. An example of this theory that has been played out in this country many times over the past century is the building of dams. Dams often lead to great benefit to society by providing stable supplies of drinking water, flood control, and recreational opportunities. However, these benefits often come at the expense of people who live in areas that will be flooded by the dam and are required to find new homes. Utilitarianism tries to balance the needs of society with the needs of the individual, with an emphasis on what will provide the most benefit to the most people.

Utilitarianism is fundamental to many types of engineering analysis, including risk–benefit analysis and cost–benefit analysis, which we will discuss later. However, as good as the utilitarian principle sounds, there are some problems with it. First, as seen in the example of the building of a dam, sometimes what is best for everyone may be bad for a particular individual or group of individuals. An example of this problem is the proposed Waste Isolation Pilot Plant (WIPP) near Carlsbad, New Mexico. WIPP is designed to be a permanent repository for nuclear waste generated in the United States. It consists of a system of tunnels bored into underground salt formations, which are considered by geologists to be extremely stable, especially to incursion of water, which could lead to seepage of the nuclear wastes into groundwater. However, there are many who oppose the opening of this facility, principally on the grounds that transportation of the wastes across highways has the potential for accidents that might cause health problems for people living near these routes.

An analysis of WIPP using utilitarianism might indicate that the disposal of nuclear wastes is a major problem hindering the implementation of many useful technologies, including medicinal uses of radioisotopes and nuclear generation of electricity. Solution of this waste disposal problem will benefit society by providing improved health care and more plentiful electricity. The slight potential for adverse health effects for individuals living near the transportation routes is far outweighed by the overall benefits to society. So, WIPP should be allowed to open. As this example demonstrates, the utilitarian approach can seem to ignore the needs of individuals, especially if these needs seem relatively insignificant.

Another objection to utilitarianism is that its implementation depends greatly on knowing what will lead to the most good. Frequently, it is impossible to know exactly what the consequences of an action are. It is often impossible to do a complete set of experiments to determine all of the potential outcomes, especially when humans are involved as subjects of the experiments. So, maximizing the benefit to society involves guesswork and the risk that the best guess might be wrong. Despite these objections, utilitarianism is a very valuable tool for ethical problem solving, providing one way of looking at engineering ethics cases.

Before ending our discussion of utilitarianism, it should be noted that there are many flavors of the basic tenets of utilitarianism. Two of these are act utilitarianism and rule utilitarianism. Act utilitarianism focuses on individual actions rather than on rules. The best known proponent of act utilitarianism was John Stuart Mill (1806–1873), who felt that most of the common rules of morality (e.g., don't steal, be honest, don't harm others) are good guidelines derived from centuries of human experience. However, Mill felt that individual actions should be judged based on whether the most good was produced in a given situation, and rules should be broken if doing so will lead to the most good.

Rule utilitarianism differs from act utilitarianism in holding that moral rules are most important. As mentioned previously, these rules include "do not harm others" and "do not steal." Rule utilitarians hold that although adhering to these rules might not always maximize good in a particular situation, overall, adhering to moral rules will ultimately lead to the most good. Although these two different types of

John Stuart Mill, a leading philosopher of utilitarianism. Courtesy of the Library of Congress.

utilitarianism can lead to slightly different results when applied in specific situations, in this text we will consider these ideas together and not worry about the distinctions between the two.

3.3 Cost–Benefit Analysis

One tool often used in engineering analysis, especially when trying to determine whether a project makes sense, is cost–benefit analysis. Fundamentally, this type of analysis is just an application of utilitarianism. In cost–benefit analysis, the costs of a project are assessed, as are the benefits. Only those projects with the highest ratio of benefits to costs will be implemented. This principle is similar to the utilitarian goal of maximizing the overall good.

As with utilitarianism, there are pitfalls in the use of cost–benefit analysis. While it is often easy to predict the costs for most projects, the benefits that are derived from them are often harder to predict and to assign a dollar value to. Once dollar amounts for the costs and benefits are determined, calculating a mathematical ratio may seem very objective and therefore may appear to be the best way to make a decision. However, this ratio can't take into account many of the more subjective aspects of a decision. For example, from a pure cost–benefit discussion, it might seem that the building of a dam is an excellent idea. But this analysis won't include other issues such as whether the benefits outweigh the loss of a scenic wilderness area or the loss of an endangered species with no current economic value. Finally, it is also important to determine whether those who stand to reap the benefits are also those who will pay the costs. It is unfair to place all of the costs on one group while another reaps the benefits.

It should be noted that although cost–benefit analysis shares many similarities with utilitarianism, cost–benefit analysis isn't really an ethical analysis tool. The goal of an ethical analysis is to determine what the ethical path is. The goal of a cost–benefit analysis is to determine the feasibility of a project based on costs. When looking at an ethical problem, the first step should be to determine what the right course of action is and then factor in the financial costs in choosing between ethical alternatives.

3.4 Duty Ethics and Rights Ethics

Two other ethical theories—duty ethics and rights ethics—are similar to each other and will be considered together. These theories hold that those actions are good that respect the rights of the individual. Here, good consequences for society as a whole are not the only moral consideration.

A major proponent of duty ethics was Immanuel Kant (1724–1804), who held that moral duties are fundamental. Ethical actions are those actions that could be written down on a list of duties: be honest, don't cause suffering to other people, be fair to others, etc. These actions are our duties because they express respect for persons, express an unqualified regard for autonomous moral agents, and are universal principles [Martin and Schinzinger, 2000]. Once one's duties are recognized, the ethically correct moral actions are obvious. In this formulation, ethical acts are a result of proper performance of one's duties.

Rights ethics was largely formulated by John Locke (1632–1704), whose statement that humans have the right to life, liberty, and property was paraphrased in the Declaration of Independence of the soon-to-be United States of America in 1776. Rights ethics holds that people have fundamental rights that other people have a duty to respect.

Duty ethics and rights ethics are really just two different sides of the same coin. Both of these theories achieve the same end: Individual persons must be respected, and actions are ethical that maintain this respect for the individual. In duty ethics, people have duties, an important one of which is to protect the rights of others. And in rights ethics, people have fundamental rights that others have duties to protect.

As with utilitarianism, there are problems with the duty and rights ethics theories that must be considered. First the basic rights of one person (or group) may conflict with the basic rights of another group. How do we decide whose rights have priority? Using our previous example of the building of a dam, people have the right to use their property. If their land happens to be in the way of a proposed dam, then rights ethics would hold that this property right is paramount and is sufficient to

Immanuel Kant, German philosopher whose work included early formulations of duty ethics. Courtesy of the Library of Congress.

stop the dam project. A single property holder's objection would require that the project be terminated. However, there is a need for others living in nearby communities to have a reliable water supply and to be safe from continual flooding. Who's rights are paramount here? Rights and duty ethics don't resolve this conflict very well; hence, the utilitarian approach of trying to determine the most good is more useful in this case.

The second problem with duty and rights ethics is that these theories don't always account for the overall good of society very well. Since the emphasis is on the individual, the good of a single individual can be paramount compared to what is good for society as a whole. The WIPP case discussed before illustrates this problem. Certainly, people who live along the route where the radioactive wastes will be transported have the right to live without fear of harm due to accidental spills of hazardous waste. But the nation as a whole will benefit from the safe disposal of these wastes. Rights ethics would come down clearly on the side of the individuals living along the route despite the overall advantage to society.

Already it is clear why we will be considering more than one ethical theory in our discussion of engineering cases. The theories already presented clearly represent different ways of looking at ethical problems and can frequently arrive at different solutions. Thus, any complete analysis of an ethical problem must incorporate multiple theories if valid conclusions are to be drawn.

3.5 Virtue Ethics

Another important ethical theory that we will consider is virtue ethics. Fundamentally, virtue ethics is interested in determining what kind of people we should be. Virtue is often defined as moral distinction and goodness. A virtuous person exhibits good and beneficial qualities. In virtue ethics, actions are considered right if they support good character traits (virtues) and wrong if they support bad character traits (vices) [Schinzinger and Martin, 2000]. Virtue ethics focuses on words such as responsibility, honesty, competence, and loyalty, which are virtues. Other virtues might include trustworthiness, fairness, caring, citizenship, and respect. Vices could include dishonesty, disloyalty, irresponsibility, or incompetence. As you can see, virtue ethics is closely tied to personal character. We do good things because we are virtuous people and seek to enhance these character traits in ourselves and in others.

In many ways, this theory may seem to be mostly personal ethics and not particularly applicable to engineering or business ethics. However, personal morality cannot, or at any rate should not, be separated from business morality. If a behavior is virtuous in the individual's personal life, the behavior is virtuous in his or her business life as well.

How can virtue ethics be applied to business and engineering situations? This type of ethical theory is somewhat trickier to apply to the types of problems that we will consider, perhaps because virtue ethics seems less concrete and less susceptible to rigorous analysis and because it is harder to describe nonhuman entities such as a corporation or government in terms of virtue. However, we can use virtue ethics in our engineering career by answering questions such as: Is this action honest? Will this action demonstrate loyalty to my community and/or my employer? Have I acted in a responsible fashion? Often, the answer to these questions makes the proper course of action obvious. To use virtue ethics in an analysis of an ethical problem, you should first identify the virtues or vices that are applicable to the situation. Then, determine what course of action each of these suggests.

As with any ethical theory, it is important to be careful in applying virtue ethics. Problems can arise with words that on the face seem to be virtues, but can actually lead to vices. For example, the concept of "honor" has been around for centuries and is often viewed positively. One sense of the word "honor" is a code of dignity, integrity, and pride. Honor may seem like a very positive thing, especially the aspects related to integrity. But the aspects related to pride can often have negative consequences. There are numerous examples in history of wars that have been fought and atrocities committed in order to preserve the honor of an individual or a nation. Individuals have often committed crimes as a way of preserving their honor. In using virtue ethics, it is important to ensure that the traits you identify as virtues are indeed virtuous and will not lead to negative consequences.

3.6 Personal vs. Corporate Morality

This is an appropriate place to discuss a tricky issue in engineering ethics: Is there a distinction between the ethics practiced by an individual and the ethics practiced by a corporation? Put another way, can a corporation be a moral agent as an individual can? This is a question that is central to many discussions of business and engineering ethics. If a corporation has no moral agency, then it cannot be held accountable for its actions, although sometimes individuals within a company can be held accountable. The law is not always clear on the answer to this question and can't be relied upon to resolve the issue.

This dilemma comes most sharply into focus in a discussion of virtue ethics. Can a company truly be expected to display honesty or loyalty? These are strictly human traits and cannot be ascribed to a corporation. In the strictest definition of moral agency, a company cannot be a moral agent, and yet companies have many dealings with individuals or groups of people.

How, then, do we resolve this problem? In their capacity to deal with individuals, corporations should be considered pseudomoral agents and should be held accountable in the same way that individuals are, even if the ability to do this within the legal system is limited. In other words, with regard to an ethical problem, responsibility for corporate wrongdoing shouldn't be hidden behind a corporate mask. Just because it isn't really a moral agent like a person doesn't mean that a corporation can do whatever it pleases. Instead, in its interactions with individuals or communities, a corporation must respect the rights of individuals and should exhibit the same virtues that we expect of individuals.

3.7 Which Theory to Use?

Now that we have discussed four different ethical theories, the question arises: How do we decide which theory is applicable to a given problem? The good news is that in solving ethical problems, we don't have to choose from among these theories. Rather, we can use all of them to analyze a problem from different angles and see what result each of the theories gives us. This allows us to examine a problem from different perspectives to see what conclusion each one reaches. Frequently, the result will be the same even though the theories are very different.

Take, for example, a chemical plant near a small city that discharges a hazardous waste into the groundwater. If the city takes its water from wells, the water supply for the city will be compromised and significant health problems for the community may result. Rights ethics indicates that this pollution is unethical, since it causes harm to many of the residents. A utilitarian analysis would probably also come to the same conclusion, since the economic benefits of the plant would almost certainly be outweighed by the negative effects of the pollution and the costs required to ensure a safe municipal water supply. Virtue ethics would say that discharging wastes into groundwater is irresponsible and harmful to individuals and so shouldn't be done. In this case, all of the ethical theories lead to the same conclusion.

What happens when the different theories seem to give different answers? This scenario can be illustrated by the discussion of WIPP presented previously. Rights ethics indicated that transporting wastes through communities is not a good idea, whereas utilitarianism concluded that WIPP would be beneficial to society as a whole. This is a trickier situation, and the answers given by each of the theories must be examined in detail, compared with each other, and carefully weighed. Generally, rights and duty ethics should take precedence over utilitarian considerations. This is because the rights of individuals should receive relatively stronger weight than the needs of society as a whole. For example, an action that led to the death of even one person is generally viewed very negatively, regardless of the overall benefit to society. After thorough analysis using all of the theories, a balanced judgment can be formed.

3.8 Non-Western Ethical Thinking

It is tempting to think that the ethical theories that have been described here are applicable only in business relations within cultures that share our Western ethical traditions: Europe and the Americas. Since the rest of the world has different foundations for its ethical systems, it might seem that what we learn here won't be applicable in our business dealings in, for example, Japan, India, Africa, or Saudi Arabia. However, this thinking is incorrect. Ethics is not geographic or cultural. Indeed, ethical thinking has developed similarly around the world and is not dependent on a Western cultural or religious tradition. Ethical standards are similar worldwide.

For example, ethical principles in Arab countries are grounded in the traditions of their religion, Islam. Islam is one of the three major monotheistic religions, along with Christianity and Judaism. It is surprising to many Westerners that Islam developed in the Middle East, just as Judaism and Christianity did, and shares many prophets and religious concepts with the other two monotheistic religions. The foundations of ethical principles relating to engineering and business in Islamic countries are thus very similar to those in Western countries. Although cultural practices may vary when dealing with the many Islamic nations that stretch from Africa and the Middle East to Southeast Asia, the same ethical principles that apply in Western countries are applicable.

Similarly, ethical principles of Hindus, Buddhists, and practitioners of all the world's major religions are similar. Although the ethical principles in other cultures may be derived in different ways, the results are generally the same, regardless of culture.

Moreover, personal ethics are not determined by geography. Personal and business behavior should be the same regardless of where you happen to be on a given day.

For example, few would find the expression "When in Rome, do as the Romans do" applicable to personal morality. If you believe that being deceptive is wrong, certainly it is no less wrong when you are dealing with a (hypothetical) culture where this behavior is not considered to be bad. Thus, the ethics that we discuss in this book will be applicable regardless of where you are doing business.

APPLICATION

Cases

The Disaster at Bhopal

On the night of December 2, 1984, a leak developed in a storage tank at a Union Carbide chemical plant in Bhopal, India. The tank contained 10,000 gallons of methyl isocyanate (MIC), a highly toxic chemical used in the manufacture of pesticides, such as Sevin. The leak sent a toxic cloud of gas over the surrounding slums of Bhopal, resulting in the death of over 2,000 people, and injuries to over 200,000 more.

The leak was attributed to the accidental pouring of water into the tank. Water reacts very vigorously with MIC, causing heating of the liquid. In Bhopal, the mixing of water with MIC increased the temperature of the liquid in the tank to an estimated 400°F. The high temperature caused the MIC to vaporize, leading to a buildup of high pressure within the tank. When the internal pressure became high enough, a pressure-relief valve popped open, leaking MIC vapors into the air.

The water had probably been introduced into the tank accidentally. A utility station on the site contained two pipes side by side. One pipe carried nitrogen, which was used to pressurize the tank to allow the liquid MIC to be removed. The other pipe contained water. It appears that instead of connecting the nitrogen pipe, someone accidentally connected the water pipe to the MIC tank. The accident was precipitated when an estimated 240 gallons of water were injected into the MIC storage tank.

As with many of the disasters and accidents that we study in this book, there was not just one event that led to the disaster, but rather there were several factors that contributed to this accident. Any one of these factors alone probably wouldn't have led to the accident, but the combination of these factors made the accident almost inevitable and the consequences worse. A major factor in this accident was the curtailment of plant maintenance as part of a cost-cutting effort. The MIC storage tank had a refrigeration unit on it, which should have helped to keep the tank temperatures closer to normal, even with the water added, and might have prevented the vaporization of the liquid. However, this refrigeration unit had stopped working five months before the accident and hadn't yet been repaired.

The tank also was equipped with an alarm that should have alerted plant workers to the dangerous temperatures; this alarm was improperly set, so no warning was given. The plant was equipped with a flare tower. This is a device designed to burn vapors before they enter the atmosphere, and it would have been able to at least reduce, if not eliminate, the amount of MIC reaching the surrounding neighborhood. The flare tower was not functioning at the time of the accident. Finally, a scrubber that was used to neutralize toxic vapors was not activated until the vapor release was already in progress. Some investigators pointed out that the scrubber and flare systems were probably inadequate, even had they been functioning. However, had any of these systems been functioning at the time of the accident, the disaster could have at least been mitigated, if not completely averted. The fact that none of them were operating at the time ensured that once the water had been mistakenly added to the MIC tank, the ensuing reaction would proceed undetected until it was too late to prevent the accident.

It is unclear on whom the ultimate blame for this accident should be laid. The plant designers clearly did their job by anticipating problems that would occur and installing safety systems to prevent or mitigate potential accidents. The management of the plant seems obviously negligent. It is sometimes necessary for some safety features to be taken off-line for repair or maintenance. But to have all of the safety systems inoperative simultaneously is inexcusable. Union Carbide also seems negligent in not preparing a plan for notifying and evacuating the surrounding population in the event of an accident. Such plans are standard in the United States and are often required by local ordinance.

Union Carbide was unable to say that such an accident was unforeseeable. Leaky valves in the MIC system had been a problem at the Bhopal plant on at least six occasions before the accident. One of these gas leaks involved a fatality. Moreover, Union Carbide had a plant in Institute, West Virginia, that also produced MIC. The experience in West Virginia was similar to that in Bhopal before the accident. There had been a total of 28 leaks of MIC over the previous five years, none leading to any serious problems. An internal Union Carbide memo from three months before the Bhopal accident warned of the potential for a runaway reaction in MIC storage tanks in West Virginia and called into question the adequacy of emergency plans at the plants. The memo concluded that "a real potential for a serious incident exists" [*US News and World Report*, Feb. 4, 1985, p. 12]. Apparently, these warnings had not been transmitted to the plant in India.

Ultimately, some share of the blame must be borne by the Indian government. Unlike in most Western nations, there was very little in the way of safety standards under which U.S. corporations must operate. In fact, third-world countries have often viewed pollution control and safety regulation as too expensive, and attempts by the industrialized nations to enforce Western-style safety and environmental regulations worldwide are regarded as attempts to keep the economies of developing countries backward [*Atlantic Monthly*, March 1987, p. 30]. In addition, the local government had no policy or zoning forbidding squatters and others from living so close to a plant where hazardous compounds are stored and used. The bulk of the blame goes to Union Carbide for failure to adequately train and supervise its Indian employees in the maintenance and safety procedures that are taken for granted in similar plants in the United States.

In the aftermath of the accident, lawsuits totaling over $250 billion were filed on behalf of the victims of the accident. Union Carbide committed itself to ensuring that the victims of the accident were compensated in a timely fashion. Union Carbide also helped set up job training and relocation programs for the victims of the accident. Ultimately, it has been estimated that approximately 10,000 of those injured in the accident will suffer some form of permanent damage [*Atlantic Monthly*, March 1987, p. 30].

The Aberdeen Three

The Aberdeen Three is one of the classic cases often used in engineering ethics classes and texts to illustrate the importance of environmental protection and the safety of workers exposed to hazardous and toxic chemicals. The Aberdeen Proving Ground is a U.S. Army weapons development and test center located on a military base in Maryland with no access by civilian nonemployees. Since World War II, Aberdeen has been used to develop and test chemical weapons. Aberdeen has also been used for the storage and disposal of some of these chemicals.

This case involves three civilian managers at the Pilot Plant at the Proving Grounds: Carl Gepp, manager of the Pilot Plant; William Dee, who headed the chemical weapons development team; and Robert Lentz, who was in charge of developing manufacturing processes for the chemical weapons [Weisskopf, 1989]. Between 1983 and 1986, inspections at the Pilot Plant indicated that there were serious safety hazards. These hazards included carcinogenic and flammable substances left in open containers, chemicals that can become lethal when mixed together being stored in the same room, barrels of toxic chemicals that were leaking, and unlabeled containers of chemicals. There was also an external tank used to store sulfuric acid that had leaked 200 gallons of acid into a local river. This incident triggered state and federal safety investigations that revealed inadequate chemical retaining dikes and a system for containing and treating chemical hazards that was corroded and leaking.

In June of 1988, the three engineer/managers were indicted for violation of RCRA, the Resource Conservation and Recovery Act. RCRA had been passed by Congress in 1976 and was intended to provide incentives for the recovery of important resources from wastes, the conservation of resources, and the control of the disposal of hazardous wastes. RCRA banned the dumping of solid hazardous wastes and included criminal penalties for violations of hazardous-waste disposal guidelines. The three managers claimed that they were not aware that the plant's storage practices were illegal and that they did things according to accepted practices at the Pilot Plant. Interestingly, since this was a criminal prosecution, the Army could not help defray the costs of the manager's defense, and each of them incurred great costs defending themselves.

In 1989, the three engineer/managers were tried and convicted of illegally storing, treating, and disposing of hazardous wastes. There was no indication that these three were the ones who actually handled chemicals in an unsafe manner, but as managers of the plant, the three were ultimately responsible for how the chemicals were stored and for the maintenance of the safety equipment. The potential penalty for these crimes was up to 15 years in prison and a fine of up to $750,000. Gepp, Dee, and Lentz were each found guilty and sentenced to three years' probation and 1,000 hours of community service. The relative leniency of the sentences was based partly on the large court costs each had already incurred.

Professional Success

Teamwork

Ethical issues can arise when working on projects in groups or teams. Many of your engineering classes are designed so that labs or projects are performed in groups. Successful performance in a group setting is a skill that is best learned early in your academic career since most projects in industry involve working as part of a team.

In order for a project to be completed successfully, cooperation among team members is essential. Problems can arise when a team member doesn't do a good job on his part of the project, doesn't make a contribution at all, or doesn't complete his assignments on time. There can also be a problem when one team member tries to do everything. This shuts out team-mates who want to contribute and learn. An analogy can be made here to team sports: clearly one individual on the team who is not performing his role can lead to a loss for the entire team. Equally true, individuals who try to do it all—"ballhogs"—can harm the team. Ethical teamwork includes performing the part of the work that you are assigned, keeping to schedules, sharing information with other team members, and helping to foster a cooperative and supportive team atmosphere so everyone can contribute.

Cost–benefit analysis	Rights ethics	Virtue ethics	**KEY TERMS**
Duty ethics	Utilitarianism		

REFERENCES

Charles E. Harris, Jr., Michael S. Pritchard, and Michael J. Rabins, *Engineering Ethics, Concepts and Cases*, Wadsworth Publishing Company, Belmont, CA, 2000.
Roland Schinzinger and Mike W. Martin, *Introduction to Engineering Ethics*, McGraw-Hill, New York, 2000.

Bhopal
Philip Elmer-DeWitt, "What Happened at Bhopal?" *Time Magazine,* April 1, 1985, p. 71.
"Bhopal Disaster—New Clues Emerge," *US News and World Report,* Feb. 4, 1985, p. 12.

Peter Stoler, "Frightening Findings at Bhopal," *Time,* Feb. 18, 1985, p. 78.
Fergus M. Bordewich, "The Lessons of Bhopal," *Atlantic Monthly,* March 1987, p. 30.

Aberdeen Three
Steven Weisskopf, "The Aberdeen Mess," *The Washington Post Magazine,* Jan. 15, 1989, p. 55.

PROBLEMS

1 Find information on the space shuttle *Challenger* accident in 1986 and analyze it, using the ethical theories developed in this chapter. What does utilitarianism tell us about this case? In your analysis, be sure to include issues regarding benefits to the United States and mankind that might result from the space shuttle program. You might also include benefits to Morton Thiokol and the communities where it operates if the program is successful.

2 What do duty and rights ethics tell us about the *Challenger* case? How do your answers to this question and to the previous question influence your ideas on whether the *Challenger* should have been launched?

3 Use contemporary newspaper accounts to find information on problems with Intel's Pentium computer chip (1995) and with runway concrete at the Denver International Airport (1994). Analyze these cases, using virtue ethics. Start by deciding what virtues are important for people in these businesses (e.g., honesty, fairness, etc.). Then see if these virtues were exhibited by the engineers working for these companies.

Bhopal

4 Use the ethical theories discussed in this chapter to analyze the Bhopal case. Topics to be considered should include the placing of a hazardous plant in a populated area, decisions to defer maintenance on essential safety systems, etc. Important theories to consider when doing your analysis are rights and duty ethics and utilitarianism.

5 Find a copy of the code of ethics of the American Institute of Chemical Engineers and use it to analyze what a process engineer working at this plant should have done. What does the code say about the responsibilities of the engineers who designed the plant and the engineers responsible for making maintenance decisions?

6 What responsibility does Union Carbide have for the actions of its subsidiaries? Union Carbide India was 50.9% owned by the parent company.

7 What duty did Union Carbide have to inform local officials in India of the potential dangers of manufacturing and storing MIC in India?

8 Some of Union Carbide's reports hinted strongly that part of the fault lay with the inadequate workforce available in a third-world country such as India. How valid is this statement? What are the ethical implications for Union Carbide if this statement is true?

9 What responsibility should the national and local government in Bhopal have for ensuring that the plant is operated safely?

10 What relative importance should be placed on keeping safety systems operating as compared to maintaining other operations? (Note: From the reports on this accident, there is no indication that Union Carbide skimped on safety to keep production going. Rather, this is a hypothetical question.)

11 In the absence of environmental or safety laws in the locality where it operates, what responsibility does a U.S. corporation have when operating overseas? Does the answer change if the locality does have laws, but they are less strict than ours? What about the ethics of a U.S. corporation selling products overseas that are banned in the United States, such as DDT?

The Aberdeen Three

12   What does utilitarianism tell us about the behavior of the Aberdeen Three? What do duty and rights ethics tell us? In analyzing this, start by determining who is harmed or potentially harmed by these activities and who benefits or potentially benefits from them.

13   Can the actions of these engineer/managers be classified as engineering decisions, management decisions, or both? Ethically, does it matter whether these decisions were engineering or management decisions?

14   Do you think that the Aberdeen Three knew about RCRA? If not, should they have? Does it really matter if they knew about RCRA or not?

15   Do you think that the Aberdeen Three were knowledgeable about the effects of these chemicals and proper storage methods? Should they have been?

16   Were the actions of the Aberdeen Three malicious?

17   In the course of this case, it came out that cleaning up the chemical storage at Aberdeen would have been paid for out of separate Army funds and would not have come from the budgets of the three managers. What bearing does this information have on the case?

18   What should the Aberdeen Three have done differently? Should the lower level workers at the plant have done anything to solve this problem?

19   The bosses of the Aberdeen Three claimed to have no idea about the conditions at the Pilot Plant. Should they have done anything differently? Should they have been prosecuted as well?

20   Apply the code of ethics of one of the professional societies to this situation. Were the managers guilty of ethical violations according to the code?

7

Ethical Problem-Solving Techniques

Objectives

After reading this chapter, you will be able to

- Apply these methods to hypothetical and real cases
- See how flow charting can be used to solve ethical problems, and
- Learn what bribery is and how to avoid it.

In the early 1990s, newspapers began to report on studies indicating that living near electrical-power distribution systems leads to an increased risk of cancer, especially in children. The risk was attributed to the effects of the weak, low-frequency magnetic fields present near such systems. Further reports indicated that there might also be some risk associated with the use of common household items such as electric blankets and clock radios. Predictably, there was much concern among the public about this problem, and many studies were performed to verify these results. Power companies began to look into methods for reducing the fields, and many engineers sought ways to design products that emitted reduced amounts of this radiation.

In designing products and processes, engineers frequently encounter scenarios like the one just described. Nearly everything an engineer designs has some health or safety risk associated with it. Often, as with the case of the weak magnetic fields, the exact nature of the hazard is only poorly understood. How then does an engineer decide whether it is ethical to work on a particular product or process? What tools are there for an engineer who needs to decide which is the ethically correct path to take?

In this chapter, we will develop analysis and problem-solving strategies to help answer these questions. These techniques will allow us to put ethical problems in the proper perspective and will point us in the direction of the correct solution.

1 INTRODUCTION

Now that we have discussed codes of ethics and moral theories, we are ready to tackle the problem of how to analyze and resolve ethical dilemmas when they occur. In solving engineering problems, it is always tempting to look for an appropriate formula, plug in the numbers, and calculate an answer. This type of problem-solving approach, while sometimes useful for engineering analysis problems, is less useful for ethical problem solving. There are theories that help us to frame our understanding of the problem, but there are no formulas and no easy "plug-and-chug" methods for reaching a solution.

In this chapter, we will examine methods for analyzing ethical problems and see how to apply them. Obviously, some problems are easily solved. If you are tempted to embezzle money from your employer, it is clear that this action is stealing and is not morally acceptable. However, as mentioned previously, many of the situations encountered by practicing engineers are ambiguous or unclear, involving conflicting moral principles. This is the type of problem for which we will most need analysis and problem-solving methods.

2 ANALYSIS OF ISSUES IN ETHICAL PROBLEMS

A first step in solving any ethical problem is to completely understand all of the issues involved. Once these issues are determined, frequently a solution to the problem becomes apparent. The issues involved in understanding ethical problems can be split into three categories: factual, conceptual, and moral [Harris, Pritchard, and Rabins, 2000]. Understanding these issues helps to put an ethical problem in the proper framework and often helps point the way to a solution.

2.1 Types of Issues in Ethical Problem Solving

Let's begin by examining in depth each of the types of issues involved in ethical problems. Factual issues involve what is actually known about a case—i.e., what the facts are. Although this concept seems straightforward, the facts of a particular case are not always clear and may be controversial. An example of facts that are not necessarily clear can be found in the controversy in contemporary society regarding abortion rights. There is great disagreement over the point at which life begins and at which point a fetus can be legally protected. *Roe v. Wade,* the original decision legalizing abortion in the United States, was decided by the Supreme Court in a split decision. Even the justices of the Supreme Court were unable to agree on this "fact."

In engineering, there are controversies over facts as well. For example, global warming is of great concern to society as we continue to emit greenhouse gases into the atmosphere. Greenhouse gases, such as carbon dioxide, trap heat in the atmosphere. This is thought to lead to a generalized warming of the atmosphere as emissions from automobiles and industrial plants increase the carbon dioxide concentration in the atmosphere. This issue is of great importance to engineers, since they might be required to design new products or redesign old ones to comply with stricter environmental standards if this warming effect indeed proves to be a problem. However, the global warming process is only barely understood, and the need to curtail emission of these gases is a controversial topic. If it were known exactly what the effects of emitting greenhouse gases into the atmosphere would be, the engineer's role in reducing this problem would be clearer.

Conceptual issues have to do with the meaning or applicability of an idea. In engineering ethics, this might mean defining what constitutes a bribe as opposed to an acceptable gift, or determining whether certain business information is proprietary. In the case of the bribe, the value of the gift is probably a well-known fact. What isn't known is whether accepting it will lead to unfair influence on a business decision. For example, conceptually it must be determined if the gift of tickets to a sporting event by a potential supplier of parts for your project is meant to influence your decision or is just a nice gesture between friends. Of course, like factual issues, conceptual issues are not always clear-cut and will often result in controversy as well.

Once the factual and conceptual issues have been resolved, at least to the extent possible, all that remains is to determine which moral principle is applicable to the situation. Resolution of moral issues is often more obvious. Once the problem is defined, it is usually clear which moral concept applies, and the correct decision becomes obvious. In our example of a "gift" offered by a sales representative, once it is determined whether it is simply a gift or is really a bribe, then the appropriate action is obvious. If we determine that it is indeed a bribe, then it cannot ethically be accepted.

Given that the issues surrounding an ethical problem can be controversial, how can these controversies be resolved? Factual issues can often be resolved through research to establish the truth. It is not always possible to achieve a final determination of the "truth" that everyone can agree on, but generally, further research helps clarify the situation, can increase the areas of agreement, and can sometimes achieve consensus on the facts. Conceptual issues are resolved by agreeing on the meaning of terms and concepts. Sometimes agreement isn't possible, but as with factual issues, further analysis of the concepts at least clarifies some of the issues and helps to facilitate agreement. Finally, moral issues are resolved by agreement as to which moral principles are pertinent and how they should be applied.

Often, all that is required to solve a particular ethical problem is a deeper analysis of the issues involved according to the appropriate principles. Once the issues are analyzed and agreement is reached on the applicable moral principles, it is clear what the resolution should be.

2.2 Application to a Case Study: Paradyne Computers

To illustrate the use of this problem-solving method, let's analyze a case study. In 1980, Paradyne, a computer company, bid to supply the Social Security Administration with new computer systems. We'll look at the factual issues first. The request for proposals clearly specified that only existing systems would be considered. Paradyne did not have any such system running and had never tested the operating system on the product they actually proposed to sell to the Social Security Administration (SSA). The employment of a former SSA worker by Paradyne to help lobby SSA for the contract is also clear. In this case, the factual issues do not appear particularly controversial.

The conceptual issues involve whether bidding to provide an off-the-shelf product when the actual product is only in the planning stages is lying or is an acceptable business practice. Is placing a Paradyne label over the real manufacturer's label deceptive? Does lobbying your former employer on behalf of your current employer constitute a conflict of interest? These questions will certainly generate discussion. Indeed, Paradyne asserted that it had done nothing wrong and was simply engaging in common business practices. The issue of the conflict of interest is so hard to decide that laws have been enacted making it illegal for workers who have left government employ to lobby their former employers for specified periods of time.

The moral issues then include the following: Is lying an acceptable business practice? Is it alright to be deceptive if doing so allows your company to get a contract? The answers to these questions are obvious: Lying and deceit are no more acceptable in your business life than in your personal life. So, if conceptually we decide that Paradyne's practices were deceptive, then our analysis indicates that their actions were unethical.

3 LINE DRAWING

The line-drawing technique that will be described in this section is especially useful for situations in which the applicable moral principles are clear, but there seems to be a great deal of "gray area" about which ethical principle applies. Line drawing is performed by drawing a line along which various examples and hypothetical situations are placed. At one end is placed the "positive paradigm," an example of something that is unambiguously morally acceptable. At the other end, the "negative paradigm," an example of something that is unambiguously not morally acceptable, is placed. In between is placed the problem under consideration, along with other similar examples. Those examples that more closely conform to the positive paradigm are placed near it, and examples closer to the negative paradigm are placed near that paradigm. By carefully examining this continuum and placing the moral problem under consideration in the appropriate place along the line, it is possible to determine whether the problem is more like the positive or negative paradigm and therefore whether it is acceptable or unacceptable.

Let's illustrate this technique using a hypothetical situation. Our company would like to dispose of a slightly toxic waste by dumping it into a local lake from which a nearby town gets its drinking water. How can we determine if this practice is acceptable? Let's start by defining the problem and the positive and negative paradigms.

Problem: It is proposed that our company dispose of a slightly hazardous waste by dumping it into a lake. A nearby town takes its drinking water supply from this lake. Our research shows that with the amount of waste we plan to put into the lake, the average concentration of the waste in the lake will be 5 parts per million (ppm). The EPA limit for this material has been set at 10 ppm. At the 5-ppm level, we expect no health problems, and consumers would not be able to detect the compound in their drinking water.

Positive paradigm: The water supply for the town should be clean and safe.

Negative paradigm: Toxic levels of waste are put into the lake.

Let's start by drawing a line and placing the positive and negative paradigms on it:

Figure 1
Example of line drawing showing the placement of the negative and positive paradigms.

Now let's establish some other hypothetical examples for consideration:

1. The company dumps the chemical into the lake. At 5 ppm, the chemical will be harmless, but the town's water will have an unusual taste.
2. The chemical can be effectively removed by the town's existing water-treatment system.
3. The chemical can be removed by the town with new equipment that will be purchased by the company.
4. The chemical can be removed by the town with new equipment for which the taxpayer will pay.
5. Occasionally, exposure to the chemical can make people feel ill, but this only lasts for an hour and is rare.
6. At 5 ppm, some people can get fairly sick, but the sickness only lasts a week, and there is no long-term harm.
7. Equipment can be installed at the plant to further reduce the waste level to 1 ppm.

Obviously, we could go on for a long time creating more and more test examples. Generally, where your problem fits along the line is obvious with only a few examples, but the exercise should be continued with more examples until it is clear what the proper resolution is. Now let's redraw our line with the examples inserted appropriately:

Figure 2

Same as Figure 1, with the addition of the examples to the line.

After setting up the examples, it may be clear that there is a gap in the knowledge. For example, in our case, we might need more information on seasonal variations in waste concentration and water usage of the town. We also could use information on potential interactions of the chemical with other pollutants, such as the runoff of pesticides from local farms. Note that there is some subjectivity in determining exactly where along the line each of the examples fits.

Now let's complete the exercise by denoting our problem by a "P" and inserting it at the appropriate place along the line. As with the previous examples, placement of the problem along the line is somewhat subjective.

Figure 3

Final version of the line-drawing example, with the problem under consideration added.

As drawn here, it is clear that dumping the toxic waste is probably a morally acceptable choice, since no humans will be harmed and the waste levels will be well below those that could cause any harm. However, since it is somewhat far from the positive paradigm, there are probably better choices that can be made, and the company should investigate these alternatives.

It should be noted that although this action seems ethically acceptable, there are many other considerations that might be factored into the final decision. For example, there are political aspects that should also be considered. Many people in the community are likely to regard the dumping of a toxin at any level as unacceptable. Good community relations might dictate that another solution should be pursued instead. The company also might want to avoid the lengthy amount of time required to obtain a permit for the dumping and the oversight by various government units. This example illustrates that line drawing can help solve the ethical aspects of a problem, but a choice that appears morally acceptable still might not be the best choice when politics and community relations are considered as well. Of course, the immoral choice is never the correct choice.

Although this problem-solving method seems to help with problem analysis and can lead to solutions, there are many pitfalls in its use. If not used properly, line drawing can lead to incorrect results. For example, line drawing can easily be used to prove that something is right when it is actually wrong. Line drawing is only effective if it is used objectively and honestly. The choice of where to put the examples and how to define the paradigms is up to you. You can reach false conclusions by using incorrect paradigms, by dishonest placement of the examples along the line, and by dishonest placement of the problem within the examples. In our example, we might have decided that the problem is somewhat like example 2 and thus placed our problem closer to the positive paradigm, making this solution seem more acceptable. Line drawing can be a very powerful analytic tool in ethical problems, but only if used conscientiously.

There is a long history of the improper use of this technique. In its early days, this method was known as "casuistry," a term that eventually came to be pejorative. In the Middle Ages, casuistry was often used in religious debates to reach false conclusions. Indeed, one of the definitions of casuistry from the American Heritage Dictionary implies the use of false and subtle reasoning to achieve incorrect solutions. Because of this negative connotation, the term "casuistry" is rarely used any more. This emphasizes the hazards of using line drawing: It is useful only if properly applied.

3.1 Application of Line Drawing to the Pentium Chip Case

In 1994–95, it was discovered and widely reported that the latest version of the Intel Pentium chip had flaws. At first, Intel sought to hide this information, but later came around to a policy of offering consumers chips in which the flaw had been corrected. We can use line drawing to get some insight into this problem.

For our positive paradigm, we will use the statement that "products should perform as advertised." The negative paradigm will be "Knowingly sell products that are defective and that will negatively affect customers' applications." A few examples that we can add to the line are as follows:

1. There is a flaw in the chip, but it truly is undetectable and won't affect any customer's applications.
2. There are flaws in the chip, the customer is informed of them, but no help is offered.
3. A warning label says that the chip should not be used for certain applications.
4. Recall notices are sent out, and all flawed chips are replaced.
5. Replacement chips are offered only if the customer notices the problem.

Of course, there are many other possible examples. One view of the line, then, is as follows:

Figure 4
Application of line drawing to the Pentium case. Negative and positive paradigms are provided along with the examples.

Where does our situation—there is a flaw, customers aren't informed, and the magnitude of the problem is minimized—fit on this line? One possible analysis is the following:

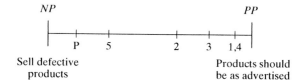

Figure 5
Final version of the Pentium chip line-drawing example, with the problem added to the line.

According to this line-drawing analysis, the approach taken by Intel in this case wasn't the best ethical choice.

4 FLOW CHARTING

Flow charts are very familiar to engineering students. They are most often used in developing computer programs, and also find application in other engineering disciplines. In engineering ethics, flow charting will be helpful for analyzing a variety of cases, especially those in which there is a sequence of events to be considered or a series of consequences that flows from each decision. An advantage of using a flow chart to analyze ethical problems is that it gives a visual picture of a situation and allows you to readily see the consequences that flow from each decision.

As with the line-drawing technique described in the previous section, there is no unique flow chart that is applicable to a given problem. In fact, different flow charts can be used to emphasize different aspects of the same problem. As with line drawing, it will be essential to be as objective as possible and to approach flow charting honestly. Otherwise, it will be possible to draw any conclusion you want, even one that is clearly wrong.

We can illustrate this technique by applying a simple flow chart to a disaster that happened at Union Carbide's Bhopal, where MIC, a toxic substance, was mixed with water, creating toxic fumes. One possible flow chart, illustrated in Figure 6, deals with the decision-making process that might have gone on at Union Carbide

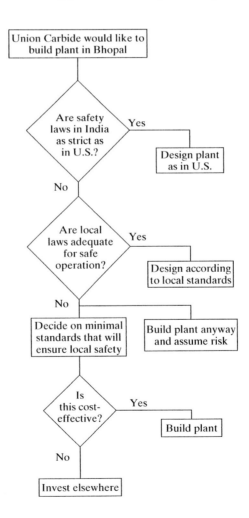

Figure 6

Application of a simple flow chart to the Bhopal case, emphasizing potential decisions made during consideration of locating a plant in India.

as they decided whether or not to build a plant at Bhopal. This chart emphasizes safety issues for the surrounding community. As indicated on the chart, there were several paths that might have been taken and multiple decisions that had to be made. The flow chart helps to visualize the consequences of each decision and indicates both the ethical and unethical choices. Of course, this flow chart should be much larger and more complex to thoroughly cover the entire problem.

Another possible flow chart is shown in Figure 7. This chart deals with the decisions required during the maintenance of the flare tower, an essential safety system. It considers issues of whether the MIC tank was filled at the time that the flare tower was taken off-line for maintenance, whether other safety systems were operating when the flare tower was taken out of operation, and whether the remaining safety systems were sufficient to eliminate potential problems. Using such a flow chart, it is possible to decide whether the flare tower can be taken off-line for maintenance or whether it should remain operating.

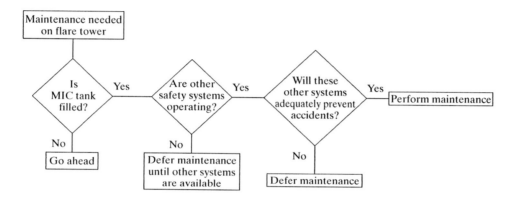

Figure 7
An alternative flow chart for the Bhopal case, emphasizing decisions made when considering deactivating the flare tower for maintenance.

The key to effective use of flow charts for solving ethical problems is to be creative in determining possible outcomes and scenarios and also to not be shy about getting a negative answer and deciding to stop the project.

5 CONFLICT PROBLEMS

An area of ethical problem solving that we will frequently encounter in this book relates to problems that present us with a choice between two conflicting moral values, each of which seems to be correct. How do we make the correct choice in this situation?

Conflict problems can be solved in three ways [Harris, Pritchard, and Rabins, 2000]. Often, there are conflicting moral choices, but one is obviously more significant than the other. For example, protecting the health and safety of the public is more important than your duty to your employer. In this type of case, the resolution of the conflict involves an easy choice.

A second solution is sometimes called the "creative middle way" [Harris, Pritchard, and Rabins, 2000]. This solution is an attempt at some kind of a compromise that will work for everyone. The emphasis here should be on the word "creative," because it takes a great deal of creativity to find a middle ground that is acceptable to everyone and a great deal of diplomacy to sell it to everyone. The sales job is especially difficult because of the nature of compromise, which is often jokingly defined as "the solution where nobody gets what they want." An example of a creative middle ground would be that rather than dumping a toxic waste into a local lake, one finds ways to re-design the production process to minimize the waste product, finds ways to pretreat the waste to minimize the toxicity, or offers to pay for and install the equipment at the municipal water system necessary to treat the water to remove this chemical before it is sent to homes. Obviously, no one will be completely satisfied with these alternatives, since redesigns and pretreatment cost money and take time. Some people will not be satisfied with even a minimized dumping of toxics.

Finally, when there is no easy choice and attempts to find a middle ground are not successful, all that is left is to make the hard choice. Sometimes, you have to bite the bullet and make the best choice possible with the information available at the time. Frequently, you must rely on "gut feelings" for which path is the correct one.

Let's illustrate the resolution-of-conflict problems by examining the *Challenger* explosion, focusing on the dilemma faced by the engineering manager, Bob Lund. The conflict was clear: There was an unknown probability that the shuttle would explode, perhaps killing all aboard. On the other hand, Lund had a responsibility to his company and the people who worked for him. There were consequences of postponing the launch, potentially leading to the loss of future contracts from NASA, the loss of jobs to many Thiokol workers, and perhaps even bankruptcy of the company. For many, the easy choice here is simply to not launch. The risk to the lives of the astronauts is too great and far outweighs any other considerations. It is impossible to balance jobs against lives. After all, most people who lose their jobs will be able to find other employment. However, not everyone will find this to be such an easy choice; clearly, Lund didn't find it to be so.

The creative middle ground might involve delaying the launch until later in the day, when the temperature will have warmed up. Of course, this option might not be possible for many reasons associated with the timing of rocket launches and the successful completion of the planned missions. Instead, perhaps, the astronauts could be informed of the engineer's concerns and be allowed to make the choice whether to launch or not. If a risk is informed and a choice is made by those taking the risk, it somewhat relieves the company of the responsibility if an accident occurs.

The hard choice is what Lund made. He chose to risk the launch, perhaps because the data were ambiguous. He might also have wanted to help ensure the future health of the shuttle program and to save the jobs of the Thiokol workers. As we know, his gamble didn't pay off. The shuttle did explode, causing the deaths of the astronauts and leading to lengthy delays in the shuttle program, political problems for NASA, and business difficulties for Thiokol.

6 AN APPLICATION OF PROBLEM-SOLVING METHODS: BRIBERY/ACCEPTANCE OF GIFTS

One of the many gray areas of engineering ethics is the acceptance of gifts from vendors or the offering of gifts to customers to secure business. The difficulty here comes because of the potential for gifts to become bribes or to be perceived of as bribes. Frequently, engineers find themselves in the position of either dealing with vendors who wish to sell them products for incorporation into the engineer's work or acting as vendors themselves and working on sales to other engineers or companies. In this section, we will look at what bribery is and see how some of the problem-solving techniques developed in this chapter can be used to decide when a gift is really a bribe.

Bribery is illegal in the United States and, contrary to popular opinion, is also illegal everywhere in the world. There are some places where bribery may be overlooked, or even expected, but it always takes place "under the table" and is never a legitimate business practice. Moreover, United States federal law forbids American businesses from engaging in bribery overseas, regardless of the local customs or expectations. In many cases, there is a fine line between bribery and a simple gift. Sometimes, the distinction has to do with the value of the gift. Always, it has to do with the intent of the gift. It is important to ensure that no matter how innocent the gift may be, the appearance of impropriety is avoided.

By definition, a bribe is something, such as money or a favor, offered or given to someone in a position of trust in order to induce him to act dishonestly. It is something offered or serving to influence or persuade. What are the ethical reasons for not tolerating bribery? First, bribery corrupts our free-market economic system and is anticompetitive. Unlike the practice of buying the best product at the best price, bribery does not reward the most efficient producer. One can argue the virtues or vices of the free-market economy, but it is the system under which our economy operates, and anything that subverts this system is unfair and unethical. Second, bribery is a sellout to the rich. Bribery corrupts justice and public policy by allowing rich people to make all the rules. In business, it guarantees that only large, powerful corporations will survive, since they are more capable of providing bribes. A small start-up company doesn't have the resources to compete in an environment where expensive favors are required to secure business. Finally, bribery treats people as commodities that can be bought and sold. This practice is degrading to us as human beings and corrupts both the buyer and the seller [Harris, Pritchard, and Rabins, 2000].

6.1 When Is a Gift a Bribe?

Frequently, the boundary between a legitimate gift and a bribe is very subtle. Gifts of nominal value, such as coffee mugs or calendars with a vendor's logo and phone number on it, are really just an advertising tool. Generally, there is no problem with accepting these types of items. Dining with a customer or a supplier is also an acceptable practice, especially if everyone pays his or her own way. It is important from the point of view of both suppliers and customers that good relations be maintained so that good service can be provided. Social interaction, such as eating together, often facilitates the type of close and successful interactions required by both sides. However, when meals or gifts are no longer of low cost and the expense of these items is not shared equally, the possibility for abuse becomes large.

6.2 Examples of Gifts vs. Bribes

To help illustrate the difference between bribes and legitimate gifts, let's look at a few potential scenarios to see how fuzzy this boundary can be. No answer will be given to the questions posed, but rather the solution of these questions will be left to the reader.

- During a sales visit, a sales representative offers you a coffee mug with his company's name and logo on it. The value of the mug is five dollars. Can you accept this item? Does the answer to this question change if this item is a $350 crystal bowl with the name of the company engraved on it? How about if there is no engraving on it?

- Your meeting with a sales representative is running into the lunch hour. She invites you to go out for lunch. You go to a fast-food restaurant and pay for your own lunch. Is this practice acceptable? Does the answer to this question change if you go to an expensive French restaurant? If she pays for lunch?

- A sales representative from whom you often purchase asks if you would like to play tennis with him this weekend at one of the local municipal courts. Should you go? Is the answer to this question different if the match is at an exclusive local club to which he belongs? What if he pays the club's guest fee for you?

- A company sales representative would like you to attend a one-day sales seminar in Cleveland. Your company will pay for your trip. Should you go? How about if the meeting is in Maui? What if the sales representative's company is going to pay for you to go? What if your family is invited as well?

Do the answers to any of these questions change if the gift is offered before you purchase anything from the company, as opposed to after you are already a steady customer? (A more detailed version of these types of scenarios can be found in [Harris, Pritchard, and Rabins, 2000].)

Keep in mind that gifts accepted even after the purchase of something from a company might be a bribe directed at securing future sales from you or might be aimed at engineers at other companies. Although nothing was said about a gift up front, now that you have received one, the expectation of gifts might affect your future purchase decisions. Similarly, an employee of a company like yours might become aware of the gift that you received. He now realizes that if he orders parts from the same supplier that you did, he will receive a gift similar to yours. He will be tempted to order from this supplier even if there is a better supplier of that product on the market. These types of gifts tend to shut out smaller companies that can't necessarily afford gifts and might also cause an increase in everyone's costs, since if everyone now expects to receive gifts, the product cost must go up. Clearly, bribery is pernicious, and even the appearance of bribery should be avoided.

6.3 Problem Solving

How can the analysis methods described in this chapter be applied to these examples concerning bribery and the acceptance of gifts? We won't go into the answer to this question in depth here, but will rather save it for the questions at the end of the chapter. However, some general ideas can be presented now. Bribery can easily be analyzed by looking at the factual, conceptual, and moral issues described previously. Frequently, the facts will be obvious: who offered a gift, what its value was, and what its purpose was. Conceptual issues will be somewhat more difficult, since it must be determined whether the gift is of sufficient value to influence a decision or whether that influence is the intent of the gift. Once the conceptual issues have been worked out and it is clear whether or not the gift is a bribe, the moral issue is often very clear.

Line drawing can be very effectively applied to the examples given previously. The subtle differences between the value of the gift, the timing of the gift, etc., are easily visualized using line drawing, and often it will be very clear what the ethical choice will be based on a well-drawn line. Likewise, flow charting can be used to examine the consequences that will result from the acceptance or offer of a gift.

6.4 Avoiding Bribery Problems

How does one ensure that accepting a gift doesn't cross the line into bribery? The first and most important method for determining this is to look at company policy. All large corporations and many smaller companies have very clear rules about what is acceptable. Some companies have very strict policies. For example, some companies say that employees are not allowed to accept anything from a vendor and that any social interaction with vendors or customers must be paid for by your company. Any deviation from this rule requires approval from appropriate supervisors. This philosophy is rooted in a sense of trying to avoid any conflict of interest and any appearance of impropriety.

Other companies realize the importance of social interactions in business transactions and allow their employees more discretion in determining what is proper. In the absence of strict corporate guidelines, a preapproval from one's management is the best guide to what is acceptable.

In the absence of any corporate guidelines, another method for determining the acceptability of an action is sometimes referred to as the "New York Times Test": Could your actions withstand the scrutiny of a newspaper reporter? Could you stand to see your name in the newspaper in an article about the gift you received? If you couldn't easily defend your action without resorting to self-serving rationalizations, then you probably shouldn't do it.

APPLICATION

Cases

Cellular Phones and Cancer

This case will seem different from many of the other cases we will study, since there is no disaster or wrongdoing that has to be analyzed after the fact. Rather, this is a case about the experimental nature of engineering and deals with issues of what engineers should do early in the design cycle for a new product or system in order to avoid possible harm to customers or the public in general. It also deals with what engineers should do after a product has been released when possible dangers are brought up.

Concerns about potential adverse health effects of cell phones began in 1992 with a lawsuit filed in Florida. In this suit, David Reynard claimed that his wife's fatal brain cancer had been caused by her use of a cell phone. Although the suit was dismissed in 1995 due to a lack of scientific evidence to support Reynard's claim, this and other similar suits received a great deal of media attention and caused some concern among frequent cell phone users.

The possible problems with cell phones are clear. In using a cell phone, you are placing a source of electromagnetic radiation in close proximity to your brain. It doesn't take much imagination to see the potential for problems: Microwave ovens use electromagnetic radiation to cook food. Of course, cell phones operate at a different frequency and at much lower power levels than do microwave ovens, but the analogy is clear. The human body evolved in an environment that did not contain significant levels of radio-frequency (rf) radiation, so it is plausible that the ubiquity of rf fields in our modern industrial world might cause some adverse health effects.

The biological effects of rf energy have been studied for many years. Some of the early studies go back to the 1940s. What types of studies were performed? Typically, these were epidemiological studies and were retrospective looks at people who have used cell phones. The goal of these studies was to try to determine the levels of exposure to rf radiation from cell phones of every person in the study and to try to correlate the levels with subsequent health effects, especially cancers. While the studies all generally indicated that there is no harm in cell phone use, problems remain. Many of the problems are due to the fact that the studies relied on self-reporting of cell phone use. They asked people to report how much time they spent talking on their phones. Of course, many people reported their phone use accurately, but many others either didn't really know how much they used their phones or misestimated their use. Epidemiological studies are also difficult to analyze, since it is hard to know the power levels each individual has been exposed to. The power emitted by the phone depends on what model of phone you use and how far you are from the base station while talking. Also, brain cancers generally take a long time to develop. There may not have been enough time since the widespread use of cell phones for a significant number of cancers to have developed. Solid links between cell phone use and brain cancers might not show up for another 10 to 20 years.

Studies have also been performed on laboratory animals. Typically, these are done by placing the animals in an environment containing rf fields designed to mimic those of cell phones. Like the epidemiological studies, the research studies on laboratory animals have not indicated any significant increase in health problems for the animals. Of course, since laboratory animals are not humans, the results may not be directly applicable to humans.

There have been some studies of the effects of rf radiation on laboratory tissue and cell cultures. The results of these studies and their applicability to human health are controversial. Some theoretical studies have examined how rf energy might be deposited into a human brain during cell phone use. These studies are very difficult to benchmark because it is difficult to make measurements of energy deposition directly into a human brain.

What is an engineer working for a cell phone company or some other company making products that emit rf radiation to do when confronted with the ongoing concerns about the health effects of rf fields? Cell phones can certainly be redesigned to reduce or eliminate this problem, but, of course, any design that will lead to reduced emission will probably cost more. We won't know for many years what the final answer is regarding cell phone health effects. For now, it seems that cell phones are probably safe to use. What is the prudent and ethical thing to do in designing such products in an atmosphere where some doubt about safety exists? This case illustrates the problems that engineers have in dealing with and managing the unknown. Many of the designs that engineers produce are experimental in nature or deal with effects that aren't fully understood. It is incumbent on the designer to be informed about the potential risks to users of her designs and to seek to minimize these risks to the extent possible.

Vice President Spiro Agnew and Construction Kickbacks in Maryland

In January of 1973, architects and consulting engineers all over Baltimore, Maryland, were seeking out any available attorneys with experience in criminal law. This activity was brought on by subpoenas issued by the U.S. Attorney for Maryland, George Beall, who was looking into charges of bribes and kickbacks given to elected officials by engineers working in the construction industry. The subpoenas required these engineers to submit the records of their firms to the U.S. attorney. One of these engineers was Lester Matz, a partner in Matz, Childs and Associates, a Baltimore engineering firm. The subsequent events described by Richard Cohen and Jules Witcover in their book *A Heartbeat Away* eventually led to the disgrace and resignation of Spiro Agnew, then the Vice President of the United States.

Matz was an engineer trained at Johns Hopkins University in Baltimore. Although his firm was doing well, it always seemed to lose out to other firms on big public-works contracts. In Maryland, engineering and architectural services for government projects were not put out for bid, but rather were awarded to individual firms using various criteria, including the firm's ability to do the work, its performance on past contracts, etc. Interestingly, unlike the situation for engineering services, the contractor for government projects was chosen through a competitive bidding process. It became clear to Matz that in acquiring government contracts, his talents and those of his firm were unimportant. What was required to get the contracts for public works was contacts in government and the requisite bribes and kickbacks.

In 1961, Matz began courting Spiro T. Agnew, an ambitious and rising politician. In 1962, Matz donated $500 to Agnew's campaign for Baltimore county executive, a post that is roughly equivalent to mayor for the areas of the county outside the city limits of Baltimore. The county executive wielded great power in determining who received contracts for the engineering services required for the numerous public-works projects undertaken by the county. The campaign contribution was given by Matz and his partner in the hopes of receiving some of the county engineering contracts that they had been locked out of. After Agnew won the election, the contribution made by Matz's engineering firm was rewarded with contracts for county engineering work. In return, the firm paid Agnew 5% of their fees from the county work, which apparently was the kickback paid by other engineering firms at the time.

With this arrangement, Matz, Childs and Associates prospered and Matz became relatively wealthy. At its peak, the firm employed nearly 350 people. Matz was able to rent an apartment in Aspen for his winter ski vacations and also had a beach condo at St. Croix in the Virgin Islands. Matz's St. Croix condo was near a condo owned by his friend, Spiro Agnew. The "business" arrangement between Agnew and Matz continued when Agnew was elected governor of Maryland, only now Matz, Childs and Associates received contracts for state work. The financial arrangement remained the same: Agnew received a payment for every contract awarded.

These payments continued even after Agnew was elected vice president on the Republican ticket with Richard Nixon in 1968. Matz testified that he met with Agnew in his office in the White House and had given him an envelope containing $10,000 in cash. Indeed, Matz also indicated that he had given $2,500 dollars to Agnew for a federal contract that a subsidiary of Matz, Childs and Associates had received. All told, Matz described payments that he had given Agnew over the years totaling over $100,000.

As a brief aside, it is interesting to describe how the money paid to Agnew was generated. Clearly, these payments had to be made in cash in order to avoid leaving records of the transactions. However, engineering firms are not paid in cash for their services and thus don't typically have large amounts of cash on hand. One method of generating cash was to give cash "bonuses" to key employees. After retaining a sufficient amount to pay the income taxes on the bonus, the employee returned the cash to the firm, where it was placed in a safe until needed. Of course, this practice is a violation of the tax code: The company books record the transaction as a bonus, yet much of the money is retained by the firm. This practice subjected Matz, Childs and Associates to prosecution under the federal tax code. This method didn't always generate the required amount of cash, so other means were also used. For example, large "loans" were made to colleagues, who cashed the money and returned it to the firm. These loans were then "repaid" slowly over a long period of time to make the books appear right.

With federal prosecutors threatening to indict Matz and Childs for income-tax evasion and other charges, they decided to provide evidence to the government of the wrongdoing of Agnew and his successor as county executive. Agnew's lawyers and the prosecutors reached an agreement whereby Agnew would resign as vice president and plead *nolo contendere* (no contest) to a single count of income-tax evasion, a felony, for payments received in 1967. This plea is the legal equivalent of a plea of guilty; the defendant doesn't admit to the crime, but does acknowledge that there is enough evidence to convict him. On October 10, 1973, Agnew resigned as vice president, the first vice president to have resigned in disgrace. Later that day, in a dramatic appearance in a Maryland courtroom, he entered his plea. The judge fined him $10,000 and honored the plea agreement whereby Agnew received no jail term, but only three years of unsupervised probation. For agreeing to cooperate with the prosecution, Matz and Childs were not prosecuted.

These events took place against the backdrop of one of the most intense government crises in U.S. history. Although Nixon and Agnew had been reelected in a landslide in the 1972 election, the Watergate scandal hung over the administration. Shortly after the events of this case, the Watergate scandal intensified, culminating in the resignation of Richard Nixon from the presidency.

Professional Success

Looking for a Job

Many ethical issues arise in the course of looking for a job. Even though as you approach graduation you are still an "amateur," ethical and professional behavior is expected during your job search. There are many ways to be unethical in searching for a job, such as exaggerating or falsifying your resume, or overstating expenses when getting reimbursed for an interview trip.

Other, less obvious, ethical concerns can occur during interview trips. For example, suppose you have had an on-campus interview with a large corporation. After the interview you have decided that you aren't really interested in this company. The company calls you later and asks you to come to company headquarters in Cleveland for a plant visit. You have a friend in Cleveland who you would like to visit. Is it acceptable to go on the plant trip? Why? Does the situation change if the plant trip is to Hawaii? Does it change if your interest level in the company is low, but you honestly feel that you could be persuaded?

How do you decide what is acceptable during your job search? The easiest thing to do is to honestly discuss your plans with the recruiter. If she feels that what you want to do isn't acceptable, then you shouldn't do it. If, however, your plans are acceptable to the company then you can proceed. In addition, the ethical analysis and problem-solving methods that we developed in this chapter and have applied to cases thus far are equally applicable to job searches.

Professional Success

Cheating on Assignments

The intense pressure to get good grades in college often leads to temptations to cheat on exams or assignments. Cheating is an issue that is likely to have arisen in educational settings even before you began your study of engineering. Of course the stakes become higher in a college or university setting, so the temptation to cheat might seem larger now than in high school. Cheating can take many forms, including copying someone else's work or using "cheat sheets" during an exam.

Although it can be analyzed using utilitarianism or rights and duty ethics, it is perhaps easiest to examine cheating using virtue ethics. Honesty is a virtue. Honesty facilitates trust between individuals whereas dishonesty causes friction. People rarely want to associate with others who they feel don't behave fairly and can't be trusted. Cheating or falsifying work is a form of dishonesty. We should seek to enhance virtues such as honesty within ourselves and others, so virtue ethics clearly tells us that cheating is unethical.

Bribery	Flow charting	Line drawing	**KEY TERMS**

REFERENCES

Charles E. Harris, Jr., Michael S. Pritchard, and Michael J. Rabins, *Engineering Ethics, Concepts and Cases,* Wadsworth Publishing Company, Belmont, CA, 2000.

Roland Schinzinger and Mike W. Martin, *Introduction to Engineering Ethics,* McGraw-Hill, New York, 2000.

Cellular Phones and Cancer

Kenneth R. Foster and John E. Moulder, "Are Mobile Phones Safe?" IEEE Spectrum, August 2000, pp.23–28.

Spiro Agnew

Richard M. Cohen and Jules Witcover, *A Heartbeat Away: The Investigation and Resignation of Vice President Spiro T. Agnew,* Viking, New York, 1974.

New York Times, October 11, 1973. Numerous articles, starting with the front-page article about Agnew's resignation and his appearance in court. Articles leading up to this event can also be found in copies of the *New York Times* up to several weeks before this date.

PROBLEMS

1 Use line drawing to assess whether the scenarios of bribery/gift giving under Examples in Section 6 are acceptable. What other examples can you think of to add to these scenarios?

2 Use flow charting to analyze whether the examples given in Section 6 are legitimate gifts or bribes. Be sure to indicate what consequences will flow from each decision.

Cellular Phones and Cancer

3   What does utilitarianism tell us about this case? What do rights and duty ethics tell us? Consider these questions from the point of view of a design engineer who must work on a product that might emit hazardous radiation. Which ethical theory applies best in this case? What does the code of ethics of the IEEE tell us about this case?

4   Analyze this case by determining the factual issues, determining the conceptual issues, and deciding which moral issues apply. Hint: This case is a perfect instance of what we discussed previously in this chapter when we said that the factual issues can be controversial.

5   If there are potential, but not well-understood, hazards in building a product, what are the future consequences of doing nothing—i.e., of making no changes in the design? Will warnings to the consumer suffice to get the designer off the hook? Must the product be engineered to be totally safe at all costs?

6   How can one best balance safety with economics in this case?

7   In their book *Ethics in Engineering,* Martin and Schinzinger state that "[e]ngineering, more than any other profession, involves social experimentation." How applicable is this statement to this case? Do you think that this statement is true in general?

8   In light of the results of various panels that indicate that there is no hazard associated with cell phone use, what should an engineer do today when designing products that will emit this rf radiation?

9   Many of the studies researching cell phone safety have been funded by the cell phone industry. What are the ethical implications of this?

10   Similar concerns about the safety of powerlines and low-frequency magnetic fields were voiced in the early 1990s. Research this case and compare it to the case study on cell phones and cancer. A good starting point is the article "Today's View of Magnetic Fields" in the December 1994 issue of IEEE Spectrum.

Spiro Agnew

11   Does the fact that paying government officials for receiving contracts seemed to be a common-place business practice in Maryland at the time make this practice ethically acceptable?

12   What should an engineer do in the face of competition from others who are willing to resort to bribery?

13   What issues does this case raise regarding competitive bidding for engineering services? Would competitive bidding for the engineering contracts in Baltimore County have solved this problem?

14   What is the ethical status of a campaign contribution given to a politician to secure future business? Is this a bribe? Is it the same as a kickback? Perhaps line drawing would help answer this question.

8

The Rights
and Responsibilities
of Engineers

Objectives

After reading this chapter, you will be able to

- Discuss the responsibilities and rights that engineers have

- Understand what a conflict of interest is and know how to manage one, and

- Determine what whistleblowing is and when it is appropriate to blow the whistle.

In the early 1970s, work was nearing completion on the Bay Area Rapid Transit (BART) system in the San Francisco Bay metropolitan area. The design for BART was very innovative, utilizing a highly automated train system with no direct human control of the trains. In the spring of 1972, three engineers working for BART were fired for insubordination. During the course of their work on the project, the three had become concerned about the safety of the automated control system and were not satisfied with the test procedures being used by Westinghouse, the contractor for the BART train controls.

Unable to get a satisfactory response from their immediate supervisors, the engineers resorted to an anonymous memo to upper management detailing their concerns and even met with a BART board member to discuss the situation. The information on the problems at BART was leaked to the press by the board member, leading to the firing of the engineers. They subsequently sued BART and were aided in their suit by the IEEE, which contended that they were performing their ethical duties as engineers in trying to protect the safety of the public that would use BART. Eventually, the engineers were forced to settle the case out of court for only a fraction of the damages that they were seeking.

There are many rights and responsibilities that engineers must exercise in the course of their professional careers. Often, these rights and responsibilities overlap. For example, the BART engineers had a responsibility to the public to see that the BART system was safe and the right to have their concerns taken seriously by management without risking their jobs. Unfortunately, in this case, their rights and responsibilities were not respected by BART. In this chapter, we will take a closer look at these and other rights and responsibilities of engineers.

1 INTRODUCTION

The codes of ethics of the professional engineering societies spell out, sometimes in great detail, the responsibilities entailed in being an engineer. However, the codes don't discuss any of the professional rights that engineers should enjoy. There is often a great deal of overlap between these rights and responsibilities. As we saw in the BART case described at the beginning of this chapter, an engineer has a duty to protect the public, by blowing the whistle if necessary, when he perceives that something improper is being done in his organization. The engineer has a right to do this even if his employer feels that it is bad for the organization.

In this chapter, we will discuss the engineer's responsibilities in more detail and also look at the rights of engineers, especially with regard to issues of conscience and conflicts with the rights of employers or clients.

2 PROFESSIONAL RESPONSIBILITIES

We will begin our discussion of professional rights and responsibilities by first looking more closely at a few of the important responsibilities that engineers have.

2.1 Confidentiality and Proprietary Information

A hallmark of the professions is the requirement that the professional keep certain information of the client secret or confidential. Confidentiality is mentioned in most engineering codes of ethics. This is a well-established principle in professions such as medicine, where the patient's medical information must be kept confidential, and in law, where attorney–client privilege is a well-established doctrine. This requirement applies equally to engineers, who have an obligation to keep proprietary information of their employer or client confidential.

Why must some engineering information be kept confidential? Most information about how a business is run, its products and its suppliers, directly affects the company's ability to compete in the marketplace. Such information can be used by a competitor to gain advantage or to catch up. Thus, it is in the company's (and the employee's) best interest to keep such information confidential to the extent possible.

What types of information should be kept confidential? Some of these types are very obvious, including test results and data, information about upcoming unreleased products, and designs or formulas for products. Other information that should be kept confidential is not as obvious, including business information such as the number of employees working on a project, the identity of suppliers, marketing strategies, production costs, and production yields. Most companies have strict policies regarding the disclosure of business information and require that all employees sign them. Frequently, internal company communications will be labeled as "proprietary." Engineers working for a client are frequently required to sign a nondisclosure agreement. Of course, those engineers working for the government, especially in the defense industry, have even more stringent requirements about secrecy placed on them and may even require a security clearance granted after investigation by a governmental security agency before being able to work.

It seems fairly straightforward for engineers to keep information confidential, since it is usually obvious what should be kept confidential and from whom it should be kept. However, as in many of the topics that we discuss in the context of engineering ethics, there are gray areas that must be considered. For example, a common problem is the question of how long confidentiality extends after an engineer leaves employment with a company. Legally, an engineer is required to keep information confidential even after she has moved to a new employer in the same technical area. In practice, doing so can be difficult. Even if no specific information is divulged to a new employer, an engineer takes with her a great deal of knowledge of what works, what materials to choose, and what components not to choose. This information might be considered proprietary by her former employer. However, when going to a new job, an engineer can't be expected to forget all of the knowledge already gained during years of professional experience.

The courts have considered this issue and have attempted to strike a balance between the competing needs and rights of the individual and the company. Individuals have the right to seek career advancement wherever they choose, even from a competitor of their current employer. Companies have the right to keep information away from their competitors. The burden of ensuring that both of these competing interests are recognized and maintained lies with the individual engineer.

2.2 Conflict of Interest

Avoiding conflict of interest is important in any profession, and engineering is no exception. A conflict of interest arises when an interest, if pursued, could keep a professional from meeting one of his obligations [Martin and Schinzinger, 2000]. For example, a civil engineer working for a state department of highways might have a financial interest in a company that has a bid on a construction project. If that engineer has some responsibility for determining which company's bid to accept, then there is a clear conflict of interest. Pursuing his financial interest in the company might lead him not to objectively and faithfully discharge his professional duties to his employer, the highway department. The engineering codes are very clear on the need to avoid conflicts of interest like this one.

There are three types of conflicts of interest that we will consider [Harris, Pritchard, and Rabins, 2000]. First, there are actual conflicts of interest, such as the one described in the previous paragraph, which compromise objective engineering judgement. There are also potential conflicts of interest, which threaten to easily become actual conflicts of interest. For example, an engineer might find herself becoming friends with a supplier for her company. Although this situation doesn't necessarily constitute a conflict, there is the potential that the engineer's judgement might become conflicted by the need to maintain the friendship. Finally, there are situations in which there is the appearance of a conflict of interest. This might occur when an engineer is paid based on a percentage of the cost of the design. There is clearly no incentive to cut costs in this situation, and it may appear that the engineer is making the design more expensive simply to generate a larger fee. Even cases where there is only an appearance of a conflict of interest can be significant, because the distrust that comes from this situation compromises the engineer's ability to do this work and future work and calls into question the engineer's judgement.

A good way to avoid conflicts of interest is to follow the guidance of company policy. In the absence of such a policy, asking a coworker or your manager will give you a second opinion and will make it clear that you aren't trying to hide something. In the absence of either of these options, it is best to examine your motives and use ethical problem-solving techniques. Finally, you can look to the statements in the professional ethics codes that uniformly forbid conflicts of interest. Some of the codes have very explicit statements that can help determine whether or not your situation is a conflict of interest.

3 PROFESSIONAL RIGHTS

We have seen how the professional status of engineering confers many responsibilities on the engineer. Engineers also have rights that go along with these responsibilities. Not all of these rights come about due to the professional status of engineering. There are rights that individuals have regardless of professional status, including the right to privacy, the right to participate in activities of one's own choosing outside of work, the right to reasonably object to company policies without fear of retribution, and the right to due process.

The most fundamental right of an engineer is the right of professional conscience [Martin and Schinzinger, 2000]. This involves the right to exercise professional judgement in discharging one's duties and to exercise this judgement in an ethical manner. This right is basic to an engineer's professional practice. However, it is no surprise that this right is not always easy for an employer to understand.

The right of professional conscience can have many aspects. For example, one of these aspects might be referred to as the "Right of Conscientious Refusal" [Martin and Schinzinger, 2000]. This is the right to refuse to engage in unethical behavior. Put quite simply, no employer can ask or pressure an employee into doing something that she considers unethical and unacceptable. Although this issue is very clear in cases for which an engineer is asked to falsify a test result or fudge on the safety of a product, it is less clear in cases for which the engineer refuses an assignment based on an ethical principle that is not shared by everyone. For example, an engineer ought to be allowed to refuse to work on defense projects or environmentally hazardous work if his conscience says that such work is immoral. Employers should be reasonably accommodating of that person's request. We will amplify this point with regard to defense work in the next section.

3.1 Engineers and the Defense Industry

One of the largest employers of engineers worldwide is the defense industry. This is by no means a modern trend; throughout history, many innovations in engineering and science have come about as the result of the development of weapons. Since fundamentally, weapons are designed for one purpose—to kill human beings—it seems important to look at this type of engineering work in the context of engineering ethics and the rights of engineers.

An engineer may choose either to work or not to work in defense-related industries and be ethically justified in either position. Many reasonable engineering professionals feel that ethically, they cannot work on designs that will ultimately be used to kill other humans. Their remoteness from the killing doesn't change this feeling. Even though they won't push the button or may never actually see the victims of the use of the weapon, they still find it morally unacceptable to work on such systems.

On the other hand, equally morally responsible engineers find this type of work ethically acceptable. They reason that the defense of our nation or other nations from aggression is a legitimate function of our government and is an honorable goal for engineers to contribute to. Both of these positions can be justified using moral theories and ethical problem-solving techniques.

Even if an engineer finds defense work ethically acceptable, there might be uses of these weapons or certain projects that he considers questionable. For example, is it acceptable to work on weapons systems that will only be sold to other nations? Is the use of weapons to guarantee our "national interests," such as maintaining a steady supply of foreign oil, an acceptable defense project?

Given the issues that surround defense work, what is an engineer to do when asked to work on a weapons project he considers questionable? As with many of the ethical dilemmas that we have discussed in this book, there is no simple solution, but rather the answer must be determined by each individual after examination of his values and personal feelings about the ethics of defense work. It is important to avoid working on any project that you deem unethical, even if it might lead to a career advancement, or even if it is a temporary job. (This principle also holds true for projects that you feel are unsafe, bad for the environment, etc.) It can be argued that weapons work is the most important type of engineering, given its consequences for mankind. Because of the implications to human life, this type of engineering requires an even more stringent examination of ethical issues to ensure responsible participation.

4 WHISTLEBLOWING

There has been increased attention paid in the last 30 years to whistleblowing, both in government and in private industry. Whistleblowing is the act by an employee of informing the public or higher management of unethical or illegal behavior by an employer or supervisor. There are frequent newspaper reports of cases in which an employee of a company has gone to the media with allegations of wrongdoing by his or her employer or in which a government employee has disclosed waste or fraud. In this section, we will examine the ethical aspects of whistleblowing and discuss when it is appropriate and when it isn't appropriate. We will also look at what corporations and government agencies can do to lessen the need for employees to take this drastic action.

Whistleblowing is included in this chapter on rights and responsibilities because it straddles the line between the two. According to the codes of ethics of the professional engineering societies, engineers have a duty to protect the health and safety of the public, so in many cases, an engineer is compelled to blow the whistle on acts or projects that harm these values. Engineers also have the professional right to disclose wrongdoing within their organizations and expect to see appropriate action taken.

4.1 Types of Whistleblowing

We will start our discussion of whistleblowing by looking at the different forms that whistleblowing takes. A distinction is often made between internal and external whistleblowing. Internal whistleblowing occurs when an employee goes over the head of an immediate supervisor to report a problem to a higher level of management. Or, all levels of management are bypassed, and the employee goes directly to the president of the company or the board of directors. However it is done, the whistleblowing is kept within the company or organization. External whistleblowing occurs when the employee goes outside the company and reports wrongdoing to newspapers or law-enforcement authorities. Either type of whistleblowing is likely to be perceived as disloyalty. However, keeping it within the company is often seen as less serious than going outside of the company.

There is also a distinction between acknowledged and anonymous whistleblowing. Anonymous whistleblowing occurs when the employee who is blowing the whistle refuses to divulge his name when making accusations. These accusations might take the form of anonymous memos to upper management (as in the BART case discussed later) or of anonymous phone calls to the police. The employee might also talk to the news media but refuse to let her name be used as the source of the allegations of wrongdoing. Acknowledged whistleblowing, on the other hand, occurs when the employee puts his name behind the accusations and is willing to withstand the scrutiny brought on by his accusations.

Whistleblowing can be very bad from a corporation's point of view because it can lead to distrust, disharmony, and an inability of employees to work together. The situation can be illustrated by an analogy with sports. If the type of whistleblowing we are discussing here was performed during a game, it would not be the referees who stopped play because of a violation of the rules. Rather, it would be one of your own teammates who stopped the game and assessed a penalty on your own team. In sports, this type of whistleblowing would seem like an act of extreme disloyalty, although perhaps it is the "gentlemanly" thing to do. Similarly, in business, whistleblowing is perceived as an act of extreme disloyalty to the company and to coworkers.

4.2 When Should Whistleblowing Be Attempted?

During the course of your professional life, you might come across a few cases of wrongdoing. How do you know when you should blow the whistle? We will start to answer this question by first looking at when you *may* blow the whistle and then looking at when you *should* blow the whistle. Whistleblowing should only be attempted if the following four conditions are met [Harris, Pritchard, and Rabins, 2000]:

1. *Need.* There must be a clear and important harm that can be avoided by blowing the whistle. In deciding whether to go public, the employee needs to have a sense of proportion. You don't need to blow the whistle about everything, just the important things. Of course, if there is a pattern of many small things that are going on, this can add up to a major and important matter requiring that the whistle be blown. For example, if an accident occurs at your company, resulting in a spill of a small quantity of a toxic compound into a nearby waterway that is immediately cleaned up, this incident probably does not merit notifying outside authorities. However, if this type of event happens repeatedly and no action is taken to rectify the problem despite repeated attempts by employees to get the problem fixed, then perhaps this situation is serious enough to warrant the extreme measure of whistleblowing.

2. *Proximity.* The whistleblower must be in a very clear position to report on the problem. Hearsay is not adequate. Firsthand knowledge is essential to making an effective case about wrongdoing. This point also implies that the whistleblower must have enough expertise in the area to make a realistic assessment of the situation. This condition stems from the clauses in several codes of ethics which mandate that an engineer not undertake work in areas outside her expertise. This principle applies equally well to making assessments about whether wrongdoing is taking place.

3. *Capability.* The whistleblower must have a reasonable chance of success in stopping the harmful activity. You are not obligated to risk your career and the financial security of your family if you can't see the case through to completion or you don't feel that you have access to the proper channels to ensure that the situation is resolved.

4. *Last resort.* Whistleblowing should be attempted only if there is no one else more capable or more proximate to blow the whistle and if you feel that all other lines of action within the context of the organization have been explored and shut off.

These four conditions tell us when whistleblowing is morally acceptable. But when is an engineer morally obligated to blow the whistle? There may be situations in which you are aware of wrongdoing and the four conditions discussed above have been met. In this case, the whistle *may* be blown if you feel that the matter is sufficiently important. You are only *obligated* to blow the whistle when there is great imminent danger of harm to someone if the activity continues and the four conditions have been met. A great deal of introspection and reflection is required before whistleblowing is undertaken.

It is important for the whistleblower to understand his motives before undertaking this step. It is acceptable to blow the whistle to protect the public interest, but not to exact revenge upon fellow employees, supervisors, or your company. Nor is it acceptable to blow the whistle in the hopes of future gains through book contracts and speaking tours.

4.3 Preventing Whistleblowing

So far, our discussion of whistleblowing has focused on the employee who finds herself in a situation in which she feels that something must be done. We should also look at whistleblowing from the employer's point of view. As an employer, I should seek to minimize the need for employees to blow the whistle within my organization. Clearly, any time that information about wrongdoing becomes public, it is harmful to the organization's image and will negatively affect the future prospects of the company. How, then, do I stop this type of damage?

In answering this question, we must acknowledge that it is probably impossible to eliminate all wrongdoing in a corporation or government agency. Even organizations with a very strong ethical culture will have employees who, from time to time, succumb to the temptation to do something wrong. A typical corporate approach to stemming whistleblowing and the resulting bad publicity is to fire whistleblowers and to intimidate others who might seem likely to blow the whistle. This type of approach is both ineffective and ethically unacceptable. No one should be made to feel bad about trying to stop ethically questionable activities.

There are four ways in which to solve the whistleblowing problem within a corporation. First, there must be a strong corporate ethics culture. This should include a clear commitment to ethical behavior, starting at the highest levels of management, and mandatory ethics training for all employees. All managers must set the tone for the ethical behavior of their employees. Second, there should be clear lines of communication within the corporation. This openness gives an employee who feels that there is something that must be fixed a clear path to air his concerns. Third, all employees must have meaningful access to high-level managers in order to bring their concerns forward. This access must come with a guarantee that there will be no retaliation. Rather, employees willing to come forward should be rewarded for their commitment to fostering the ethical behavior of the company. Finally, there should be willingness on the part of management to admit mistakes, publicly if necessary. This attitude will set the stage for ethical behavior by all employees.

APPLICATION

Cases

The BART Case

The cities surrounding San Francisco Bay form one of the largest metropolitan areas in the United States. Due to the geographical limits imposed by the bay, much of the commuting that takes place in this area must be across just a few bridges. The Bay Area Rapid Transit system (BART) had its genesis in late 1947 when a joint Army–Navy review board recommended the construction of a tunnel underneath San Francisco Bay for high-speed train service between San Francisco and Oakland [Friedlander, 1972]. The California state legislature then formed the San Francisco Bay Area Rapid Transit Commission, which was to study the transportation needs of the Bay area and make recommendations to the legislature. This effort culminated in the formation of the Bay Area Rapid Transit district in 1957. By 1962, this group had done a preliminary design of a rapid train system, including a transbay tube, and had laid the groundwork for fund-raising for the project. In 1962, a bond issue to fund the project was approved by the voters and the project was begun.

As envisioned, BART was to be a high-tech rail system serving many of the outlying communities along San Francisco Bay. There were three distinct engineering issues involved in BART: the design and construction of railbeds, tunnels, bridges, etc.; the design and manufacture of the railcars; and the design and implementation of a system for controlling the trains. The control system will be the focus of our discussion.

BART was to incorporate much new technology, including fully automated control systems. The trains would have "attendants," but would not be under direct control by humans. In many respects, BART was an experiment on a very large scale. None of the control technologies that were to be used had been previously tested in a commuter rail system. Of course, any innovative engineering design is like this and has components that have not been previously tested.

The Automatic Train-Control (ATC) system was an innovative method for controlling train speed and access to stations. In most urban mass transit systems, this function is performed by human drivers reading trackside signals and receiving instructions via radio from dispatchers. Instead, BART relied on a series of onboard sensors that determined the train's position and the location of other trains. Speeds on the track were automatically maintained by monitoring the location of the train and detecting allowed speed information. One of the unique and problematic features of the system was that there were no fail-safe methods of train control [Friedlander, 1972]. Rather, all control was based on redundancy. This distinction is very important. *"Fail safe"* implies that if there is a failure, the system will revert to a safe state. In the case of BART, this would mean that a failure would cause the trains to stop. Redundancy, on the other hand, relies on switching failed components or systems to backups in order to keep the trains running.

There are two distinct phases of this type of engineering project, construction and operation, each requiring different skills. For this reason, early on, BART decided to keep its own staff relatively small and subcontract most of the design and construction work. This way, there wouldn't be the need to lay off hundreds of workers during the transition from construction to operation [Anderson, 1980]. This system also encouraged the engineers who worked for BART not only to oversee the design and construction of the system, but also to learn the skills required to run and manage this complex transportation system. Contracts for design and construction of the railroad infrastructure were awarded to a consortium of large engineering firms known as Parsons, Brinkerhoff, Tudor, and Bechtel (PBTB). PBTB began construction on the system in January of 1967. The transbay tube was started in November of that year. Also in 1967, a contract was awarded to Westinghouse to design and build the ATC. In 1969, Rohr Industries was awarded a contract to supply 250 railroad cars.

A little bit should be said about the management structure at BART. By design, BART was organized with a very open management structure. Employees were given great freedom to define what their jobs entailed and to work independently and were encouraged to take any concerns that they had to management. Unfortunately, there was also a very diffuse and unclear chain of command that made it difficult for employees to take their concerns to the right person [Anderson, 1980].

The key players in this case were three BART engineers working on various aspects of the ATC: Roger Hjortsvang, Robert Bruder, and Max Blankenzee. The first to be employed by BART was Hjortsvang. As part of his duties for BART, Hjortsvang spent 10 months in 1969–70 in Pittsburgh at the Westinghouse plant working with the engineers who were designing the ATC. During this time, he became concerned about the lack of testing of some of the components of the ATC and also about the lack of oversight of Westinghouse by BART. After returning to San Francisco, Hjortsvang began raising some of these concerns with his management.

Soon after Hjortsvang returned from Pittsburgh, Bruder joined BART, working in a different group than Hjortsvang. He also became concerned about the Westinghouse test procedures and about the testing schedule, but was unable to get his concerns addressed by BART management. Both Hjortsvang and Bruder were told that BART management was satisfied with the test procedures Westinghouse was employing. Management felt that Westinghouse had been awarded the contract because of its experience and engineering skills and should be trusted to deliver what was promised.

Around this time, both engineers also became concerned about the documentation that Westinghouse was providing. Would the documentation be sufficient for BART engineers to understand how the system worked? Would they be able to repair it or modify it once the system was delivered and Westinghouse was out of the picture? Being unable to get satisfaction, Hjortsvang and Bruder dropped the matter. It is important to note that the concerns here were not just about testing, *per se,* but also about the effect that untested components might have on the safety and reliability of BART.

Blankenzee then joined BART and worked at the same location as Hjortsvang. Before joining BART, Blankenzee had worked for Westinghouse on the BART project, and so he knew about how Westinghouse was approaching its work. He too was concerned about the testing and documentation of the ATC. When Blankenzee joined BART, it rekindled Hortsvang's and Bruder's interest in these problems. To attempt to resolve these concerns, Hortsvang wrote an unsigned memo in November of 1971 to several levels of BART management that summarized the problems he perceived. Distribution of an anonymous memo was, of course, viewed with suspicion by management.

In January 1972, the three engineers contacted members of the BART board of directors, indicating that their concerns were not being taken seriously by lower management. This action was in direct conflict with the general manager of BART, whose policy was to allow only himself and a few others to deal directly with the board [Anderson, 1980]. As defined previously in this chapter, this action by the engineers constituted "internal whistleblowing." The engineers also consulted with an outside engineering consultant, Edward Burfine, who evaluated the ATC on his own and came to conclusions similar to those of the three engineers.

One of the members of the board of directors, Dan Helix, spoke with the engineers and appeared to take them seriously. Helix took the engineers' memos and the report of the consultant and distributed them to other members of the board. Unfortunately, he also released them to a local newspaper, a surprising act of external whistleblowing by a member of the board of directors. Naturally, BART management was upset by this action and tried to locate the source of this information. The three engineers initially lied about their involvement. They later agreed to take their concerns directly to the board, thus revealing themselves as the source of the leaks. The board was skeptical of the importance of their concerns. Once the matter was in the open, the engineers' positions within BART became tenuous.

On March 2 and 3, 1972, all three engineers were offered the choice of resignation or firing. They all refused to resign and were dismissed on the grounds of insubordination, lying to their superiors (they had denied being the source of the leaks), and failing to follow organizational procedures. They all suffered as a result of their dismissal. None was able to find work for a number of months, and all suffered financial and emotional problems as a result. They sued BART for $875,000, but were forced to settle out of court, since it was likely that their lying to superiors would be very detrimental to the case. Each received just $25,000 [Anderson, 1980].

As the legal proceedings were taking place, the IEEE attempted to assist the three engineers by filing an *amicus curiae* (friend of the court) brief in their support. The IEEE asserted that each of the engineers had a professional duty to keep the safety of the public paramount and that their actions were therefore justified. Based on the IEEE code of ethics, the brief stated that engineers must "notify the proper authority of any observed conditions which endanger public safety and health." The brief interpreted this statement to mean that in the case of public employment, the proper authority is the public itself [Anderson, 1980]. This was perhaps the first time that a national engineering professional society had intervened in a legal proceeding on behalf of engineers who had apparently been fulfilling their duties according to a professional code of ethics.

Safety concerns continued to mount as BART was put into operation. For example, on October 2, 1972, less than a month after BART was put into revenue service, a BART train overshot the station at Fremont, California and crashed into a sand embankment. There were no fatalities, but five persons were injured. The accident was attributed to a malfunction of a crystal oscillator, part of the ATC, which controlled the speed commands for the train. Subsequent to this accident, there were several investigations and reports on the operation of BART. These revealed that there had been other problems and malfunctions in the system. Trains had often been allowed too close to each other; sometimes a track was indicated to be occupied when it wasn't and was indicated not to be occupied when it was. The safety concerns of the three engineers seemed to be borne out by the early operation of the system [Friedlander, 1972, 1973].

Ultimately, the ATC was improved and the bugs worked out. In the years since, BART has accumulated an excellent safety record and has served as the model for other high-tech mass transit systems around the country.

The Goodrich A7-D Brake Case

This case is one that is very often used as an example in engineering ethics texts, especially to study whistleblowing. In studying this case, it is important to keep in mind that much of the information presented here is derived from the writing of the whistleblower. An individual who is deeply embroiled in a controversial situation such as this one will have different insights and viewpoints on the situation than will management or other workers. Little is publicly known about what Goodrich management thought about this case.

In the 1960s, the B. F. Goodrich corporation was a major defense contractor. One of their main defense-related industries was the production of brakes and wheels for military aircraft. This activity was located in Troy, Ohio. Goodrich had developed a new and innovative design: a four-rotor brake that would be considerably lighter than the more traditional five-rotor designs. Any reduction in weight is very attractive in aircraft design, since it allows for an increase in payload weight with no decrease in performance.

In June of 1967, Goodrich was awarded the contract to supply the brakes for the A7–D by LTV, the prime contractor for the airplane. The qualifying of this new design was on a very tight schedule imposed by the Air Force. The new brake had to be ready for flight testing by June of 1968, leaving only one year to test and qualify the design. To qualify the design for the flight test, Goodrich had to demonstrate that it performed well in a series of tests specified by the Air Force.

After the design had been completed, John Warren, the design engineer, handed the project over to Searle Lawson, who was just out of engineering school, to perform the testing of the brakes. Warren moved on to other projects within the corporation. Lawson's first task was to test various potential brake-lining materials to see which ones would work best in this new design. This test would be followed by the testing of the chosen linings on full-scale prototypes of the brakes. Unfortunately, after six months of testing, Lawson was unable to find any materials that worked adequately. He became convinced that the design itself was flawed and would never perform according to the Air Force's specifications.

Lawson spoke with Warren about these problems. Warren still felt that the brake design was adequate and made several suggestions to Lawson regarding new lining materials that might improve performance. However, none of these suggestions worked and the brakes still failed to pass the initial tests. Lawson then spoke about these problems with Robert Sink, the A7-D project manager at Goodrich. Sink asked Lawson to keep trying some more linings and expressed confidence that the design would work correctly.

In March of 1968, Goodrich began testing the full brake prototypes. After 13 tests, the brake had yet to pass the Air Force's specification for temperature. The only way to get the brakes to pass the test was to set up cooling fans directed at the rotors. Obviously, brakes that required extra cooling would not meet the Air Force's specification. Nevertheless, Sink assured LTV that the brake development was going well.

Kermit Vandivier was a technical writer for Goodrich who was responsible for writing test reports and was assigned to write the report for the new A7-D brakes. This report would be an integral part of the Air Force's decision-making process. Vandivier was not an engineer, but he did have experience in writing up the results of this type of test. In the course of writing the report on the A7-D brake tests, Vandivier became aware that some of the test results had been rigged to meet the Air Force's specifications. Vandivier raised his concerns about the report he was writing, feeling that he couldn't write a report based on falsified data. His attempts to write an accurate report were not allowed by management, and Goodrich submitted a report using the jury-rigged data. Based on this report, the brake was qualified for flight testing.

Vandivier was concerned about the safety of the brake and wondered what his legal responsibility might be. He contacted his attorney, who suggested that he and Lawson might be guilty of conspiracy to commit fraud and advised Vandivier to meet with the U.S. Attorney in Dayton. Upon advice of the U.S. Attorney, both Lawson and Vandivier contacted the FBI.

In July, the Air Force asked Goodrich to supply the raw test data for review. This request led to efforts at Goodrich to control the damage that would ensue when the real nature of the tests became known. Not being satisfied with the report presented to it, the Air Force refused to accept the brake. Knowing that the four-rotor brake was not going to work, Goodrich began an effort to design a five-rotor replacement. Vandivier continued meeting with the FBI and supplied FBI agents with Goodrich documents related to the A7-D brake tests.

Apparently, Lawson had impressed LTV because after the flight testing was over, LTV offered him a job. Lawson accepted and left Goodrich on October 11, 1968. With the only other person who really knew about the test procedures gone, Vandivier also decided to resign from Goodrich. In his letter of resignation, he included a series of accusations of wrongdoing against Goodrich regarding the brake tests. Vandivier went to work for the *Troy Daily News,* the local newspaper.

At the *Daily News,* Vandivier told his editor about the situation at Goodrich. From there, the story made its way to Washington, where it came to the attention of Senator William Proxmire, among others. In May of 1969, Proxmire requested that the General Accounting Office (GAO) review the issue of the qualification testing of the A7-D brakes. The GAO investigation led to an August 1969 Senate hearing chaired by Proxmire. By then, the new five-rotor brake had been tested and qualified for use on the A7-D. At the hearing, Vandivier's concerns and the GAO findings were publicly aired. The GAO report confirmed Vandivier's statements about testing discrepancies, though the report also showed that there was no additional cost to the government in obtaining a working brake and that the brake problems didn't cause any substantial delays in the overall A-7D program.

No official action was taken against Goodrich as a result of this incident, and there does not seem to have been any negative impact on the careers of those at Goodrich involved in the A7-D project. Lawson went on to a successful career at LTV. Vandivier later wrote a chapter of a book and an article in *Harper's* magazine detailing his version of the story.

The Therac-25 Accidents

The Therac-25 was a radiation therapy machine produced by the Atomic Energy Commission Ltd. (AECL), a Canadian company. AECL had previously collaborated with CGR, a French company in the development of earlier versions of this machine. The Therac-25 was a dual-mode linear accelerator designed to deliver X-ray photons at 25 MeV, or electrons over a range of energies. The electrons are used to treat tumors relatively close to the surface, while the X-rays can be used therapeutically on deeper tumors. The Therac-25 was not the first radiation therapy machine produced by this partnership; similar machines, the Therac-6 and Therac-20, had been in use for a number of years. Although the previous Therac machines had utilized some level of computer control, they also relied heavily on hardware interlocks to ensure the safe operation of the machine. From the start, the Therac-25 was designed to be controlled by software and did not incorporate the level of hardware safety devices found on the early machines.

The accidents involving the Therac-25 date back to the months between June 1985 and January 1987, comprising at least six known events of improper dosing of patients. There were eleven Therac-25 machines installed in the US and in Canada, with accidents occurring on both sides of the border. The six accidents involved overdosing of patients receiving radiation therapy for various types of cancer. Typical of these accidents was what happened to a patient at the East Texas Cancer Center in Tyler, Texas, in March of 1986. At the time of this accident, the Therac-25 had been in operation at this center for two years and had been used to treat over 500 patients. The patient in this case was being treated for a tumor in his back and was undergoing his ninth treatment with this machine. The prescribed treatment was to be 180 rads of 22 MeV electrons over a 10×17 cm area of his upper back. As the treatment was started, the machine shut down, giving the operator an error code labeled "Malfunction 54." The meaning of this code was not identified in the manual that came with the machine. The machine also showed a "Treatment Pause" and an underdose, indicating that only about 3% of the requested dose had been delivered. Thinking that the treatment was incomplete, the operator told the machine to proceed, but it immediately shut down again. Because the video monitor was not working, the operator was unable to see the patient and didn't know that after the first dose, the patient had experienced what he described as an electric shock in his back. Knowing that something was wrong, he was attempting to get up when the second dose was delivered with the same painful effect. It was later estimated that the patient had received a total dose of between 16,500 and 25,000 rads, far higher than the 180 rads he was supposed to receive. In addition, the dose was concentrated in an area of approximately 1 cm^2. As a result of this malfunction, the patient developed symptoms of severe radiation poisoning and eventually died of complications related to the accident. The other six accidents were similar in nature, with similar consequences [Leveson, 1993].

The proximate cause of these accidents was a "bug" in the software. As the operators became comfortable with the software, they became quite proficient and fast at entering the data that set the type of treatment, dose, and energy. However, the hardware of the system required several seconds to reset when a command was changed on the computer keyboard. If the operator input the wrong information initially, quickly changed the settings to the correct ones, and hit the key that turned the beam on, the machine would go ahead and energize the beam resulting in an incorrect dose being delivered. Basically, the software didn't wait for the hardware to reset before turning the beam on. Compounding the problem, there were no hardware interlocks available to shut the beam off when excessive doses were detected. The earlier versions of the Therac machines had this type of hardware safety system, but the Therac-25 relied on software to provide this protection. [Casey, 1993].

In the wake of these accidents, investigations took place into the reasons for the malfunction of the machine. Two major areas of concern were identified:

- Systems engineering–In this complicated system, there was an almost exclusive reliance on the software to work correctly and ensure the safe operation of the machine. The lack of hardware safety systems was cited as one of the main problems with the Therac-25.
- Software engineering–Many software engineering errors were made during the development of the Therac-25, including inadequate documentation and testing of the software modules and the software.

The Hartford Civic Center Collapse

The new Hartford Civic Center opened in 1975 as the centerpiece of a downtown revitalization project for the city of Hartford, Connecticut. Perhaps the most important part of the Center was a new arena, designed to seat 12,500 people for sporting events, concerts, and conventions. Nearly three years after opening, on the night of January 18, 1978, the roof of the arena collapsed during a snowstorm. The snow was only 4.8 inches deep, not a particularly bad storm for Hartford. Naturally, the specifications for the roof structure called for it to withstand snow loads much greater than this. The roof collapse occurred around 4 A.M. when the building was unoccupied, so fortunately there were no injuries. The disaster could have been much worse since just a few hours earlier, the arena was packed with spectators watching the University of Connecticut men's basketball team defeat the University of Massachusetts [*Time*, 1978].

The project architect was Vincent Kling & Associates, a well-known East Coast architecture firm, with structural engineering performed by Fraioli-Blum-Yesselman Associates. The building was constructed by Gilbane Building, William L. Crow Construction, and the Bethlehem Steel Companies. The arena incorporated several innovative design and construction features. Perhaps most significant in these innovations was the use of computer software to perform and verify the structural analysis and design.

The space spanned by the arena's roof was 330×360 feet, and a "space frame" design was chosen for the roof structure. As with all engineering projects, the engineers looked for ways to save money both in the building and in the design process. The engineers developed several cost-saving innovations in the space frame, and used computer software to analyze the stresses in the structure. Of course, in current engineering practice, it is not at all unusual to rely on computer software for analysis of structures. However, in 1975 computer software was not as sophisticated as it is today and few engineers were trained in the proper use of this type of software. Fraioli-Blum-Yesselman chose to use computers for structural analysis as a cost-cutting measure; calculating the expected stresses would otherwise be a time-consuming and tedious process. Among the items calculated using the computer were the loading capacities of various structural members, and the expected sag, or downward deflection of the roof.

An interesting aspect of the space-frame design was that it was light enough to be assembled on the ground and then lifted into place when completed. After assembly, the frame was to be raised onto the building using four jacks, and then the roofing was to be added. As soon as the roof frame was built and raised into place, excessive deflection was noticed. A contractor documented a deflection of 8.4 inches with no roof decking in place. As completed, the deflection of the roof was supposed to be only 7.35 inches [Ross, 1984]. Thus the incomplete roof had already exceeded the expected deflection of the completed roof.

Later, as workers attempted to install the roof panels, they noted that the panels didn't fit into place correctly due to the sagging of the structure. When the roofing subcontractor reported this in writing, he was told the sagging was to be expected, and to make the necessary adjustments to get the job done on time. Afterwards, when deflection of the completed roof was twice what computer results had predicted, the engineers disregarded it, claiming that "such discrepancies between actual and the theoretical should be expected" [Martin, 2001]. Concerns about the sagging of the roof were repeatedly brought to the attention of the engineers. Still, the engineers dismissed these concerns stating that the deflection was normal and that they didn't expect the actual measurements to exactly match computer calculations.

Another contributing factor to the collapse was that several construction details did not match the original design. For example, the plans called for the 30-ft cross members in the top layer of the frame to be braced at their midpoint. During construction, this bracing was omitted, and the omission was not caught during inspections [Ross, 1984]. This, and other omissions, further weakened an already inadequate design.

In the aftermath of the accident, Lev Zetlin Associates, another civil engineering firm, was hired to investigate the reasons for the collapse. Their major findings indicate that

- The exterior top chord compression members on the east and west faces were overloaded by as much as 852%.
- The exterior top chord compression members on the south and north faces were overloaded by as much as 213%.
- The interior top chord compression members in the east–west direction were overloaded by as much as 72% [Ross, 1984].

They also noted a discrepancy in the weight of the space frame: the designer's estimate was that the frame would weigh 18 pounds per square foot, while in reality the weight was 23 pounds per square foot, a 20% difference [Ross, 1984]. As finished, the capacity of the roof was to have been 140 pounds per square foot. It was estimated that with the snowfall the night of the collapse, the roof and frame load was no more than 73 pounds per square foot. Clearly, this design which relied so heavily on computer-aided analysis was inadequate.

KEY TERMS   Conflict of interest   Confidentiality   Whistleblowing

REFERENCES

Charles E. Harris, Jr., Michael S. Pritchard, and Michael J. Rabins, *Engineering Ethics, Concepts and Cases*, Wadsworth Publishing Company, Belmont, CA, 2000.

Roland Schinzinger and Mike W. Martin, *Introduction to Engineering Ethics*, McGraw-Hill, New York, 2000.

Boris Rauschenbakh, "Computer War," in *Breakthrough; Emerging New Thinking*, A. Gomyko and M. Hellman, Eds., Walker, New York, 1988.

BART

Robert M. Anderson, *Divided Loyalties*, Purdue University Press, West Lafayette, IN, 1980.

Gordon D. Friedlander, "The Grand Scheme," *IEEE Spectrum*, Sept. 1972, p. 35.

Gordon D. Friedlander, "BART's Hardware—from Bolts to Computers," *IEEE Spectrum*, Oct. 1972, p. 60.

Gordon D. Friedlander, "More BART Hardware," *IEEE Spectrum*, Nov. 1972, p. 41.

Gordon D. Friedlander, "Bigger Bugs in BART?," *IEEE Spectrum*, March 1973, pp. 32–37.

Gordon D. Friedlander, "A Prescription for BART," *IEEE Spectrum*, April 1973, pp. 40–44.

Goodrich A7-D Brake

John Fiedler, "Give Goodrich a Break," *Business and Professional Ethics Journal*, vol.7, Spring 1988, p. 21.

Kermit Vandivier, "Why should my conscience bother me?", in Robert Heilbroner, Ed., *In the Name of Profit*, Doubleday, 1972.

Kermit Vandivier, "The Aircraft Brake Scandal," *Harpers Magazine*, April 1972, p. 45.

The Therac-25 Accidents

Nancy Leveson, and Clark S. Turner, "An Investigation of the Therac-25 Accidents," IEEE Computer, vol 26, No. 7, July 1993, pg. 18.

Steven M. Casey, "Set Phasors on Stun, and Other True Tales of Design, Technology, and Human Error," Aegean Publishing Company, 1993, pg. 13.

The Hartford Civic Center Collapse

Rachel Martin, and Norbert J. Delatte, "Another Look at the Hartford Civic Center Coliseum Collapse," *Journal of Performance of Constructed Facilities,* vol. 1, no. 1 (February, 2001), pp. 31–35.

Steven S. Ross, *"Construction Disasters: Design Failures, Causes, and Prevention,"* McGraw-Hill, New York, NY, 1984.

Time Magazine," The Night the Roof Fell In," *Time* magazine, Jan. 30, 1978.

PROBLEMS

1   An engineer leaves a company and goes to work for a competitor.

(a) Is it ethical for the engineer to try to lure customers away from the previous employer?

(b) Is it alright for the engineer to use proprietary knowledge gained while working for the previous employer at the new job? How would the answer to this question change if the new job weren't for a competitor?

    (c) At the new job, is it acceptable for the engineer to use skills developed during his previous employment?

2 If you are an engineer working for a state highway department with the responsibility for overseeing and regulating construction companies that work for the state, is it a conflict of interest to leave the state and accept a position with a construction company that you formerly regulated as a government relations manager? Is the opposite acceptable: leaving a private company to take a position in government regulating that company? How about if you have substantial stock in the company in a pension or other plan?

3 You are an engineer who has taken a new job with a competitor of your previous company. At a meeting you attend, a research engineer describes her plans for developing a new product similar to one developed by your former company. You know that the direction this engineer is taking will be a dead end and will cost the company a lot of time and money. Do you tell her what you know? Does the answer to this question change if the new company is not a direct competitor of the previous one?

4 You are a civil engineer working for an engineering consulting firm and have just finished work on a new bridge project. This project involved some innovative designs developed by you and other engineers in the firm. You have decided that you now have enough experience to start your own consulting firm. The first project that comes to you is a bridge. Can you use the innovation pioneered at your previous firm in this new design? How does this situation differ from that in Question 3?

BART

5 BART was a very innovative design that went well beyond other mass transit systems then in existence. What guidance does "accepted engineering practice" provide in such an innovative design?

6 When pointing out safety problems, an engineer is rightfully concerned about maintaining his job. However, how effective is an anonymous memo? Can anyone be expected to pay attention to something that a person won't sign?

7 Did the three engineers meet the criteria for whistleblowing discussed previously in this chapter?

8 Should the IEEE have intervened in the court case?

9 In what ways could the BART structure and chain of command have been changed to make the whistleblowing unnecessary?

10 At what point should an engineer give up expressing her concerns? In this case, when several levels of management appeared not to share the engineers' concerns, how much more effort does professional ethics dictate is necessary?

11 What level of supervision should an organization have over its contractors? Is it sufficient to assume that they are professional and will do a good job?

12 One of the perceived problems with BART was a lack of adequate documentation from Westinghouse. What are the ethical considerations regarding the documentation of work? What responsibility does an engineering organization have after the design is complete?

13 It is important to remember that from our perspective, it is impossible to know whether the Westinghouse test procedures and schedule were adequate. The subsequent accidents and problems really don't tell us much about this issue: Anything new and this complex should be expected to have some bugs during the early periods of operation. Given this understanding, were the engineers' concerns adequately addressed by management? What actions short of going to the board and whistleblowing might the engineers have taken?

Goodrich A7-D Brake

14   Was an unethical act taking place when test results on the brake were falsified?

15   Was this mitigated at all by the fact that Goodrich was planning to redesign the brakes anyway?

16   Was this mitigated by the fact that the brake design was a new one for which the old test methods might not be applicable? This was a claim by Goodrich. If the old test methods were not applicable to the new design, what should Goodrich have done?

17   Can some of the problem here be attributable to sloppy management? For example, should the original designer be allowed to hand off the test work to a new hire with no further participation? What are the ethical implications of this type of management?

18   Did Vandivier meet the criteria set out in the previous section for whistle-blowing? In other words, was there need for the whistle to be blown? Did he have proximity? Was he capable? Was it a last resort? Does the fact that nothing seems to have been done to Goodrich following the Senate investigation change your answer?

19   What could Goodrich have done to solve the problem without public disclosure of the falsified tests?

20   Was Goodrich engaged in a "bait and switch?" In other words, did it use claims about the innovative brake design as a means to get the contract with the intent of ultimately supplying a conventional brake? What is the ethical status of this type of tactic?

The Therac-25 Accidents

21   What do the engineering codes of ethics say about the Therac-25 case?

22   Are engineering codes adequate to analyze this case, or should we look at codes specific to computer professionals such as the codes of the Association for Computing Machinery (ACM)?

23   The Therac-25 evolved from earlier models of the machine. How should engineers safeguard against safety hazards when new designs are derived from older designs?

24   What is the appropriate balance between hardware and software safety features in an engineered system?

25   Engineers often have training in the basics of computer code writing. Sometimes engineers acquire considerable software expertise through on-the-job learning. When can an engineer trained in this way write and test software, and when should a software expert be called in?

The Hartford Civic Center Collapse

26   How does an engineer ensure that the software he is using is applicable to the problem he's working on?

27   When discussing computers, it is often said, "Garbage in, garbage out." This expression indicates that if a wrong number is inserted into a calculation, then a wrong answer will result. What methods can be used to verify that the results of a computer analysis or design are correct?

28   If a design is innovative and outside the realm of accepted engineering practice, what steps should be taken to ensure that a computer-generated design or analysis is adequate?

9

Ethical Issues in Engineering Practice

Objectives

After reading this chapter, you will be able to

● Determine what ethical issues arise in engineering practice with regard to the environment

● Decide how engineering practice is impacted by computer technology, and

● Learn about ethical issues that arise in the course of research.

Between June of 1985 and January of 1987 at least six patients receiving treatment using the Therac-25 were exposed to high doses of radiation, leading to serious injury or death. The Therac-25 was a radiation therapy machine capable of irradiating tumors with either electrons or X-rays. Based on earlier versions of the machine, the Therac-25 was the first to incorporate significant computer controls.

The use of radiation for treating cancer is a well-established medical tool. Machines have been developed that deliver precisely controlled doses to tumors and the surrounding tissue without causing harm to healthy tissue in the patient. The Therac-25 was one of these machines and was based on earlier models produced by the same company. These machines had successfully treated thousands of patients. The problem with the Therac-25 was that the computer software used to control the machine and monitor the dose delivered to the patient was inadequate. Under certain circumstances, the software allowed the machine to be energized when it wasn't in the correct configuration. When this happened, patients could receive doses orders of magnitude larger than planned. Investigations in these cases determined that accepted standards for writing, testing, and documenting the software that controlled the Therac-25 had not been followed, directly leading to the accidents.

During the course of their careers, engineers frequently use computers and software in performing design and analysis, or incorporate these into systems they design. Computers don't really create new ethical issues in engineering practice. However, computers do create news ways in which ethical issues confront engineers. In this chapter, we will look at the special ethical challenges that computers present to engineering professionals.

1 INTRODUCTION

Many engineers will become involved in research and experimentation in the course of their academic and professional careers. Even engineers who are not employed in research laboratories or academic settings can be involved in research and development work or the testing of a new product or design. In this chapter, we will examine some of the unique ethical issues that are encountered in research.

2 ENVIRONMENTAL ETHICS

One of the most important political issues of the late 20th century has been environmental protection and the rise of the environmental movement. This movement has sought to control the introduction of toxic and unnatural substances into the environment, to protect the integrity of the biosphere, and to ensure a healthy environment for humans. Engineers are responsible in part for the creation of the technology that has led to damage of the environment and are also working to find solutions to the problems caused by modern technology. The environmental movement has led to an increased awareness among engineers that they have a responsibility to use their knowledge and skills to help protect the environment. This duty is even spelled out in many of the engineering codes of ethics.

Sometimes the engineer's responsibility for the environment is denoted with phrases such as "sustainable design" or "green engineering." These concepts incorporate ideas about ensuring that our designs do not harm the environment. By using sustainable design principles, engineers will help to maintain the integrity of the environment and ensure that our quality of life can be sustained. Sustainable design includes not only ensuring that a product has minimal environmental impact during its use, but also that it can be manufactured and disposed of without harming the natural world. These concepts have been incorporated into some of the engineering codes of ethics which specifically use the word "sustainable."

As concern about the environment has grown, ethicists have turned their attention to the ethical dimensions of environmentalism. In the late 1960s, an area of study called environmental ethics was formulated, seeking to explore the ethical roots of the environmental movement and to understand what ethics tells us about our responsibility to the environment.

Fundamental to discussing ethical issues in environmentalism is a determination of the moral standing of the environment. Our Western ethical tradition is anthropocentric, meaning that only human beings have moral standing. Animals and plants are important only in respect to their usefulness to humans. This type of thinking is often evident even within the environmental movement when a case is sometimes made for the protection of rare plants based on their potential for providing new medicines. If animals, trees, and other components of the environment have no moral standing, then we have no ethical obligations toward them beyond maintaining their usefulness to humans. There are, however, other ways to view the moral standing of the environment.

One way to explore the environment's moral status is to try to answer some questions regarding the place of humans in our environment. Do we belong to nature, or does nature belong to us? If animals can suffer and feel pain like humans, should they have moral standing? If animals have moral standing, how far does this moral standing then extend to other life forms, such as trees? Clearly, these questions are not easily answered, and not everyone will come to the same conclusions. However, there are significant numbers of people who feel that the environment, and specifically animals and plants, do have standing beyond their usefulness to humans. In one form, this view holds that humans are just one component of the environment and that all components have equal standing. For those who hold this view, it is an utmost duty of everyone to do what is required to maintain a healthy biosphere for its own sake.

Regardless of the goal (i.e., either protecting human health or protecting the overall health of the biosphere for its own sake), there are multiple approaches that can be taken to resolving environmental problems. Interestingly, these approaches mirror the general approaches to ethical problem solving. The first approach is sometimes referred to as the "cost-oblivious approach" [Martin and Schinzinger, 2000]. In this approach, cost is not taken into account, but rather the environment is made as clean as possible. No level of environmental degradation is seen as acceptable. This approach bears a striking resemblance to rights and duty ethics. There are obvious problems with this approach. It is difficult to uphold, especially in a modern urbanized society. It is also very difficult to enforce, since the definition of "as clean as possible" is hard to agree on, and being oblivious to cost isn't practical in any realistic situation, in which there are not infinite resources to apply to a problem.

A second approach is based on cost–benefit analysis, which is derived from utilitarianism. Here, the problem is analyzed in terms of the benefits derived by reducing the pollution—improvements in human health, for example—and the costs required to solve the problem. The costs and benefits are weighed to determine the optimum combination. In this approach, the goal is not to achieve a completely clean environment, but rather to achieve an economically beneficial balance of pollution with health or environmental considerations.

There are problems associated with the cost–benefit approach. First, there is an implicit assumption in cost–benefit analysis that cost is an important issue. But what is the true cost of a human life or the loss of a species or a scenic view? These values are difficult, if not impossible, to determine. Second, it is difficult to accurately assess costs and benefits, and much guesswork must go into these calculations. Third, this approach doesn't necessarily take into account who shoulders the costs and who gets the benefits. This is frequently a problem with the siting of landfills and other waste dumps. The cheapest land is in economically disadvantaged areas, where people don't necessarily have the political clout, education, or money required to successfully oppose a landfill in their neighborhood. Although dumps have to go somewhere, there should be some attempt to share the costs as well as share the benefits of an environmentally questionable project. Finally, cost–benefit analysis doesn't necessarily take morality or ethics into account. The only considerations are costs and benefits, with no room for a discussion of whether what is being done is right or not.

Given the complexity of these issues, what then are the responsibilities of the engineer to the environment? When looking at the environmental aspects of his work, an engineer can appeal to both professional and personal ethics to make a decision. Of course, the minimal requirement is that the engineer must follow the applicable federal, state, and municipal laws and regulations.

Professional codes of ethics tell us to hold the safety of people and the environment to be of paramount importance. So clearly, engineers have a responsibility to ensure that their work is conducted in the most environmentally safe manner possible. This is true certainly from the perspective of human health, but for those who feel that the environment has moral standing of its own, the responsibility to protect the environment is clear. Often, this responsibility must be balanced somewhat by consideration of the economic well-being of our employer, our family, and our community.

Our personal ethics can also be used to determine the best course when we are confronted with an environmental problem. Most of us have very strong beliefs about the need to protect the environment. Although these beliefs may come into conflict with our employer's desires, we have the right and duty to strongly express our views on what is acceptable. As we will see later in this chapter, as professionals, engineers have the right to express their opinions on moral issues such as the environment. An engineer should not be compelled by his employer to work on a project that he finds ethically troubling, including projects with severe environmental impacts.

In trying to decide what the most environmentally acceptable course of action is, it is also important to remember that a basic tenet of professional engineering codes of ethics states that an engineer should not make decisions in areas in which he isn't competent. For many environmental issues, engineers aren't competent to make decisions, but should instead seek the counsel of others—such as biologists, public health experts, and physicians—who have the knowledge to help analyze and understand the possible environmental consequences of a project.

3 COMPUTER ETHICS

Computers have rapidly become a ubiquitous tool in engineering and business. There are ways in which computers have brought benefits to society. Unfortunately, there are also numerous ways in which computers have been misused, leading to serious ethical issues. The engineer's roles as designer, manager, and user of computers bring with them a responsibility to help foster the ethical use of computers.

We will see that the ethical issues associated with computers are really just variations on other issues dealt with in this book. For example, many ethical problems associated with computer use relate to unauthorized use of information stored on computer databases and are thus related to the issues of confidentiality and proprietary information discussed in section 6.2. Ethical problem-solving techniques used for other engineering ethics problems are equally applicable to computer ethics issues.

There are two broad categories of computer ethics problems: those in which the computer is used to commit an unethical act, such as the use of a computer to hack into a datebase and those in which the computer is used as an engineering tool, but is used improperly.

3.1 Computers as a Tool for Unethical Behavior

Our discussion of computer ethics will start with an examination of ways in which computers are used as the means for unethical behavior. Many of these uses are merely extensions to computers of other types of unethical acts. For example, computers can be used to more efficiently steal money from a bank. A more traditional bank-robbery method is to put on a mask, hand a note to a bank teller, show your gun, and walk away with some cash. Computers can be used to make bank robbery easier to perform and harder to trace. The robber simply sits at a computer terminal—perhaps the modern equivalent of a mask—invades the bank's computer system, and directs that some of the bank's assets be placed in a location accessible to him. Using a computer, a criminal can also make it difficult for the theft to be detected and traced.

It is clear that from an ethical standpoint, there is no difference between a bank robbery perpetrated in person or one perpetrated via a computer, although generally the amounts taken in a computer crime far exceed those taken in an armed robbery. The difference between these two types of robbery is that the use of the computer makes the crime impersonal. The criminal never comes face to face with the victim. In addition, the use of the computer makes it easier to steal from a wide variety of people. Computers can be used to steal from an employer: Outsiders can get into a system and steal from an institution such as a bank, or a company can use the computer to steal from its clients and customers. In these cases, the computer has only made the theft easier to perpetrate, but does not alter the ethical issues involved. Unfortunately, the technology to detect and prevent this type of crime greatly lags behind the computer technology available to commit it. Those seeking to limit computer crime are always playing a catch-up game.

Similar computer ethics issues arise with regard to privacy. It is widely held that certain information is private and cannot be divulged without consent. This includes information about individuals as well as corporate information. Computers did not create the issues involved in privacy, but they certainly have exacerbated them. Computers make privacy more difficult to protect, since large amounts of data on individuals and corporations are centrally stored on computers where an increasing number of individuals can access it. Before we look at the ways that privacy can be abused by the use of computers, we will discuss the issues surrounding privacy and see what the ethical standing of privacy is.

By privacy, we mean the basic right of an individual to control access to and use of information about himself [Martin and Schinzinger, 2000]. Why is privacy an ethical issue? Invasions of privacy can be harmful to an individual in two ways. First, the leaking of private information can lead to an individual's being harassed or blackmailed. In its simplest form, this harassment may come in the form of repeated phone calls from telemarketers who have obtained information about an individual's spending habits. The harassment might also come in the form of subtle teasing or bothering from a coworker who has gained personal knowledge of the individual. Clearly, individuals have the right not to be subjected to this type of harassment. Second, personal information can also be considered personal property. As such, any unauthorized use of this information is theft. This same principle applies to proprietary information of a corporation.

How do computers increase the problems with privacy protection? This phenomenon is most easily seen by looking at the old system of record keeping. For example, medical records of individuals were at one time kept only on paper and generally resided with the individual's physician and in hospitals where a patient had been treated. Access to these records by researchers, insurance companies, or other healthcare providers was a somewhat laborious process involving searching through storage for the appropriate files, copying them, and sending them through the mail. Unauthorized use of this information involved breaking into the office where the files were kept and stealing them or, for those who had access to the files, surreptitiously removing the files. Both of these acts involved a substantial risk of being caught and prosecuted. Generally, these records have now been computerized. Although computerization makes the retrieval of files much easier for those with legitimate needs and reduces the space required to store the files, it also makes the unauthorized use of this information by others easier.

Ethical issues also arise when computers are used for "hacking." This has been widely reported in the newspapers and in popular culture, sometimes with the "hacker" being portrayed as heroic. Hacking comes in many forms: gaining unauthorized access to a database, implanting false information in a database or altering existing information, and disseminating viruses over the Internet.

These activities are by no means limited to highly trained computer specialists. Many hackers are bored teenagers seeking a challenge. Computer hacking is clearly ethically troublesome. As mentioned before, accessing private information violates the privacy rights of individuals or corporations, even if the hacker keeps this information to himself. In extreme cases, hackers have accessed secret military information, which has obvious implications for national security. Altering information in a database, even information about yourself, is also ethically troubling, especially if the alteration has the intent of engaging in a fraud.

The issuance of computer viruses is also unethical. These viruses frequently destroy data stored on computers. In extreme cases, this act could lead to deaths when hospital records or equipment are compromised, to financial ruin for individuals whose records are wiped out, or even to the loss of millions of dollars for corporations, individuals, and taxpayers, as completed work must be redone after being destroyed by a virus.

Oftentimes, hackers are not being malicious, but are simply trying to "push the envelope" and see what they and their computers are capable of. Nevertheless, hacking is an unethical use of computers.

Copyright infringement is also a concern in computer ethics. Computers and the internet have made it easy to share music, movies, software, and other copyrighted materials. A full discussion of the issues surrounding copyright is beyond the scope of this text. Briefly, copyright exists to protect the rights of authors, musicians, and others to profit from their creations. Copyright gives the creator the exclusive right to profit from his or her creation. The protection of copyright has become increasingly difficult as court cases related to music sharing websites such as Napster and other copycat websites have illustrated. Although computers make copyright violation easy to do and hard to detect, it is still illegal and unethical. If creators can no longer profit from their work—if their work is freely distributed without their consent—then the incentive to create will diminish and this type of creative activity that enriches everyone's lives will diminish as well. There are those who advocate eliminating copyright altogether, mostly from the practical standpoint that modern technology makes copyright impossible to enforce and therefore useless. Nevertheless, copying music or software without permission of the owner of the copyright is illegal and unethical.

3.2 Computers as an Engineering Tool

Computers are an essential tool for all engineers. Most often, we use computers for writing documents using a word processing software package. We also keep track of appointments with scheduling software, use spreadsheets to make financial calculations, databases to keep records of our work, and use commercially available software to develop plans for how our projects will proceed. The use of these types of software is not unique to engineering—indeed, they are useful in various areas of business. Unique to engineering are two uses of computers: as design tools and as components integrated into engineered systems.

Computer Design Tools

Numerous software packages are available for the design of engineered devices and structures. This software includes CAD/CAM, circuit analysis, finite element analysis, structural analysis, and other modeling and analysis programs. Software also exists that is designed to aid in the process of testing engineered devices by performing tests, recording data, and presenting data for analysis. These all serve to allow an engineer to work more efficiently and to help take away some of the tedious aspects of an engineer's work. However, the use of this type of software also leads to ethical issues.

For example, who is responsible when a flaw in software used to design a bridge leads to the failure of the bridge? Is it the fault of the engineer who designed the bridge? Or is it the fault of the company that designed and sold the defective software? Who is at fault when a software package is used for a problem that it isn't really suited for? What happens when existing software is used on a new and innovative engineering design that software hasn't yet been developed for?

These questions all have the same answer: Software can never be a substitute for good engineering judgment. Clearly, the engineer who uses software in the design process is still responsible for the designs that were generated and the testing that was done using a computer. In order to do this, engineers must be careful to make sure that the software is appropriate to the problem being worked on, and should be knowledgeable about the limitations and applicability of a software package. Engineers must also keep up to date on any flaws that have been discovered in the software and ensure that the most recent version of the software is being used—software companies make patches and updates available, and engineers must check to make sure they have the most up-to-date version. Finally, it is important to verify the results of a computer-generated design or analysis. Sometimes it's a great idea to sit down with a piece of paper and a pencil to make sure that the output of a computer program makes sense and is giving the right answer.

Computer software can also give an engineer the illusion that he is qualified to do a design in fields beyond his expertise. Software can be so easy to use that you might imagine that by using it, you are competent in the area that it is designed for. However, it takes an expert in a field to understand the limitations and appropriate use of software in any engineering design.

Integration of Computers into Engineered Systems

Computers have also become a component of many engineered systems. For example, modern automobiles contain multiple computers, dedicated to specific tasks. Computers control the emissions and braking systems on automobiles, and allow modern vehicles to operate more efficiently and safely. However, the ability to control aspects of system performance using software removes humans from the control loop. There are numerous examples of situations in which computerized systems malfunctioned without giving the operator any indication that a problem existed. In some cases, the operator was unable to intervene to solve a problem because the software design wouldn't allow it. It is essential when designing systems with embedded computers and software that engineers ensure that software is adequately tested, that humans can intervene when necessary, and that safety systems have enough hardware redundancy without relying solely on software to ensure the safe operation of the system.

3.3 Autonomous Computers

Other ethical concerns arise because of the increasingly autonomous nature of computers. Autonomy refers to the ability of a computer to make decisions without the intervention of humans. Some of the negative implications of this autonomy are chillingly spelled out in *2001: A Space Odyssey*, by Arthur C. Clarke, in which an autonomous computer responsible for running a spaceship headed for Jupiter begins to turn against the humans it was designed to work for. Certainly, there are applications for which autonomy is valuable. For example, manufacturing processes that require monitoring and control at frequent intervals can greatly benefit from autonomous computers. In this case, the autonomy of the computer has very little impact beyond the interests of the manufacturer.

Other autonomous computer applications are not so benign. For example, by the 1980s, computers were widely used to automate trading on the major U.S. stock exchanges. Some brokerages and institutional investors utilized computers that were programmed to sell stocks automatically under certain conditions, among them when prices drop sharply. This type of programming creates an unstable situation. As prices drop, computers automatically start selling stocks, further depressing the prices, causing other computers to sell, and so on until there is a major market crash.

This scenario actually occurred on October 19, 1987, when the Dow Jones Industrial Average (a widely used market-price indicator) dropped by 508 points, a 22.6% drop in the overall value of the market. Interestingly, during the famous October 1929 stock market crash that launched the Great Depression, the percent drop in overall market value was only half of this amount. The 1987 crash was widely attributed to automated computer trading. Federal regulations have since been implemented to help prevent a recurrence of this problem.

Autonomy of computer systems has also been called into question with regard to military weapons. Many weapons systems rely heavily on computer sensors and computer controls. Due to the speed with which events can happen on a modern battlefield, it would seem valuable to have weapons that can operate autonomously. However, weapons systems operating without human intervention can suffer from the instability problems described with regard to the financial markets. For example, a malfunctioning sensor might lead a computer to think that an enemy has increased its military activity in a certain area. This would lead to an increased readiness on our part, followed by increased activity by the enemy, etc. This unstable situation could lead to a conflict and the loss of life when really there was nothing happening [Rauschenbakh, 1988]. This problem is of special concern due to the implications for the loss of human life. It is clear from this example that although autonomous computers can greatly increase productivity and efficiency in many areas, ultimately there must be some human control in order to prevent disasters.

3.4 Computer Codes of Ethics

To aid with decision making regarding these and other computer-related ethics issues, many organizations have developed codes of ethics for computer use. The purposes of ethical codes and the way in which codes of ethics function are equally true for codes related to computer use. They are guidelines for the ethical use of computing resources, but should not be used as a substitute for sound moral reasoning and judgement. They do, however, provide some guidance in the proper use of computer equipment.

APPLICATION

Cases

Avanti Corp. vs. Cadence Design Systems

One of the most important assets a high-technology company can have is its intellectual property. Intellectual property includes new inventions, innovative ways of producing products, and computer codes. Intellectual property can be protected through the patent and trademark system of the federal government, or simply by maintaining "trade secrets." How computer software fits into the intellectual property protection scheme has been slowly developing. At first, software could not be patented, and it was unclear whether it could receive a copyright either. More recently, federal patent law has changed to allow software to be patented. Patenting does provide protection for intellectual property for a period of time, but in order to gain this protection, a software developer must divulge the code. This makes it easy for competitors to use ideas from the patent by designing around it. The best way to protect intellectual property is to keep it a trade secret.

Cadence Design Systems is the largest supplier of electronic design automation (EDA) products. Among other things, EDA products are used to do the layout of complex integrated circuits. EDA products are used by the various computer chip manufacturers. Avanti Corporation is a rival company in this field. In December of 1995, the headquarters of Avanti was raided by police and FBI agents looking for evidence that trade secrets belonging to Cadence had been stolen by Avanti and incorporated into Avanti products. Specifically, Cadence claimed that up to 60,000 lines of code developed by its own software engineers had been used by Avanti. Cadence also filed a civil suit seeking damages from Avanti. In 1997, eight Avanti employees, including the chairman of the board, were indicted on criminal charges in the case. All of those who were indicted were former Cadence employees.

In order to understand the implications of this case, it is important to set it in the context of the high-tech industry in the United States. Both Cadence and Avanti are located in the Silicon Valley region of California. It is common for employees of one company to quit and move to a competing company just down the street. It is also common for a group of employees of a large company to leave and start a new company in the same field. It is often hard to determine the dividing line between skills and information learned at a former job and intellectual property belonging to your former employer.

The legal proceedings continued for several years, including a 1997 ruling by a court barring the sales of Avanti products containing the disputed computer code. The criminal cases culminated in a plea of "no contest" by seven of the Avanti defendants. (Charges against the eighth had already been dropped.) A no-contest plea is not an admission of guilt, but is an acknowledgment that if the case goes to trial, the defendant would likely be convicted. Five of the defendants faced jail time, one up to six years. All received various fines, some in the millions of dollars. In a separate civil case, Cadence sought hundreds of millions of dollars in compensation from Avanti for the use of Cadence's intellectual property.

4 ETHICS AND RESEARCH

There are two major ethical issues related to research: honesty in approaching the research problem and honesty in reporting the results. The first relates to a state of mind essential to successfully performing research. This state of mind includes avoiding preconceived notions about what the results will be, being open to changing the hypothesis when such action is warranted by the evidence, and generally ensuring that an objective frame of mind is maintained. As we will see in the cases at the end of this chapter, this attitude is not necessarily easy to assume, but it is essential to producing useful research or test results. More will be said about this topic later in this chapter in the section on pathological science.

Results must also be accurately reported. Once an experiment or test has been performed, the results of the experiment must not be overstated, but rather an accurate assessment and interpretation of the data must be given. The environment that most researchers work in fosters temptations and rewards for overstating research results. Academic researchers must publish significant research results in order to get tenure at their universities. If an experiment isn't working out, it is tempting to "massage" the results to achieve the desired outcome. Even for researchers in industrial environments or faculty who are already tenured, the quest for fame or the desire to be the first with new results can be overwhelming and can lead to falsification of data. Often, the pressure to get a new product to market leads the test engineer to "fudge" data to qualify the product.

It is important to note the distinction between intentional deception and results or interpretations that are simply incorrect. Sometimes, results are published that, upon further research, turn out to be incorrect. This situation is not an ethical issue unless a clarification of the results is never presented. Rather, this issue indicates that great care must be taken before results are initially reported.

It is also important to ensure that proper credit is given to everyone who participated in a research project. Rarely is research performed by a single investigator working alone in her laboratory. Generally, there is participation by other people, who should be acknowledged for their contributions such as discussions or guidance, construction of experimental apparatus, or substantial help with performing experiments or interpreting data.

It is tempting to think that fraud and deception in research are rare and only perpetrated by lower level scientists, but this perception is decidedly untrue. There are many examples of well-known and even Nobel prize–winning scientists who have had lapses of ethical judgement with respect to their research. For example, Robert Millikan was a physicist from the University of Chicago who won the 1923 Nobel Prize in physics for experiments that measured the electrical charge of the electron. Studies of Millikan's unpublished data indicate that he excluded 49 of the 140 experimental observations from the paper that he published [Holton, 1978, and Franklin, 1981]. However, in the paper, he stated that the published work contained all of the data. Inclusion of this data wouldn't have changed his conclusions, but would have made the result seem more certain and the experiment more clearly definitive.

4.1 Analyzing Ethical Problems in Research

How can ethical issues relating to research best be analyzed? Perhaps the easiest means to determine the best ethical course in performing research and experiment is to consult the codes of ethics of the engineering professional societies. All of the codes include language requiring engineers to be honest in reporting the results of work and assigning credit for work done. For example, the code of the American Institute of Chemical Engineers states that "members shall … treat fairly all colleagues and co-workers, recognize the contributions of others …," and "issue statements and present information only in an objective and truthful manner." These statements apply equally well to all professional activities of an engineer, including research, experiment, and testing.

Several ethical theories can be used to analyze issues involving research. Utilitarianism or rights and duty ethics can be applied to research, but it is perhaps easiest to examine research issues using virtue ethics. One of the virtues is honesty. Honesty facilitates trust and good relations between individuals, whereas dishonesty leads to doubts and misgivings about others. People rarely want to associate with those who they feel don't behave fairly and can't be trusted. Making false claims about the results of experiments is certainly a form of dishonesty. We should seek to enhance virtues such as honesty within ourselves and others, so virtue ethics clearly tells us that the inaccurate reporting of experimental results is unethical. Likewise, not giving credit to everyone who has participated in a project is dishonest, and virtue ethics indicates that this practice is unacceptable.

4.2 Pathological Science

As mentioned previously, self-deception is one of the biggest impediments to the successful completion of a research or experimental project. Self-deception in research is a frequent occurrence in many areas of science and has led to some notorious cases throughout history. Irving Langmuir, a well-known physicist working at General Electric Research Laboratories, coined a term for this phenomenon: "pathological science." He proposed the following six characteristics of pathological science [Langmuir, 1968]:

1. The maximum effect that is observed is produced by a causative agent of barely detectable intensity, and the magnitude of the effect is substantially independent of the intensity of the cause.

   This characteristic implies that it doesn't matter how close the causative agent is or how intense it is; the effect is the same. This practice, of course, goes against all known forces and effects.

2. The effect is of a magnitude that remains close to the limit of detectability; or, many measurements are necessary because of the very low statistical significance of the results.

   The problem here is that when things are at the edge of statistical significance or of detectability, the tendency is to discard values that don't "seem" right. To measure anything at the edge of detectability requires a lot of data. With a lot of data to work with, the measurements can be massaged to fit the conclusion that is being sought. In fact, what often happens is that data are rejected on the basis of their incompatibility with the preconceived theory, rather than on their true significance.

3. Claims of great accuracy.

4. Fantastic theories contrary to experience.

5. Criticisms are met by ad hoc excuses thought up on the spur of the moment.

6. Ratio of supporters to critics rises up to somewhere near 50% and then falls gradually to oblivion.

The term "pathological science" doesn't imply any intentional dishonesty, but only that the researcher comes to false conclusions based on a lack of understanding about how easy it is to trick yourself through wishful thinking and subjectivity.

This shows that a great deal of objectivity and care in the pursuit of research or testing is required. Drawing conclusions on very subtle effects is very tricky, and these conclusions should be confirmed by as many colleagues as possible. Ultimately, the goal of research is not publicity and fame, but rather the discovery of new knowledge.

APPLICATION

Cases

The City of Albuquerque vs. Isleta Pueblo Water Case

The city of Albuquerque, New Mexico, straddles the Rio Grande and is bounded on the north and south by two Indian pueblos (reservations). Several other pueblos are nearby. According to federal law, Indian tribes are sovereign nations with the wide-ranging ability to self-regulate and are subject to federal laws and some restrictions imposed by the states. Overall, however, their status is closer to that of an equal of state governments rather than a subordinate.

Isleta Pueblo is located on the Rio Grande, downstream from Albuquerque, and is contiguous to the Albuquerque metropolitan area, which contains approximately

650,000 people. Traditionally, the Pueblo used water directly from the river for drinking during religious ceremonies. In more recent times, this practice has been difficult due to runoff entering the river—storm runoff is directly input to the river—and from treated sewer effluent placed into the river by Albuquerque. Similar effluent is probably discharged into the river by other municipalities farther upstream.

Of great concern to Isleta Pueblo is the concentration of arsenic in the river water. The Albuquerque sewage treatment plant puts water into the Rio Grande that meets all applicable Environmental Protection Agency (EPA) regulations, including the standard for arsenic concentration. Of course, the water placed into the river is not of drinking quality, since it is assumed that any municipality using river water for drinking must treat the water anyway.

Isleta Pueblo has used its sovereign status to try to enforce a stricter water quality standard for the water discharged by Albuquerque and seeks to bring the water quality to the point where it can be consumed directly from the river. This involves a standard for arsenic discharge that is roughly twice as stringent as the EPA regulations permit. The EPA has sided with the pueblo, citing federal law giving Indian reservations the right to set their own pollution standards. This case is analogous to the situation that might occur if Mexico decided that it wanted stricter regulation of the quality of water in the Rio Grande flowing from the United States south along the Mexican border.

The city of Albuquerque has argued that the pueblo's standards are too strict and are unnecessary, since the concentration of arsenic in the water that the city discharges into the river is lower than what naturally exists in the river upstream from Albuquerque, although this point is under debate. Albuquerque contends that the cost of meeting the standard would be prohibitive, approximately $300 million. The city also argues that the standard is a violation of the First Amendment's prohibition of government-established religion. Albuquerque pressed this case all the way to the U. S. Supreme Court, but the court turned down consideration of Albuquerque's appeal in 1997 and thus will allow new EPA arsenic standards based on Isleta's requirements to stand. Albuquerque and other similarly affected municipalities are currently seeking federal government aid in meeting these new standards. Many other states and municipalities, especially in the west, are interested in this case.

The N-Ray Case

After the discovery of X-rays in the late 19th century, there was a great deal of interest among scientists in finding other similar types of rays. Many scientists joined this search in the hopes of achieving the fame that such a discovery would bring. In many ways, this scenario was similar to the frenzy in the scientific community in the 1980s upon the discovery of superconductivity at temperatures above the boiling point of liquid nitrogen. Many researchers dropped everything else they were doing and began searching for new materials with even higher superconducting temperatures, especially hoping to find one at room temperature. The search to find new rays was joined by a well-known French physicist, René Blondlot, at the University of Nancy. His case is discussed in depth in an interesting article published in 1980 by *Scientific American* [Klotz, 1980].

The apparatus used at the time for detecting such rays was the spark gap. This device consisted of two electrodes that were close enough together so that a spark developed between them in air when a large electric potential was applied between them. What we now know as electromagnetic radiation in the form of light or X-rays directed through the spark gap increased the ionization in the gap, increasing the current flow and the brightness of the spark. The brightness of the spark could be used to measure the intensity of the radiation present in the gap. Of course, by modern standards this is a very crude means for detecting X-rays, but at the time, this method was state of the art.

In order to see the change in brightness, care had to be taken in establishing the measuring environment. For example, the researcher had to stay in a darkened room sufficiently long so that his eyes would become dark adapted. Even then, the change in intensity of the spark could be very subtle, and care had to be taken to be honest in the assessment of the change.

In 1903, Professor Blondlot was working with gas discharges that produced the newly discovered X-rays. His previous experience was in the study of electromagnetic phenomena, and he was hoping to discover if X-rays were a wave or particle by determining if the X-rays could be polarized as visible light can be. Using a spark gap and an apparatus similar to the one that Roentgen had used to discover X-rays, Blondlot attempted to determine the polarization of X-rays by rotating the spark gap in the X-ray field. In his initial study, Blondlot discovered that, indeed, the spark gap became brighter when rotated to a certain angle with respect to the discharge tube. This was an important discovery.

Subsequent experiments indicated that the radiation impinging on the spark gap could be bent by a quartz prism. This feature was a major problem, since X-rays had already been shown by many scientists to be unaffected by lenses and prisms. The fact that the radiation he was measuring appeared to be bent by the prism convinced Blondlot that he had discovered a new form of radiation that he called N-rays (for the University of Nancy). He quickly published this work.

The reports of the discovery of a new type of ray set off a flurry of activity in other laboratories around the world, and Blondlot himself continued to study the phenomenon. Many discoveries were made about N-rays: Materials were found that transmitted them (metals, wood, mica, quartz) and some that didn't transmit the rays (water and rock salt). Natural sources of N-rays were also discovered, including the sun and the human body. Despite the explosion of research on N-rays, there were also some doubts about Blondlot's findings. Many researchers outside of France, including Lord Kelvin in England, had been unable to reproduce the results reported by Blondlot.

Prof. J. W. Wood of Johns Hopkins University was also unable to reproduce the results and traveled to Nancy to observe the experiments firsthand. In a paper published in *Nature,* he described the experiments that he had witnessed. Wood reported that when he observed the spark gap and someone placed a hand in the path of the N-rays, Wood didn't see the expected changes in intensity. Told that his eyes weren't sensitive enough, he exchanged positions with the French researchers and placed his hand in the path. The research team incorrectly reported whether his hand was in or out of the beam as they claimed to see changes in intensity. Wood reported that there was no correlation between the position of his hand and their reports of intensity.

Wood also observed a different experiment designed to spread the N-rays into a spectrum. The dispersion of the N-rays was accomplished using an aluminum prism and was observed using a thin phosphor strip painted onto a cardboard screen. Wood was unable to observe the variations in intensity from the phosphor that the French team claimed to see. Indeed, when Wood surreptitiously removed the prism from the apparatus, the researchers still claimed to see the effect! Wood was convinced after this incident that there were no N-rays and that the researchers had deluded themselves.

Publication of Wood's findings ended research into N-rays everywhere except in France. Blondlot responded to the criticisms and continued to present results of new, more controlled experiments. He even published a set of instructions for properly observing the phenomenon. For example, the instructions stated that the observer had to avoid gazing directly at the spark gap and instead had to look at it obliquely. The observer had to remain silent, avoid smoke, and had to look at the detector in the "way an impressionist painter would view a landscape" [Klotz, 1980]. Acquisition of this ability required a great deal of practice and might be impossible for some people. In other words, the key to the measurement was the sensitivity of the observer, rather than the validity of the phenomena. As more research was performed, it became clear even to the French that there were no N-rays.

The Case of Cold Fusion at Texas A&M University

On March 23, 1989, Stanley Pons and Martin Fleischmann of the University of Utah announced that they had produced excess heat in a tabletop electrochemical cell. The excess heat was presumed to be due to nuclear fusion, and the process was dubbed "cold fusion." Pons and Fleischmann's results were widely reported in newscasts and daily newspapers and led to great excitement among scientists around the world.

The apparatus used by Pons and Fleischmann was a fairly standard electrochemical cell. They found that when palladium electrodes were immersed in heavy water (water with the normal hydrogen atoms replaced by the heavier deuterium isotope) and an electric current run through them, heat far in excess of levels expected was produced. This heat production was attributed to the breakdown of the heavy water due to electrolysis, diffusion of the deuterium into the palladium, where the deuterium was thought to get to a density sufficient to initiate fusion, leading to the release of the excess heat.

Although Pons and Fleischmann were well-respected electrochemists, their results were treated with great skepticism by many scientists, especially those who had worked in conventional fusion and nuclear physics. This skepticism arose because, according to the contemporary understanding of the fusion process, the reaction of deuterium should produce copious amounts of tritium (another hydrogen isotope) and neutrons. Neither of these products was seen in the Pons–Fleischmann experiments. The response of many of the believers in cold fusion to this criticism was that they had discovered some new form of fusion that didn't behave according to the old rules. Indeed, there were some claims of professional jealousy: Physicists who had worked for years to make conventional fusion practical would not be happy to be upstaged by chemists who couldn't possibly know anything about fusion. Despite the controversy, the potential benefits if this process proved to be real were so enormous that many researchers worldwide began setting up similar electrochemical cells in their laboratories and trying to reproduce the results. John Bockris at Texas A&M University was one of these scientists.

Bockris's research group built electrochemical cells like those of Pons and Fleischmann and set out to verify the Utah work. By April 22, 1989, this group had observed a surprising result. A graduate student working with Bockris, Nigel Packham, had removed samples of the electrolyte from three of the cells in the laboratory and took them to another campus building, the Cyclotron Center, for tritium measurements. Two of the three samples were "hot," containing 10^9 tritium

Stanley Pons and Martin Fleischmann, who started a frenzy in the scientific research community when they announced that they had discovered a way to control nuclear fusion in a tabletop electrochemical cell.
AP/Wide World Photos.

atoms/ml, an amount far in excess of the expected background level. Subsequently, tritium was detected in four more cells.

When this work was reported at scientific meetings, there was immediate concern, since the data was too amazing. More work was performed, designed to control the experimental conditions more carefully, including work by other researchers at Texas A&M. For example, Kevin Wolf, a nuclear chemist, ran a cell in front of neutron detectors in his laboratory, hoping to find the telltale sign that should accompany tritium production. No neutrons were detected, although tritium did appear in the electrolyte when tested. Packham also performed an experiment in which electrolyte samples were taken at four different intervals over twelve hours while the cell was running. At the beginning of the experiment, tritium was at background levels. Two hours later, it was slightly above background level. A few hours later, the level had climbed greatly to 5 trillion atoms, and at 12 hours it had climbed to 7.6 trillion atoms [Taubes, 1990]. Although this data seemed to confirm that tritium was being produced in the cell, skeptics also pointed out that this result was consistent with someone "spiking" the sample with tritium sometime toward the middle of the experiment. Indeed, there was a supply of tritium stored in the laboratory.

In response to these allegations, Bockris and his team failed to take steps to ensure that intentional spiking couldn't occur. Offers to place the experiment in the locked laboratory of colleague Charles Martin, another electrochemist, were refused, and the bottle of tritiated water in the lab was not locked up or thrown away. While Bockris continued his work, Wolf and Martin continued their own similar studies with the same type of cell used by Bockris. Martin even took the precaution of taking cells home to ensure that there would be no sabotage. Martin's cells never showed signs of tritium.

In late September, after nearly three months with no results, two more cells turned up with tritium. The discovery of new cells containing tritium coincided with a scheduled visit from officials of the Electric Power Research Institute (EPRI), which had funded some of the research at Texas A&M. This incident and coincidences with other visits from funding sources cast more suspicion on the tritium results.

On November 27, 1989, Packham, who had not been involved with this work for several months, decided to test samples from two previously untested cells with titanium electrodes. These samples proved to be hot as well. The coincidence was too much for several of the workers in the lab. They took their concerns to Bockris, who dismissed their claims. These scientists subsequently went to other laboratories or sought employment outside the university.

Through most of the controversy, the university had taken a hands-off approach. There had been inquiries of Bockris as to his results and why they appeared so anomalous. However, the university allowed the situation to continue. In June of 1990, Gary Taubes published an article on this situation in *Science*. The negative publicity, especially the statements that the university appeared to be doing nothing, prompted an internal investigation by the university. The three-member panel appointed by the university concluded that intentional spiking of the samples could not be ruled out, but that it was more probable that the results were due to inadvertent contamination or other unexplained problems with the measurements. The panel did find that there were lapses in proper scientific procedure caused by the excitement surrounding the study of a new discovery that was receiving so much media attention. These lapses included categorizing experiments that supported the hypothesis of cold fusion as "successful" and those that didn't support it as "failures" [Pool, 1990].

Unable to reproduce the Pons–Fleischmann results, many researchers stopped their investigations of cold fusion. Funding for this work has dried up, although there are still a few people who believe in the phenomenon and continue to study it. Fraud was certainly a possibility at Texas A&M, although it is unclear who was responsible if this is true. However, all of the researchers were responsible for performing their experiments in an objective manner. In the face of charges of fraud, steps should have been taken to ensure that spiking was not possible. The reputations of senior scientists as well as of students and the university were tarnished by this episode.

Professional Success

Falsifying Experimental Results

Experimental work is an important part of an engineering student's education. It is no surprise that ethical issues often arise in the course of laboratory work. Most ethical issues in experimentation relate to honesty in reporting results. For example, it is often tempting to "massage" data to get the desired result. Or sometimes, it seems easier to "dry run" an experiment by recording measurements and results in your lab book even though you haven't actually performed the experiment. Fundamentally, these are very similar to cheating.

How do you decide what is ethical in experimentation? It is easiest to look at ethical issues related to experimentation using virtue ethics. Honesty is a virtue that should be fostered within ourselves. So, virtue ethics tells us that the utmost care must be taken to ensure that experiments are performed carefully and the results reported honestly.

Computer ethics	Ethics in research	Pathological science	**KEY TERMS**

REFERENCES

Wayne Leibel, "When Scientists are Wrong: Admitting Inadvertent Error in Research," *Journal of Business Ethics,* vol. 10, 1991, pp. 601–604.

Alexander Kohn, *False Prophets*, Basil Blackwell, Oxford, 1986.

Gerald Holton, "Subelectrons, presuppositions, and the Millikan-Ehrenhaft dispute," *Historical Studies in Physical Sciences,* vol. 11, 1978, p. 185.

A. D. Franklin, "Millikan's published and unpublished data on oil drops," *Historical Studies in Physical Sciences,* vol. 58, 1981, p. 293.

Irving Langmuir, "Pathological Science," in R. N. Hall, Ed., General Electric Research and Development Center Report No. 68-C-035, April 1968.

Cadence vs. Avanti

Richard Goering, "Avanti Pleads No Contest," *EE Times*, May 28, 2001, pg. 1.

Isleta Pueblo Water

Tania Soussan, "8 States Watching Water Quality Suit" *Albuquerque Journal*, Section C, June 24, 1997, p. 1.

Tania Soussan, "Isleta's Water Demands Upheld" *Albuquerque Journal*, Section A, Nov. 11, 1997, p. 7.

N-Rays

Irving M. Klotz, "The N-ray Affair," *Scientific American*, May 1980, vol. 242, no. 14, pp. 168–70.

Cold Fusion

Articles in *New York Times*, March 24 and 28, 1989, and numerous subsequent articles. Also, this story was widely reported at the same time in many daily newspapers across the country.

Robert Pool, "Cold Fusion at Texas A&M: Problems, But No Fraud," *Science,* 14 December 1990, vol. 250, pp. 1507–8.

Gary Taubes, "Cold Fusion Conundrum at Texas A&M," *Science*, 15 June 1990, vol. 248, pp. 1299–1304.

PROBLEMS

1   Write a code of ethics for computer use.

2   Is there an ethical obligation to ensure that the information you post on your Internet website is accurate and true? Or is it up to the Web user to be discriminating and to realize that some material might not be accurate?

3   There is much in the news about the use of the Internet to disseminate pornographic images, especially in the context of the availability of this material to children. What ethical issues do "cyberporn" and efforts to limit it raise? Do employers have the right to fire employees who access pornography on their computers at work?

4   Many desktop computers come with games already installed on them. In addition, there are many websites where users can download games onto their computers. Is it alright to play computer games at work? How about during lunch? After hours?

5   Should computer and software designers be concerned about possible abuse of their products? Should designs incorporate methods for preventing the misuse of computers?

6   Is it acceptable for employees to use their computers at work to send and receive personal e-mail?

7   There has been some discussion of having the federal government maintain a computer database of medical information on everyone in the United States. Some medical researchers feel that such a database might save lives by allowing access to a larger base of medical records for research purposes. Certainly, this database would make certain legitimate government functions more efficient. Is this a good idea?

8   How can utilitarianism or rights and duty ethics be applied to issues surrounding the proper conduct of research?

9   Think about ways in which ethical issues regarding experimentation or research have come up during your academic career. Analyze these cases and decide if you handled them ethically or not.

10   Read the papers by Holton and Franklin listed in the references and obtain a copy of Millikan's original paper. Do you think that there are ethical problems in Millikan's actions?

Avanti

11   Suppose you are a user of EDA products. Knowing that the Avanti products contain pirated software, is it ethical to purchase it? Is the answer the same even if the Avanti product is superior to Cadence products?

12   When you move from a company to a competitor, what is your responsibility for protecting your former employer's trade secrets? Does the answer change if your new employer is not in competition with your former employer?

13   How do you separate out skills that you have acquired from previous employers from the previous employer's intellectual property? In other words, where is the dividing line between knowledge and skills you have acquired on the job, and your former employer's trade secrets?

Isleta Pueblo Water

14   What does utilitarianism tell us about this case? What do rights and duty ethics say?

15   Is the religious use of water a valid claim against a municipality? If this were a claim by a large mainline religious denomination (for example, some Christian

denominations might want to use the river for baptisms), does the answer to this question change?

16 Engineers frequently participate in setting standards for pollution limits through consulting with governments. If you were an engineer working for the EPA, what would your advice be? How would this advice change if you worked for the city of Albuquerque? How would this advice change if you worked for Isleta Pueblo?

17 Nearly every municipality in the United States has some pollution problems and controversies. Research a local pollution issue and apply the problem-solving techniques discussed in this book to determine what you think is the ethical solution to the problem.

N-Rays

18 How well is the N-ray case described by Langmuir's six characteristics of pathological science?

19 What ethical mistakes were made by Blondlot and his colleagues in researching N-rays?

20 Once Wood's article was published in *Nature*, what should Blondlot have done?

Cold Fusion

21 How seriously should Bockris have taken the suggestions or charges of fraud made against his results? How seriously should the university have taken these charges?

22 Do some further reading on the early claims about cold fusion. Analyze the claims of Pons and Fleischmann in terms of the description of characteristics of pathological science.

23 Using the code of ethics of one of the engineering professional societies and analyze the behavior of Bockris's research group. According to the code, did this group operate in an ethical manner?

10

Engineering and Communication

1 I AM AN ENGINEER, NOT A PROFESSIONAL COMMUNICATOR

Maybe nobody has told you yet, but the truth is this: To be an engineer is to be a technical communicator. Engineering is a problem-solving profession, and clear communication leads to the effective solutions. As an engineer, you will solve problems for people (often, large groups of people). Whether your specialty is civil, mechanical, electrical, chemical, biomedical, computer, aerospace, or any other engineering discipline, you will develop products, services, and built environments needed by some segment of the public. In order to produce those goods and services, you will work collaboratively with dozens of other engineers, experts, and support personnel, designing, analyzing, refining, and building solutions. You, your collaborators, and your clients will have to understand exactly what each of you is doing every step of the way. That is why communication skills are critical to engineering work.

Communication means writing, speaking, and showing visuals to other people, as well as listening to and observing others and reading their work. Of course, most of us think of writing as the most difficult skill to master (although, for some of us, speaking in front of a crowd seems not only difficult, but also terrifying). Yet, writing well is critical for communicating your ideas and solutions. Let us say you have designed a new type of bus shelter for a large city in a rainy part of the United States. Your design is rendered very professionally, either in CAD or as an artist's rendering, and you have submitted the design to the municipal transportation authority. In addition to presenting the

SECTIONS

OBJECTIVES

By reading this chapter, you will learn the following:

- why writing and speaking well are critical to your success as an engineer;
- how writing and speaking can help you better understand your work as an engineer;
- for whom you will be writing at different times;
- why it is important to present data in a useful format;
- how to write different parts of a document for different audiences.

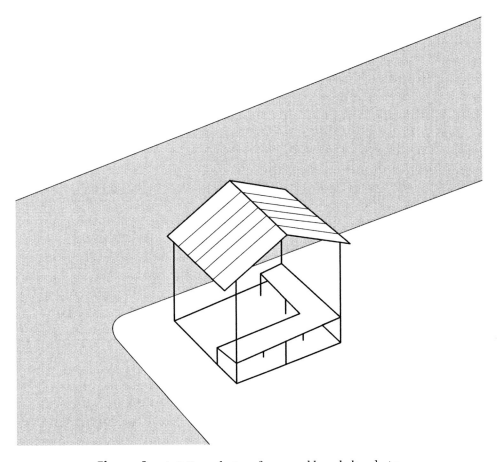

Figure 1. Artist's rendering of proposed bus-shelter design.

design (see Figure 1), you will want to explain in a proposal the main features of the design and the criteria you used to develop it, such as the following:

- Keeps out rain effectively
- Allows enough openness to discourage theft and crime
- Trash does not collect inside

You will use pictures and words to argue that this design should be accepted and built. You may also include a line graph displaying the drop in bus-shelter crime experienced by another city that adopted a similar design. But your design improves on the previous one by being less costly: It can be assembled away from the site and installed on-site within a matter of hours. Sounds good ... but only as good as you make it sound with your words and make it look with your visuals.

Communication is a part of almost every phase of engineering work. This chapter presents some basic tenets to remember throughout your career.

2   WRITING DEMONSTRATES MY COMPETENCE AS AN ENGINEER

Someone can point to a proposal you write for, as an example, a new type of bus shelter and say, "See what a good solution this is; see this clear explanation of how this design solves the problems." Your competence as an architectural engineer is proven by that proposal. The same concept is true for all the engineering disciplines. Inside your own organization as well, writing demonstrates that you understand the work you do and the jobs of the people with whom you work. Even your informal writing, such as memos and e-mail messages, demonstrates this understanding. When you give people truly useful information, you have shown that you know how they will use that information; otherwise, the information would not be useful. People read information in order to discover what they need to do. Whether your intention is to persuade or simply to inform people, your writing must clearly show them what actions are suggested or required.

RESEARCH SHOWS...

Readers often understand technical writing by forming a "concrete story or event" in their mind. They do this with even the most technical of documents, because they need to *use* the information in some way. They need to know "agents and action." So, the readers in one study actually *restructured* the information to be more active (Flower et al., 1986, p. 45).

3   WRITING AND SPEAKING CAN HELP ME DISCOVER WHAT I REALLY THINK

In the process of producing solutions, you will use many different kinds of oral and written communication. As you move through your career, no matter where you work—whether a large Fortune 500 firm, a small consulting firm, or a public agency—writing and speaking can help you plan, develop, and revise your engineering solutions. Writing can solve problems for you as well as for your reader.

Imagine, for a moment, that you must do some research for your boss on nanocrystalline coatings that protect microchips. There are many of these new coatings on the market, and your company needs information on similarities and differences among coatings before investing research-and-development time and money in adapting a coating for use on its chips. What do you do? How do you start? You probably start by reading as much as you can, collecting information on coatings and trying to organize it. Then you have to look for similarities and differences and make judgments about which coatings fit better with your company as products. How do you capture what you are learning? You probably take notes and make summaries of informative articles and websites. So, you are already writing, even before you have started drafting the report you have to produce. You are also probably talking to people, asking questions and getting their feedback on your findings.

When you do start drafting the report, you probably begin with the lists you have been making of each coating's qualities (strengths and limitations). If you do not have enough information about a particular coating, you will notice, because your list will not be complete. The simple act of putting down words shows you what you need to find out more about. And as you start drafting and making an argument for one kind of coating over the other, you may notice that you never say why, for example, coating 3 will not work. Your argument is thus not complete, because you had assumed early on in your investigation that coating 3 would never work, but forgot to explain why. And then when you start to explain why, you realize that you were mistaken about one of the attributes of coating 3, and it might work after all.

In these and many other ways, writing helps you see your own thoughts in front of you, so you can clarify and finish them. Without writing, you probably cannot know what you understand and what you do not. Just remember that writing happens over time, as a recursive process of outlining, drafting, and revising. You have to give it time. Computers can help us create and revise documents faster, but they probably cannot help us think faster. And your writing is simply the clear arrangement of your thoughts—after you have rearranged them a few dozen times. Remember that when you see someone else's writing, you are seeing a final product; you cannot see the hours of drafting and thinking that went into that written product. So, do not think that most people write faster than you. Almost no one writes very quickly!

EXPERTS SAY...

According to engineer Henry Petroski, there is a clear connection between the practice of engineering and the practice of writing, since both involve creating something new: "Writing no less than engineering consists of ideas to be realized" (p. 10). In his book *Beyond Engineering* (1986), Petroski draws a parallel between an engineer as a bridge builder and as a writer when he describes an engineer as "the designer of a bridge of words" (p. 10). He also explains how writing about bridge building helps the engineer understand the actual process of bridge building better, because writing is "the test of an engineer's understanding of his own theoretical work" (p. 11).

4   MY READER OR LISTENER (MY AUDIENCE) IS ALWAYS MY CLIENT

As an engineering professional, to whom will you be writing and speaking? Those of you who have worked in engineering-related firms, private or public, know that, as an entry-level engineer, you make reports (orally and in writing) to your boss, to colleagues, and sometimes to middle managers from other divisions or offices. For the first few years of your career, you probably will not be writing directly to outside clients. In fact, one survey found that, three years after graduating with a B.S. degree, most engineers were writing more often to people inside their organization than to people outside it (Anderson, 1986). So, in light of this finding, why should you consider your reader a client? Because the other finding from this study was that most of those in-house readers knew less than the writer about the subject matter. So, if you are the writer, your job is to help your readers understand the subject matter and act on that information.

Treat your reader or listener like a valued client—someone with whom you want to maintain a positive professional relationship. And think about how to talk to that client, in writing or by speaking. For example, suppose that you have to present that design for a bus shelter to the city council. How do you explain a design to people who may not look at designs very often? City councils are usually composed of ordinary citizens from many walks of life who happen to care about their city. Do you show them a plan view of your design? A schematic? Will your readers know how to "read" these visuals? Should you refer to the "postmodern use of space"? Will your readers understand that terminology? You would want to examine your communication options ahead of time, including vocabulary, visuals, and even tone of voice.

RESEARCH SHOWS...

In the workplace, chances are good that you know more than your readers—even in-house readers—about the subject matter of your writing (Anderson, 1986). This means that you must explain technical processes, concepts, and vocabulary more than you might think.

5   IT IS MY RESPONSIBILITY TO TURN DATA INTO INFORMATION MY READERS CAN USE

Engineers deal with lots of data; they collect and generate test results, experimental results, specifications, standards, all sorts of numbers, and raw facts. In order to make your communication useful for all your readers and listeners, you need to help them understand the meaning and the relationships of your data. Data are just raw facts. For example, consider the statement, "It is 100°F outside." That piece of data will not be very informative to a child who does not understand what "degrees" means or to a visitor from Indonesia who is not familiar with the Fahrenheit system. Data are bits of information (test results, raw facts) that must be interpreted, organized, and synthesized in order to make sense and to have meaning. As one cognitive scientist put it, "Data plus meaning is information" (Reeves, 1996). Your job is to turn the data you produce into useful information by anticipating the needs of your reader. Sure, many of your readers will be technical folks like you, but they still need to know the relationships among the data you present.

The information, for instance, that air density changes with temperature can be demonstrated only by presenting the correlation between air density and temperature at successive measurements. You would probably use an x–y scatter graph, with a line drawn through the series of points plotted, to convey this information, as in Figure 2. You would *not* give the temperature readings in one paragraph and the corresponding density readings in another paragraph! You could present the data that way, but doing so would make it way too hard for the reader to perceive how rapidly air density changes with temperature (especially by contrast with water density, for instance). And you would be very far from imparting knowledge to your reader that he or she could use later on. The x–y graph provides the best context (a visual context) for the reader to understand the correlations. And then your words can enhance and support the visual context:

"At standard atmospheric pressure, the density of air drops steadily with increasing temperature." Graphical and verbal presentation of data, working side by side—bingo, you have created information, and maybe even knowledge, your reader can use.

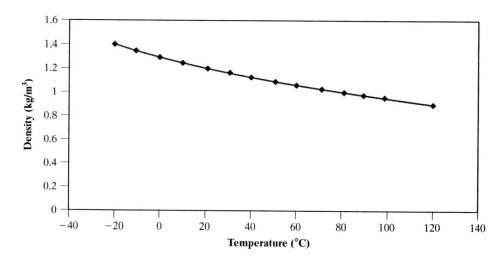

Figure 2.   Relationship between density and temperature of air at standard atmospheric pressure. *Source of data:* Crowe, C.T., et al. 2001. *Engineering Fluid Mechanics*, 7th ed.

6   MY AUDIENCES WILL CHANGE, AND SO MUST MY WRITING AND SPEAKING

One of the challenges of learning how to write for engineering work is that, in school, you are not writing for a typical engineer as audience. You professors and teaching assistants are not your boss; they are not paying you to solve problems. Neither are they typical readers of your engineering documents. Unlike your future supervisors, clients, and colleagues, your instructors want to know how much you have learned about what they already know. So it is sometimes difficult for instructors to respond to your writing the way typical readers might, with thoughts such as these:

> "What does she mean by 'picocuries'?"
> "I thought he was going to give me credit for my part of the design."
> "This looks too long to read."
> "Doesn't she know we don't use that pollutant-removal process here anymore?"

The reality is that engineers must communicate daily with listeners and readers who have a variety of educational and professional backgrounds. To give you an example, assume for the moment that you are an environmental engineer. For a final report on your study of methods to clean up a particular hazardous-waste site, you may be addressing regulators who are familiar with some of the terminology in your discipline ("*in situ* remediation," for instance), but who do not have a strong background in the science of sampling or of assessing risk. If you then write instructions for the technicians who will implement the cleanup, you will have yet a different audience, one who may not understand the regulatory terms or the science, but who will need clearly written procedures for handling hazardous materials. And sometime later, you may need to help write a description of the remediation process for local news reporters who know very little about engineering. See examples of these three styles of writing in Figures 3 through 5. Each of these audiences has different needs for your documents, needs that must be met if your documents (and presentations) are to communicate meaningfully and get the particular job done.

How many different audiences will you have in your career as an engineer? The answer will depend partly on whether you go into management or not. Chances are that you will become a manager within five years of graduation from college. At the very least, you will be writing for and speaking to people whose role in your organization falls

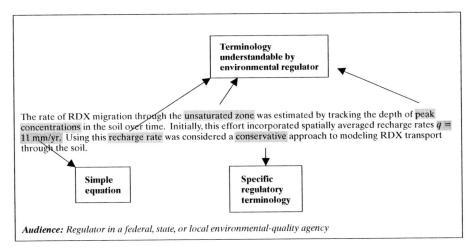

Figure 3.   Excerpt from a *technical report* on RDX contamination at a site.

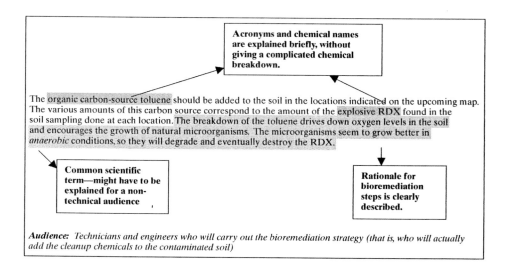

Figure 4. Excerpt from the introduction to a *set of instructions* on implementing a bioremediation system to clean up explosive RDX in contaminated soil.

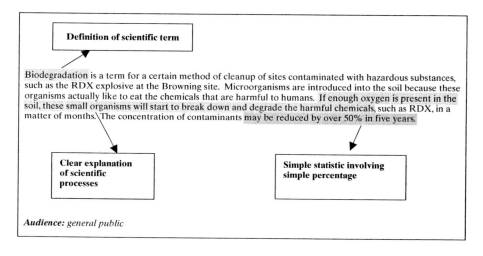

Figure 5. Excerpt from a *newspaper article* on cleaning up RDX contamination.

into one of the three categories defined by Paul Anderson (1986): Decision-makers, advisors, implementers.

Decision makers make things happen in a company or organization. They are ordinarily top management or those managers with some budgetary control. They are "big-picture" people who must allocate resources, keep an eye on the bottom line, and keep the organization moving forward at a healthy, but not out-of-control, pace. They want summaries of information and quick answers to questions such as, "How much will this solution cost?" and "How long will the solution take to implement?" They want to read conclusions and recommendations, not report sections containing lots of details. They want to listen to talks that get to the bottom line quickly.

Advisors are indispensable to decision makers, because advisors *do* care about details and methodology. Their job is to advise the decision makers about the credibility of solutions and of the procedures used to develop those solutions. They want to see descriptions of procedures and discussions of results. They will even check the appendices of reports to make sure that the investigation or proposal follows good science and that the computations are correct.

The final audience type, implementers, usually do not have much decision-making power. Instead, they have to do things on the basis of your writing: recalibrate a machine, build a new component to filter out "bad" air from a manufacturing building, etc. They are often technicians. These readers need clear instructions and rationale for the changes they will be making. They do not need theoretical details, financial justifications, or lengthy discussions of procedures used to arrive at the changes.

There are other audiences inside your own organization who may not quite fit into those categories: colleagues (engineers at the same level as you), support staff, and sales and marketing staff. The first audience is easy to communicate with; the others need clear explanations of concepts and terminology with which they are probably not familiar. And then there are the audiences outside your organization: customers, regulatory agencies, financial institutions, vendors, and perhaps the news media. As a manager, you will be called on to communicate with at least the first four of these audiences and possibly with the last one as well.

PRACTICE QUESTION: DIFFERING AUDIENCES

As an audience for your writing or speaking, how does a workplace engineer (manager or nonmanager) differ from an academic engineer (such as your engineering professors or instructors)?

SUGGESTED ANSWER

Workplace engineers are extremely busy, typically involved in a number of projects, and usually responsible for keeping costs as low as possible for the company and the client. Managers often do not do any engineering work, but rather manage people and other resources. Academic engineers are usually most interested in underlying causes of problems that need solving, and they want to pass their expertise on to younger engineers. Your instructors want to know how much you know and how well you know it; workplace engineers want to know what you know that can help them solve a problem.

SUMMARY

- For engineers, writing is not an extra set of skills that it would be nice to possess, but rather an integral part of doing engineering work every day.
- Writing helps you solve problems by helping you discover what you really think about the connections among the data and facts you have collected.

- *Data* are raw facts and numbers; *information* shows relationships among data and thereby becomes useful for solving problems. Your job as an engineer is to turn data into information.
- You will have many different audiences for your technical writing and speaking, and you must learn to adjust your language and graphics to fit the understanding of the particular audience.

Problems

1. Interview an engineer in the workplace. Choose any sort of engineer; he or she may or may not be working in an engineering firm. Ask him or her to describe a typical day in their workweek: what tasks does he or she perform and how long does each take? Ask especially about how much time your interviewee spends writing and reading, including e-mail and other forms of digital communication. Write up a short summary of the interview and compare with summaries written by other students. How much time (expressed as a range) do engineers spend doing communication tasks?

2. Talk to a family member or a friend who is not an engineer and describe a project you hope to work on, either at work or in college. Or describe the latest concept you just learned in your engineering studies. Be as specific as possible. Then, answer the following questions:

    Does your listener ask questions as you describe the engineering project? If so, write down those questions.
    Can you characterize the questions? Are they primarily requests for definitions, for more description?

3. Based on the questions asked by the non-technical person you interviewed, write a short analysis of the types of information needed by a non-technical audience.

4. Make a sketch of a particular piece of lab equipment in an engineering laboratory. If you don't have access to a lab, choose another available piece of hardware equipment (such as an electric drill or a coffee maker). Show the sketch to a non-technical person and ask him or her to describe how the piece of equipment works, based on your sketch.

5. If the non-technical person had trouble describing how the piece of lab or other equipment works, write a brief analysis of why. How might you redo the sketch, knowing what you know now? If the person had no trouble, write a brief analysis of the strengths of your sketch in communicating practical facts about the piece of equipment.

6. Chances are, your engineering instructor is which kind of audience for you?

    Decision maker
    Advisor
    Implementer

7.   Does the following sentence contain "data" or "information"?

Subjects in the behavioral experiment had a 90% likelihood of pushing the blue rather than the red buzzer.

8.   Does the following sentence contain "data" or "information"?

The findings from this experiment reveal that the number of total fish in the Hudson River has decreased by 23% since the 1950s.

FURTHER READING

Anderson, P.V. 1986. "What Survey Research Tells Us about Writing at Work," in *Writing in Nonacademic Settings*, Odell, L., and Goswami, D., eds. Guilford Press: New York.

This book is a groundbreaking work that looked seriously for the first time at writing in places other than schools. Paul Anderson pioneered research that looked at writing from the point of view of the reader rather than the writer. His essay in this volume is a clear and readable presentation of his study of alumni of Miami University (Ohio) and their experiences with writing at work.

Crowe, C.T., Elger, D.F., and Robertson, J.A. 2001. *Engineering Fluid Mechanics*, 7th ed. John Wiley & Sons: New York.

This is the textbook from which I took the data to construct the graph in Figure 1.2. You can learn a lot about good technical writing by looking at a good textbook for undergraduate students (who have, after all, a variety of educational backgrounds). Notice the way information is broken up into many sections with headings and visual items such as shaded boxes and illustrative figures.

Flower, L, Hayes, J.R., and Swarts, H. 1986. "Revising Functional Documents: The Scenario Principle," in *Writing in Nonacademic Settings*, Odell, L., and Goswami, D., eds. Guilford Press: New York.

Everyone knows that scenarios are good to construct when you are making a video or film, but most technical writers still balk at the idea of telling a story. This article demonstrates persuasively that even knowledgeable readers will reconstruct a passage in their mind to resemble a story with "agents and actions" (p. 45). So we may as well write that way, at least in functional documents such as instructions and procedures.

Petroski, Henry, 1986. *Beyond Engineering: Essays and Other Attempts to Figure without Equations*. St. Martin's Press: New York.

This small book is much beloved by both engineers and communication professionals who are interested in convincing other people that engineering and writing are not mutually exclusive activities; they actually support each other. Written by an engineer with much experience in both industry and academia, the text is down to earth and conversational.

Reeves, W.W. 1996. *Cognition and Complexity*. The Scarecrow Press: Lanham, MD, and London.

This volume is a wonderful little book that explains very readably what cognitive science has to say about how we process information and how we are all coping with the anxiety of information overload. Chapter 2 explains succinctly the similarities and differences among "data," "information," and "knowledge" and why it is important to use clear presentation to turn data into knowledge.

Spilka, R., ed. 1993. *Writing in the Workplace: New Research Perspectives*. Southern Illinois University Press: Carbondale, IL.

This collection of articles extends the work of *Writing in Nonacademic Settings* to present more conclusions about the interplay between writing at work and working. In particular, Spilka's article ("Moving between Oral and Writing Discourse to Fulfill Rhetorical and Social Goals") clearly shows how both speaking and writing help individuals and organizations achieve their professional goals.

Zinnser, W.K. 1988. *Writing to Learn*. Harper & Row: New York.

This wonderful, easy-to-read book presents the connection between writing and thinking. Especially useful to engineering students are Chapters 2 ("Writing across the Curriculum"), 9 ("Writing Mathematics"), and 10 ("Writing Physics and Chemistry").

11

Writing: It's about Control

1 WRITING FOR CONTROL COMES *AFTER* DRAFTING FOR CONTENT

When you draft a document, you are trying to get your thoughts down on paper or screen. You are trying to wrap your arms around the content of what you need to say, the data you need to present, and the arguments you need to make. You should not worry during the drafting phase about grammar, punctuation, and all those other things that the word "writing" may mean to you. If you worry about them too much, you will slow yourself down. You want your draft to be as complete as possible, and *then* you can go back and correct it for writing errors.

When you have completed a good first draft—that is, when you have written something about all the items on your outline or you just believe that you have covered the territory of what you have to say or present—then you are ready to focus on the quality of your writing. If you have already cognitively absorbed the guidelines presented in this chapter, you will of course have a better quality draft than if you know very little about crafting clear sentences and paragraphs. But either way, be easy on yourself and remember that you will still need to get external feedback before you deliver a final document.

2 READABLE STYLE

The style of technical writing has long been thought to be different from the styles of other types of writing, such as creative writing, essay writing, and journalism. And it *is*, although not as different as many people think. As a technical writer, you still have to grab a reader's attention, make logical arguments, and carry the reader along in a flow of words that gets your message across. The difference is that technical writing focuses less on you, the writer, and more on the ideas or facts you are presenting. As with all writing, you are

OBJECTIVES

By reading this chapter, you will learn the following:

- to use a readable style for your technical documents;
- to recognize passive-voice constructions and use them appropriately;
- how to construct logical, organized paragraphs;
- to recognize sentence fragments and avoid them;
- how to choose the correct spelling of commonly misspelled words;
- how to choose the proper verb tense;
- how to control sentences through punctuation.

From *Introduction to Engineering Communication*, Hillary Hart. Copyright © 2005 by Pearson Education, Inc. Published by Prentice Hall, Inc.

responsible for helping the reader understand the message, but the message in this case often involves complex data and information.

Even in the most technical documents, you will want to be as concrete as possible so that the reader does not have to work too hard to learn the new information you are offering. Research shows that we read at two levels of comprehension as we process information: superficial processing and deeper processing. In the first type, we simply try to retain facts; in the second, we attempt to comprehend relationships among the facts (Der Meer and Hoffmann, 1987, p. 119). In addition, we try to remember new facts by seeing whether they link up with what we already know. If the link is clear (for example, if the author uses transitions and sequences information logically), the reader has good help; if new and important information is highlighted, the reader has even more good help in understanding the content.

RESEARCH SHOWS...

Cognitive psychologists study how people read and understand information. Their studies have shown that these elements enhance the processing of information for the reader:

visual imagery

examples

comparisons

descriptions

questions

(Der Meer and Hoffmann, 1987)

Let us look at an example of clear technical writing. Even if you know nothing about phase-sensitive X-ray imaging, you will probably easily understand this passage from *Physics Today* (July 2000, p. 23):

> Clinical and biological studies stand particularly well poised to benefit from the development of phase-sensitive techniques. Absorption contrast works well in distinguishing between hard and soft tissue: Heavier elements—like calcium in bones and teeth—have a much higher absorption cross section than the lighter elements that constitute soft tissues. However, in many clinical situations, such as mammography, there is a need to distinguish between different kinds of soft tissue—between tumors and normal tissue, for instance. Because the absorption is small to begin with, and differences in density and composition are slight, standard x-ray imaging is not as successful at this task.

Readable style is generally grammatically correct, but it is also a lot more than just that. In fact, grammatical correctness may be less important overall than presenting information logically and leading the reader carefully along the trail of your thought. To lead your readers, you need to prune your writing of deadwood, make the sequence of your thought explicit, avoid ambiguity, and keep the reader focused on the most important points. The keys to good writing, outlined in the upcoming box, are just as important in technical writing as in any other type of writing. They are not so much rules of grammar as strategies for writing clearly and concisely and for helping your reader remember the information.

Passive and Active Voice: What Is All the Fuss?

Perhaps the largest difference between technical and other kinds of writing is the increased use of passive voice in the former. The word "voice" as applied to writing just

How many elements listed in the previous "Research Shows…" box can you discover in the passage from *Physics Today*?

SUGGESTED ANSWER

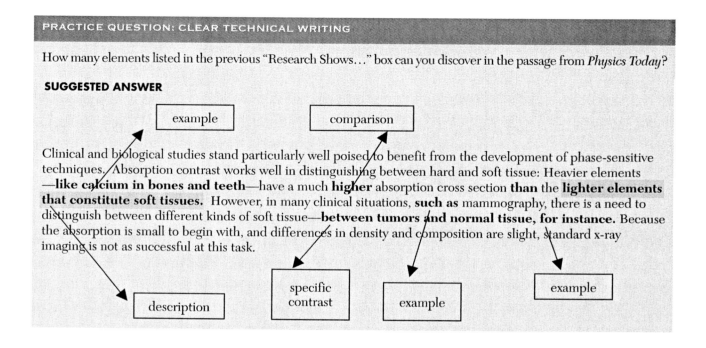

HINT

Keys to Powerful Writing

There are five keys to good writing. The last three contribute to both the big picture (paragraphs and sections) and the smaller picture (individual sentences). The first two keys keep your sentences clear, concise, and communicative. The five keys to powerful writing are

> **prune your writing**
> **control passive voice**
> **maintain logical linkage**
> **maintain focus**
> **maintain parallelism**

means how you "sound" on the page, instead of at the lectern. Your writing has a voice because the reader, in some not-very-well understood way, "hears" the words on your page in his or her head. Voice in writing is different than in talking, because the reader can slow down and "listen" again to your words. So, you have to make sure that your "tone" is exactly what you intend. Both passive voice and active voice can strike the wrong tone when used inappropriately.

What is the difference between passive and active voice, and why should you care? Well, compare these two sentences:

> I threw the ball.
> The ball was thrown by me.

The first is in active voice, the second in passive. Say these sentences aloud to yourself. The first is the way we would describe the event when talking; the second kind of sentence usually occurs in writing only, not in speaking. The agent (or doer) of the action is clear in the first sentence; the doer may not be so clear in the second version, especially (as often happens with passive sentences) if the doer is left off entirely, as in "The ball was thrown."

When to use which voice is an ongoing issue for technical writers, who often present information in which the doer of the action is not important, as in "The material was heated to a temperature of 100°C." In that sentence, the reader does not care who heated up the water sample, so naming the doer of the action simply wastes the reader's time. We do not need to use the active-voice construction, "The technician heated the material to a temperature of 100°C," because we do not need to know who is the agent of the action of heating (the technician). Teachers of creative and essay writing encourage students to use only active voice, because active-voice sentences are usually clearer and more direct. But technical writers, including you, must decide what they want to emphasize before they can construct a good sentence and use the appropriate voice.

HINT

When to Use Which Voice?

Active Voice	Passive Voice
• **to emphasize the agent of the action:** Previous researchers established the relationship between chemical qualities and model parameters.	• **to emphasize the object:** The relationship between chemical qualities and model parameters was established by previous researchers.
• **to be concise and direct:** JMC Consulting recommends that the agency adopt a risk-communication plan.	The water sample was heated to a temperature of 100°C.

Wordiness: Learn to Prune

A big complaint about technical writing is its wordiness. A sentence like the following is typical of much technical writing:

> An important conclusion extracted from the result is that there is a correlation between the mixing length and the volumetric flow.

The sentence is not terribly long, but it wastes words. And those "dead" words get in the way of our quick and easy understanding of the meaning of the sentence. The following is a better way to write it:

> The result demonstrates a correlation between mixing length and volumetric flow.

The revised sentence has 11 words, almost half the length of the original, which has 21 words. The second sentence relates the important conclusion without wasting time announcing that we are about to hear an important conclusion. If the word "important" seems important, there are other ways of declaring importance to a reader, such as italicizing the sentence or making sure that the sentence begins or ends a paragraph.

Our writing models are often not very good, and we pick up habits of using unnecessary words and legalisms. Also, the way we first write something when we are drafting is often the long way around explaining it. *Pruning* is the process of going through your own draft and removing the deadwood—the words that really do not add anything to the meaning you are trying to convey. Just as pruning a tree makes it stronger and eventually more beautiful, pruning your sentences will strengthen what you are trying to convey. See Table 1 for some examples of how to prune common deadwood phrases.

TABLE 1   Words and Phrases that Can often be Pruned

Deadwood	Pruned wood
different aspects	aspects
make a measurement	measure
give consideration to	consider
relative to	about *or* of
it should be noted that . . .	note that . . .
regardless of the fact that	although
due to the fact that	because
subsequent to	after
in the course of	during

PRACTICE QUESTION: PRUNING

How many words can you remove from this sentence without changing the meaning?

The following report outlines the different aspects relating to the current feasibility of constructing a magnetically levitated bullet train in Central Texas.

SUGGESTED ANSWER

This

~~The following~~ report outlines ~~the different aspects relating to~~ the *current* feasibility of constructing a magnetically levitated bullet train in Central Texas.

The word "current" is also a candidate for pruning; it depends on whether you want to emphasize the report's timeliness (perhaps in comparison with another report from last year) or not. Normally, feasibility studies cover only current feasibility.

But do not prune just to make sentences shorter! Shorter sentences are not necessarily better than longer sentences. Consider this string of short sentences:

This report is a final report. It presents final results for the design of a wastewater treatment plant. The design is for the process sequence, piping, flow distribution, and hydraulics. It includes the pump station and biological-treatment units. It also includes the disinfection and sludge-handling processes for the plant.

Notice how confusing those sentences become as they keep stopping and starting. What does "it" refer to at the beginning of three of the sentences: the report, the design, or some process? "It" is a very small word that does not mean anything by itself. Not only are the sentences choppy, but also we have to keep reading backwards to figure out what "it" means each time. Here, the best solution is to combine some of these sentences, not to shorten them:

> This final report presents the design of a wastewater treatment plant, including the process sequence, piping, flow distribution, and hydraulics. **The design** also includes the pump station, the biological-treatment units, and the disinfection and sludge-handling processes for the plant.

We have lengthened the sentences in this passage, but by combining some sentences, we have actually *shortened the passage*. Productive pruning can be a two-step process in which you actually lengthen a sentence in order to strengthen the passage. Again, pruning is not better for its own sake, but only when it removes deadwood. Here, some of the deadwood is the meaningless word "it" that keeps cropping up, which leads us to the next major problem with much technical writing: empty pronouns.

PRACTICE QUESTION: COMBINING SENTENCES

Consider the following sentences:

> The population explosion in and around the Austin area has proved to be problematic regarding water-drainage structures. It has particularly affected the Brushy Creek area in southern Williamson County.

- Does combining these sentences improve their readability?
- What problems does combining the sentences solve?

SUGGESTED ANSWER

> The population explosion in and around the Austin area, particularly in the Brushy Creek area in southern Williamson County, has proved to be problematic regarding water-drainage structures.

By taking the geographic details of the second sentence and inserting them into the first sentence, we can keep "population explosion" as the subject of one clear sentence with one predicate ("has proved to be"). Longer sentences may produce a shorter passage! Of course, we can prune this sentence even more—see next Practice Question.

Empty Pronouns

Isn't it annoying to read sloppy sentences that use the word "this" instead of a word with some meaning, such as the following?

> In the United States, the chemical and petroleum industries consume eight million tons of hydrogen annually. **This** is produced from natural gas by a process called steam reforming that extracts hydrogen from hydrocarbons. **This** can occur by one of two methods.

When you use "this" without any noun attached to it, especially at the beginning of a sentence, you are cheating the reader. Guessing what the author means by "this" is a stupid game that we readers would rather not play. In the second sentence of the foregoing example, we would like to be sure that the word "this" refers to hydrogen. (Actually, it refers to the eight million tons of hydrogen consumed by the U.S. chemical and petroleum industries.) Hydrogen, however, is not particularly emphasized in the previous sentence; it is tucked into a prepositional phrase ("of hydrogen"). So why not say, "**This hydrogen** is produced . . ."? And what does "this" refer to in the third sentence? As readers, we prefer the clarity of "**This process** can occur by one of two methods," or better yet, "**Steam reforming** can occur. . . ."

HINT

> **Simple Rule:** Never use "this" by itself at the beginning of a sentence. Always use "this" to modify a noun—for example, "this *process*" or "this *chemical reaction*."

Use of "it" at the beginning of a sentence can also be a problem. Generally, when we begin a sentence with "it," we are delaying getting to the point. For example, consider the sentence, "It is the case that hydrogen occurs naturally." We can prune away the first five words without changing the meaning of that sentence! "It" has its place, but watch out for cases where you are using "it" because you do not know exactly what you want to say or because you are being unthinkingly wordy.

Noun Compression: Let Some Air in

Another barrier for readers of technical writing is long noun phrases, such as *process design revamp project* or *multireservoir water resources systems*. Even if you have seen these phrases before, it is difficult to know exactly what they mean. Here is a sentence that invites you to skip right over it:

> The scope of work provides technical service support to continue to improve the quality of the company's Advanced Science and Technology Plan and **develop a gap-analysis-based, site-specific Integrated Technology Plan** that includes Plant Directed Research and Development Thrusts.

Problems abound with this sentence, including the prevalence of strings of capitalized nouns that mean nothing to a reader unfamiliar with these "plans" and "thrusts." But even the noncapitalized noun phrases are problematic. What does "gap-analysis-based" mean? "Based" is actually an adjective, not a noun, but it does not help us much to discover the meaning. Does the phrase mean an analysis based on identifying the gaps in the current plan? If so, that part of the sentence should read this way:

> develop **a site-specific Integrated Technology Plan that fills in the gaps in the current plan**

If we insert this more understandable phrase into the original sentence, however, we will make the sentence even longer, so perhaps in this case we should split the sentence in two:

> The scope of work provides technical service support to continue to improve the quality of the company's Advanced Science and Technology Plan. **The scope should also** develop a site-specific Integrated Technology Plan that fills in the gaps in the current plan and includes Plant Directed Research and Development Thrusts.

The new passage is longer than the original, but it is much clearer. Of course, we can always work on pruning it. For example, do you think "technical service support" means anything more than "technical support"?

Noun phrases clog up our writing because they try to stuff so much meaning into a small place that there is no room to understand the meaning. Sometimes you have to add words to clarify the relationship of words to each other. Look at this sentence, for instance:

> This report on statewide outdoor burning describes the **activity data collection process**.

Surely some of the nouns in the indicated phrase are being made to act as adjectives, but we are uncertain about what is referring to what. Adding prepositions and pronouns may help to clarify compressed noun phrases. What kind of activity are we talking about? The incidents of outdoor burning? In that case, a better version would look like this:

> This report describes **the process <u>of</u> collecting data <u>on</u> incidents <u>of</u>** outdoor burning statewide.

The solution is to add some prepositions that indicate the relationship of certain words to each other. Here, too, the new sentence is *longer* than the original, but the changes *add* to the meaning rather than detract from it.

HINT   **Simple Rule:** Shorter is not always better. Clearer *is* always better.

PRACTICE QUESTION: MORE PRUNING

We previously produced the following sentence by combining the original two sentences:

> **The population explosion in and around the Austin area, particularly in the Brushy Creek area in southern Williamson County, has proved to be problematic regarding water-drainage structures.**

Can you make it even more concise (without losing meaning) by pruning it some more?

SUGGESTED ANSWER

Here is the sentence with changes shown and then with the changes incorporated.

> **The population explosion in and around the Austin area, particularly in the Brushy Creek area in southern Williamson County, has ~~proved to be~~ *created* problem~~atic~~ ~~regarding~~ *for* water-drainage structures.**

> **The population explosion in and around the Austin area, particularly in the Brushy Creek area in southern Williamson County, has created problems for water-drainage structures.**

The changes have made this sentence both shorter and clearer.

---

3   CONSTRUCTING POWERFUL PARAGRAPHS

Here are the three keys to writing clear paragraphs and sections of a document:

- maintain logical linkage;
- maintain focus;
- maintain parallelism.

Maintaining links, focus, and parallelism is a matter of style and emphasis; using these keys requires that you think hard about exactly which bits of information and data are most important.

Maintain Logical Linkage

Good technical writing is not list making. We do not learn anything from lists unless we already know the context for all the items on the list. When you go to the grocery store, you already know that you are buying items for dinner, for instance. But you probably do not write down, "dinner for four people." And yet knowing that information is critical to understanding how much of each item to buy. You cannot really use your grocery list—e.g., chicken, lettuce, tomatoes—without understanding that unwritten context. Good writing helps the reader understand the context by making explicit connections between ideas or pieces of information. These connections are like signposts that say "A is like B" (comparison), "A caused B" (cause and effect), "A is different from B" (contrast), or "A is more important than B" (degree of control). These signposts use conventional words and phrases such as "similarly," "consequently," and "on the other hand" to show the reader where your thought is heading.

PRACTICE QUESTION: MAINTAINING LINKAGE

Here is a paragraph from the Work Remaining section of a progress report. Do you know in what direction the thought is headed in each sentence? If not, can you diagnose what is missing from the paragraph?

The evaluation of diamond film based on the final criterion will be completed when the analysis of its qualities is received from the Institute for Advanced Technology (IAT). A request for the resource files on diamond film will be submitted to Bolton Manufacturing. An additional comparison of the results received from IAT will be made with information provided by Bolton. The evaluation of diamond dust will be used for the comparison of the other nanocrystalline coatings.

SUGGESTED ANSWER

There are no links between these sentences, no words that establish a conceptual connection. Every sentence seems to start the thought process all over again.

Let us take a closer look at the paragraph in the foregoing practice question to understand what has gone wrong:

> The evaluation of diamond film based on the final criterion will be completed when the analysis of its qualities is received from the Institute for Advanced Technology (IAT). A request for the resource files on diamond film will be submitted to Bolton Manufacturing. An additional comparison of the results received from IAT will be made with information provided by Bolton. The evaluation of diamond dust will be used for the comparison of the other nanocrystalline coatings.

The sentences generally describe what will happen, but we do not know the connection between each of these promises. Are they listed in chronological order? Will the most important steps be taken care of first? Do certain steps depend on others and require that the others be accomplished first? What does Bolton Manufacturing have to do before the author can accomplish certain steps? The paragraph is simply a list of unrelated steps and reveals almost nothing about the sequence of this process (except for the word "when" in the first sentence).

Part of the problem with this paragraph is overuse of the passive voice; we are not sure who is doing what when. But even if we retain most of the passive-voice constructions, we can greatly improve the readability of the paragraph by adding links. Lets us look at a revised version of the paragraph. Why is this revision so much easier to understand?

> The evaluation of diamond film based on the final criterion will be completed when the analysis of its qualities is received from the Institute for Advanced Technology (IAT). **In addition**, a request for the resource files on diamond film will be submitted to Bolton Manufacturing, **so that we may compare** the results received from IAT with information provided by Bolton. **Once our evaluation of diamond film is completed**, we can compare diamond film with the other nanocrystalline coatings.

The paragraph now includes some links between sentences and between the concepts of the second, long sentence. We know a lot more about where each sentence is going. What made the difference in this paragraph? Transitional phrases.

HINT

Transitions establish strong links between these elements:

parts of a sentence;
whole sentences;
whole paragraphs.

PRACTICE QUESTION: TRANSITIONS

How many words or phrases can you think of that would fit in the blank at the beginning of the second of the following two sentences?

> *The project manager will be in Japan for the next two weeks. _____, the project engineers will remain in town at the branch office.*

SUGGESTED ANSWER

Any of these words would make sense as a link for the two sentences:

However

Nevertheless

Therefore

Unfortunately

There are other possible links as well. Each one produces a different meaning. You have to provide the *right* link to the reader to convey the right meaning (the one you intend).

When you consider these two sentences and the relationship between them, you realize that lots of different relationships are possible:

> The project engineer will be in Japan for the next two weeks. _____, the project engineers will remain in town at the branch office.

Each of those relationships would be indicated by a different word or phrase in that blank space at the beginning of the second sentence, such as "On the other hand," "Therefore," or "However." Each of these transitions imparts a different meaning to the sentences. Which is the right meaning? As the writer, you want to establish control and guide your readers to the right meaning. You may want to emphasize contrast ("However") in order to make clear the difference between the situations of managers and nonmanagers. Or you may want to emphasize cause and effect ("Therefore") in order to explain why the engineers cannot travel even locally during the next two weeks. **If you do not establish the correct connection between sentences and phrases, your reader will attempt to establish the connection anyway.** And that might be the wrong connection or meaning. For example, do you want your readers to assume that the missing word in the blank is "Unfortunately"? (This example also shows that sometimes two sentences are better constructed as one: Especially if you use "However," you would want to make one sentence, with a semicolon before and a comma after: "; however,".)

Table 2 lists some useful transitional words and phrases. Note, however, that this list does not begin to cover all the varieties of transitional words and phrases.

TABLE 2   Partial List of Transitions and the Relationships They Indicate

Relationship of One Phrase, Sentence, or Paragraph to Another	Transitional Word or Phrase
Comparison	similarly
Cause and effect	therefore; consequently; as a result
Contrast	but; however
Sequence	first; second; finally
Addition	and; also
Example	for example
Classification	partly; the other half
Spatial relationship	upwind; downwind; to the left; to the right; in back; in front
Relative importance	most importantly; secondarily

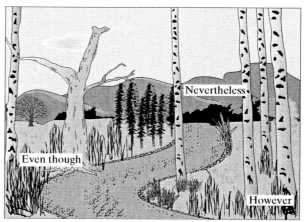

The right transitions guide the
reader down the right path.

Transitions also create organization. In a paragraph such as the next example, the transitional phrases establish the organizing pattern—comparison and contrast—that helps us make quick sense of the writing. In this paragraph, the author (in *Physics Today*, August 2002, p. 17) is talking about how a team of researchers is attempting to quantify the amount and distribution of water ice on Mars:

> For the ice's depth distribution, the team considered **two simple cases. In one**, the ice-bearing soil extends right to the surface; **in the other**, a dry layer of variable thickness tops the ice-containing layer. Thermal and epi-thermal neutrons, thanks to their **different behavior in the two cases**, provide the discrimination.

We can see classification also at work here ("two" cases, "the other").

You will notice that we have already looked at several of these patterns, since making clear the precise relationship among facts, ideas, or events is the main goal of much technical writing. In addition, the patterns often overlap within the same paragraph or section of a document. Which patterns are operating in this paragraph from an article on X-ray imaging (*Physics Today*, July 2000, p. 26)?

> A monochromator throws much of the x-ray flux away, and when used with an x-ray tube source, would make the time needed to record an image unacceptably long for clinical uses. The ability to use the polychromatic output of an x-ray tube is **therefore** important for potential clinical applications. The large beam divergence from such a source has the **additional** advantage of providing magnification, with a corresponding increase in spatial resolution. The spreading beam **also** allows the imaging of large areas in a single step.

Notice that in this paragraph, the transitions are located inside the sentences rather than primarily at the beginning. Nonetheless, they link parts of whole thoughts. By making it easy for the reader to follow the pattern of your thought, you maintain flow and help keep the reader focused on what is important.

Maintain Focus

When it comes to helping the reader focus on critical information, the most powerful writing tool you have is the topic sentence. Think about how you read paragraphs. Usually, you read the first sentence for a clue as to what the paragraph is about. (Every so often, a topic sentence will come second or third, after a sentence or two that link to a previous paragraph.) Then you want to hear mainly about *that* subject; if the paragraph tries to cover too many subjects or if it has no clear topic sentence, you will understandably become confused. The topic sentence is like a welcoming door to a house: If the door is closed and locked, you will feel unwelcome and not go in. If it is slightly open and you peek inside, you will want to know where you are entering. Is this a place of good, clear information?

Consider the following paragraph:

> The State does not appropriate funds to maintain and/or build surface parking lots, parking facilities, or parking garages. All parking on campus, including surface parking and the parking garage, is operated and maintained from the parking system revenues. Revenues include the annual parking permit fee, incomes from citations issued by The University Police, and fees charged to use the University parking garage. The construction of a second parking garage is necessary. To meet the required funding to construct this parking garage, it will be necessary to increase the campus parking revenue by raising the annual parking permit fee. The parking permit fee will increase over a two-year period to accomplish this.

Does the first sentence make you want to "enter" the paragraph? Do you feel that the first sentence is a good indicator of the subject matter covered by the rest of the paragraph? If you answered "no" to both questions, you are not alone. Most people would not read this paragraph all the way through. Knowing the sources of the state's funds does not seem important at the beginning because we are not given a clue as to the real subject matter of this paragraph. Of course, the real subject is bad news: The parking fee will go up. So we can understand why the writer did not want to use the last sentence—*The parking permit fee will increase over a two-year period*—as the topic sentence. But the problem is that hiding bad news may mean that someone simply does not read the entire paragraph and is therefore shocked when receiving a higher bill in the mail. If you really do not want to inform your readers, do not write anything, because badly organized writing will only *misinform* them. If you *do* want to inform them, figure out a way of organizing the paragraph so that you keep the reader focused on the most positive message—in this case, the fact that a garage will be built to help solve the university's parking problems.

Looking at the foregoing paragraph about constructing a new parking garage at a university, can you come up with a topic sentence that emphasizes a positive message? What would be a better second sentence?

SUGGESTED ANSWER

- Here is one suggestion for a better topic sentence:

  To solve the problem of increased traffic on campus, the university is building a second parking garage.

This sentence focuses on the solution to the problem of increased numbers of cars on campus.

- Here is a suggestion for the second sentence:

  To fund this initiative, the parking fee will increase over a two-year period.

Another way to maintain focus in every sentence of a paragraph is to keep the reader's eye on the ball—that is, on the most important pieces of information. Consider this pair of sentences:

> The proposal does not conform to our research goals as outlined in the five-year strategic plan. For instance, the potential for discovering new laser techniques is discussed only briefly and does not form a major part of the proposal.

The topic sentence here seems fine. But the second sentence does not tie in well with the first, in spite of the helpful transitional phrase "For instance." The second sentence is confusing because it does not emphasize at the beginning what is important: the proposal. In the following revision, the noun that is the main subject is repeated in the position of subject:

> The **proposal** does not conform to our research goals as outlined in the five-year strategic plan. For instance, the **proposal** fails to emphasize our potential for discovering new laser techniques; these techniques are discussed only briefly.

Placing "the proposal" in the position of subject of the second sentence greatly increases our comprehension of the content. We know now to keep focusing on the proposal and what it does and does not do.

HINT

Maintaining Focus

- Tie new information to old information.
- Place repeated information in the subject position.

Research has shown clearly that readers want new information to be tied explicitly to information they already know. Study this passage from *Physics Today* (August 2002, p. 21) and notice how seamlessly it weaves new information into the fabric of given information by repeating key words and concepts in the "subject" position:

> After setting a **wave** in motion, the researchers take an **image** of the tray with a video camera. **The wave** is brighter than its unexcited surroundings, and its size and location are easily **measured**. **These measurements** go

into the feedback step: determining the pointing direction and brightness of the reaction-controlling spotlight. By comparing the current **image** with an image taken two seconds earlier, the researchers can tell whether the **wave** needs a bigger or smaller dose of light to maintain its stability.

This passage also makes good use of parallelism to channel the reader's attention. What is parallelism? Read on . . .

Maintain Parallelism

When you present a series of facts, findings, or steps in a process, you want readers to remember how the items are similar and dissimilar. Mostly, you want them to remember the facts or steps themselves. To make clear the similarity of certain items and to aid reader's memories, you need to use parallel structure (parallelism). A sentence such as this one is unnecessarily wordy and potentially confusing because it does not maintain parallelism:

> The architectural engineer finished the mechanical plan, made five copies, and then it was forwarded to the client.

Of the three actions the engineer took, two are presented in the active voice and one in the passive voice. Maintaining parallelism means being consistent with your grammatical constructions for each item in your list, especially with your verb forms.

To maintain parallelism, you must choose a grammatical form of presentation (based on parts of speech, usually) and stick to it. Here is a set of instructions that is not in parallel form:

Recommended Procedure for Characterizing Emodin:

1. *Obtain emodin from reliable chemical manufacturing company. (See list.)*
2. *Identification should be made with nuclear magnetic resonance spectroscopy.*
3. *Determining purity should be done by elemental analyses.*

In this example, if we agree that the first instruction ("Obtain emodin . . .") is the best form for a set of instructions, then we should stick to that form for the other items. Here, the chosen form sets up each item in the following sequence of parts of speech:

*command form of a **verb/** noun as object/ **prepositional phrase***
        obtain/ emodin/   **from ... company**

If we rewrite steps 2 and 3 in parallel form with step 1, we come up with something like this revision:

Recommended Procedure for Characterizing Emodin:

1. ***Obtain*** *emodin from reliable chemical manufacturing company. (See list.)*
2. ***Identify*** *emodin by using nuclear magnetic resonance spectroscopy.*
3. ***Determine*** *purity through elemental analyses.*

HINT

Present parallel ideas in parallel form in the following structures:

- lists;
- sentences (series or pairs).

Pay special attention to the first few words of each clause or phrase.
Remember that parallel constructions channel the reader's attention and aid his or her memory.

As we have seen, parallelism clarifies sentences as well as vertical lists. Let us return to our original example:

> The architectural engineer finished the mechanical plan, made five copies, and then **it was forwarded** to the client.

This sentence is easy to fix, right? We simply stick with the past-tense verb form of the first two actions. The final phrase then becomes active instead of passive: ". . . and then **forwarded it** to the client."

Here is an example that includes more than one "and":

> We researched and compared the performance capabilities and FAA records of each aircraft, **as well as conducting** a pilot survey.

The phrase after the comma is not in the same grammatical form as the other items in this sentence list, right? You have to change "conducting" to a past-tense verb: "conducted." Then you can make explicit the fact that the research involved at least two distinct steps—researching and comparing, and conducting a survey—not one big simultaneous step. Readers like processes and information to be explicitly broken down into understandable steps or ideas. Here is one possible revision:

> We researched and compared the performance capabilities and FAA records of each aircraft, and then **we conducted** a pilot survey.

4   GRAMMAR AND SENTENCE STRUCTURE: DIAGNOSING AND CURING THE PROBLEMS

Some problems with sentences are matters of clarity and style, and some problems are matters of grammatical correctness. Focus on the clarity first; then fix the grammar. There are several well-described methods available for pinpointing the weakness and wordiness of so many of our sentences. The best writing guides include Strunk and White's *The Elements of Style* (1979) and Richard Lanham's "Paramedic Method," developed in *Revising Business Prose* (2000). The best methods all work to counteract the vague and bureaucratic writing that Lanham calls the "Official Style." You may think the Official Style is the best way to write, because you see so much business and professional writing that is artificially pumped up with extra words and roundabout explanations. Actually, much of that writing is simply imitating a pompous style to which *those* writers were exposed. The fact is that most technical writers have never been taught how to revise their writing.

Let us look at a sentence on the experimental results of a study of liquid-jet-gas pumps:

> An important conclusion extracted from the result **is that there is** a correlation between the mixing length and the volumetric flow.

Thinking about the words "An important conclusion . . . is that there is . . . ," we realize how empty they are. Conclusions should simply be stated, not backed into. If we follow Richard Lanham's advice, we should improve our sentences by always asking the question, "Where is the action?" Most sentences focus on their verbs because we are most interested in what happened (or will happen or could happen). That something simply "is" is rarely enough information about it. The main action of the original sentence might be "extracted." But is the fact that the conclusion was "extracted" really important to the reader? Are we not interested mainly in the conclusion itself, in what the result demonstrates?

Something important has been proven, or at least demonstrated. Can we express that result in a straightforward verb? Consider the following revision:

> The result demonstrates a correlation between mixing length and volumetric flow.

Pruning this particular sentence has also involved changing a passive construction ("conclusion extracted from . . . is") to an active construction ("result demonstrates").

We already know that excessive and inappropriate use of passive voice can be a problem for the reader, but how do you recognize passive voice in your own writing and test whether it is appropriate or not? Let us look at a paragraph from the Work Remaining section of a progress report:

> The evaluation of diamond film based on the final criterion **will be completed** when the analysis of the qualities **is received** from the Institute for Advanced Technology (IAT). A request for the resource files on diamond film **will be submitted** to Bolton Manufacturing. An additional comparison of the results received from IAT **will be made** with information provided by Bolton. The evaluation of diamond dust **will be used** for the comparison of the other nanocrystalline coatings.

The passive-voice constructions are printed in boldface. To test for passive voice, just check each verb and see whether you can easily ask the question, "By whom?" For instance, "will be completed" brings up the question, "By whom?" If you have read the progress report up until this point, you have a pretty good idea that the agent of the action of "completing" is the writer, so you are probably not confused at that point in the paragraph. But you are forced to keep asking yourself, "By whom?" for every single action in this paragraph. There are, however, other potential agents of action (IAT and Bolton), so eventually you get tired of having to answer that darned question at least once in every sentence. Excessive use of passive voice wears us out! Reading is time consuming enough without having to worry about who is the agent of the action all the time!

Of course, not all uses of passive voice are wrong. Especially in technical writing, we may not need to know who is the doer of the action. Sometimes the sentence itself will answer the question, as in this example:

> The report **was disseminated** by the Department of Justice.

In that case, the verb is still passive, but the question gets answered, and so we are not confused. But if many sentences take this form, the document will be longer than it needs to be. As a writer, think about what is more important: the object of the action or the doer of the action.

Of course, putting verbs in active voice means inserting what is missing: the agent of the action. If the agent is the writer, technical style has long dictated that the writer may not appear as "I." In many contemporary journals, however, "we" is now perfectly acceptable. If you are told that you cannot use "I" or "we," then you may want to restructure some of your sentences to include active verbs nonetheless. Consider the following example:

> The evaluation of diamond film based on the final criterion will be completed when the analysis of its qualities is received from the Institute for Advanced Technology (IAT). A request for the resource files on diamond film will be submitted to Bolton Manufacturing. An additional comparison of the results received from IAT will be made with information provided by Bolton. The evaluation of diamond dust will be used for the comparison of the other nanocrystalline coatings.

We may revise this paragraph as follows:

> The evaluation of diamond film based on the final criterion **will be completed** when the analysis of its qualities **is received** from the Institute for Advanced Technology (IAT). Once Bolton Manufacturing **responds** to a request for resource files on diamond film, an additional comparison of the results received from IAT **will be made**. The evaluation of diamond dust **will be used** for comparison with the other nanocrystalline coatings.

Of the five verbs with a subject in the foregoing paragraph, four are still in passive voice, but one is now in active voice—"responds." Turning just one verb form into active voice helps the flow of this paragraph and helps prune away other unnecessary words. Of course in this case—an industry progress report—there is no reason not to use "we." The writer is probably doing work for a client.

Another test for good writing is determining the number of prepositional phrases. Check out the original version of the last two sentences again:

> An additional comparison <u>of</u> the results received <u>from</u> IAT **will be made** <u>with</u> information provided <u>by</u> Bolton. The evaluation <u>of</u> diamond dust **will be used** <u>for</u> the comparison <u>of</u> the other nanocrystalline coatings.

In these two sentences, totaling only 33 words, there are seven almost-consecutive prepositional phrases. Those phrases slow down our reading, because prepositions do not involve action. They do establish relationship; something belongs *with* something else or comes *after* it. But too many in a row pull us away from the main thread of action that we are always trying to follow. As a rule, stick to no more than three prepositional phrases in a row. If we look again at our revised sentences, we can make them even stronger if we get rid of a couple of those phrases:

> Once Bolton Manufacturing sends us its resource files <u>on</u> diamond film, an additional comparison <u>with</u> the results received <u>from</u> IAT will be made. The evaluation <u>of</u> diamond dust will then provide a comparison <u>with</u> the other nanocrystalline coatings.

HINT

> **Remember: No more than three prepositional phrases in a row!**
>
> This report describes ***the process <u>of</u> collecting data <u>on</u> incidents <u>of</u>** outdoor burning statewide.*
>
> **That is the limit!**

5   WORDS: PICKY, PICKY

Paying attention to every word you use makes for good writing. You want to be sure that you are saying exactly what you mean. Be sure to keep a list handy of the words you know you tend to use improperly or are unsure of. See Table 3 for good examples of words that trip up many people.

Verb Tenses

Many technical writers get confused about which verb tenses to use in which sections of a report. Do we say, "research show<u>s</u>" or "research show<u>ed</u>"? Proposals are easier in this regard because they describe a plan for doing something in the future: "We will do x, y, and z." Here is an outline of sensible assumptions about verb tense and when to use which.

TABLE 3 Words That are Often Misspelled or Misused

Diction: Watch out for these pairs of words!	
affect/effect	"affect" is usually the verb "effect" is usually the noun
among/between	"among" for more than two
cite/site	"cite" is the verb form of "citation" "site" is the place
criteria/criterion	"criteria" is plural
data/datum	"data" is plural
fewer/less	"fewer" refers to number: *fewer tons* "less" refers to volume: *less capacity*
imply/infer	"Imply" is your intention "Infer" is your discovery

Past tense is used mainly to describe the work you or others did to come up with the findings you have. Present tense is used in technical communication to indicate that you are speaking of something that is (apparently) eternally true—$e = mc^2$—or that you are speaking of what the reader is reading: "This report analyzes lab-test results for the air samples." Future tense is used solely for statements that project into the future with plans or visions. Figure 1 gives more examples of how to use past, present, and future tense in specific sections of a report or paper.

Past Tense:

- **describes what you did**
- **speaks biographically of another researcher's actions**
- **sets up a historical continuum**

Use mainly in Procedures, Methodology, and Background sections (also in parts of the Introduction).

Example:
  "Researchers have long known that microbes can destroy contaminants in soil." (historical continuum)

Present Tense:

- **states theory or established knowledge**
- **says what your document does**

Use mainly in Introduction and Conclusions.

Example:
  "This research shows that microbes can destroy contaminants in soil." (conclusion)

Future Tense:

- **outlines recommendations for future work or action**
- **envisions a future state of affairs**

Use mainly in the Recommendations section.
  "Implementing this water treatment system will ensure safe drinking water.

Do not use this tense to state what your report does!

"This report will present the results of the study."

"This report presents the results of the study."

Figure 1.   Uses of past, present, and future tense in engineering reports and papers.

6   PUNCTUATION: WHY SHOULD I CARE?

Do you think of punctuation as a set of unfathomable rules that mostly do not matter, except that teachers like to make corrections on your papers? If so, you are not alone: Many students get conflicting messages about various marks of punctuation, especially commas. Should the comma always follow an introductory clause, as in the following sentence?

> After the initial tests were run, the material was sealed in an airtight container.

Should the comma always follow the last item in a series, coming before the final "and" or "or," as in the following sentence?

> The three steps of this process are gas separation, sulfur recovery, and excess gas disposal.

Actually, neither of these questions has one right answer; as a rule of grammar, the comma is generally considered to be optional in both cases. Practicing writers, however, will tell you that using the comma in these two places often helps reader comprehension and provides fewer confusing choices for the writer. In particular, the final comma in a series sometimes has to be there, such as if the items themselves in the series contain "and." See the following example, in which the final comma is necessary to avoid confusion:

> Engineers learned to isolate **and** separate the gasses, identify **and** recover the sulfur, **and** dispose of the excess gas.

Using the final comma routinely means that the writer doesn't have to worry about whether it is required or not. At least one revered style guide, however, advises *not* using the comma when the only "and" is the final "and" (Strunk and White, 1979).

The main reason to bother about punctuation is to control and clarify your meaning in any given sentence. Even hyphens can be critical in conveying the correct meaning. For instance, which of these phrases is correct?

fast-sailing ship
fast sailing ship

Well, of course, it depends on whether you are referring to a ship (any kind) that sails fast or a sailing ship (in particular) that is fast. Many engineering disciplines have noun phrases that are commonly used without hyphens; remember to think of your audience before you omit the hyphens from a phrase such as this: *antibiotic resistant infections*. If you want to be sure that no reader will mistakenly assume that you are talking about resistant infections *caused by* antibiotics, then you should write the phrase this way: *antibiotic-resistant infections*. Check with your instructor or boss about the punctuation of commonly used phrases in your field, and read around in your field's technical journals to see how the phrases are handled there.

In general, the best practice is to familiarize yourself with punctuation rules as outlined in some reference guide and then simply place the guide on your desk for easy reference when writing. Here is an annotated list of a few of the best guides:

Strunk, W., and White, E.B. 1979. *The Elements of Style*, 3d. ed. Macmillan: New York.
Though originally written almost 50 years ago, this concise guide to writing style is a bible for many technical professionals. (Actually, the original book was privately printed by William Strunk in 1918!) It covers only those elements and issues of punctuation that are most relevant, according to the authors—issues such as

whether to incorporate the comma in a series before the final "and." But because the book is short and written in the style it recommends—direct, brief, and precise—its "essential" rules of punctuation, grammar, and style are easy to remember and have stood many, many writers in good stead for decades.

Chicago Manual of Style, 15th ed., 2003. University of Chicago Press: Chicago.
This is the mothership of style manuals. This big volume focuses on style and publication issues, but also has an extensive chapter on punctuation (almost 40 pages long) that is a terrific reference tool for engineers.

Harris, M. 2003. *Prentice Hall Reference Guide to Grammar and Usage*, 5th ed., Prentice Hall: Upper Saddle River, NJ.
This volume is more reader friendly than the mammoth *Chicago Manual*; it uses tabs, section indices, and other formatting techniques to make finding information easy. The chapter on punctuation is comprehensive without being overwhelming and includes useful exercises.

Nagle, J.G. 1996. *Handbook for Preparing Engineering Documents: From Concept to Completion*. IEEE Press: New York.
This handbook contains a nice summary, in an easy-to-read chart form, of the major punctuation rules and usage.

SUMMARY

- The keys to effective writing are to prune away the deadwood (vague and useless words), control passive voice, and maintain focus by linking thoughts together clearly.
- Empty pronouns drive readers crazy; "it or "this" at the beginning of a sentence means nothing without a specific noun to modify. Combining sentences can be a good way to avoid empty pronouns.
- If you can write a good paragraph, you have got it made. Effective paragraphs have a topic sentence that acts like a miniature thesis, and all the sentences that follow fit together logically and derive from that topic sentence. The direction of thought *moves*.
- Transitional words and phrases connect ideas and link data together. Making connections is what writing technical information is all about. Otherwise, you are just making lists.
- Use a good style guide to pinpoint and fix grammatical errors and weaknesses of style in your sentences.

Problems

1.   In the following paragraph, change the passive constructions (italics) to active verb constructions. Passive constructions are discussed in section 1.

     The evaluation of diamond film based on the final criterion *will be completed* when the analysis of the qualities *is received* from the Institute for Advanced Technology (IAT). A request for the

resource files on diamond film *will be submitted* to Bolton Manufacturing. An additional comparison of the results received from IAT *will be made* with information provided by Bolton. The evaluation of diamond dust *will be used* for the comparison of the other nanocrystalline coatings.

2. After changing the passive verb constructions in the paragraph in #1, answer these questions:

Does this exercise force you to add additional words?
Are those words mainly transitions, or do they have another function?
How do these additional words help keep the paragraph moving along?

3. Write a list of all the words or phrases that could fill in the blank in the following pair of sentences. Which transitional word or phrase is best and why?

The technician heated the material to a temperature of 100° C. _____, the material changed color slightly.

4. Rewrite the pair of sentences in #3 as one sentence. How did you punctuate it? Is the information clearer when expressed as one sentence or as two sentences?

5. Add correct punctuation to the following sentence:

Spending limit balances will carry forward for some financial accounts however we will remove expenditure limits against IT accounts on August 31 2004.

6. True or false? In a report, you use past tense to state theory or established knowledge.

7. True or false? The word "criteria" is used properly in the following sentence:

The design criteria is one reason we decided to shorten the length of the rod.

8. Which word in the following sentence is used improperly?

Among the two of us researchers, there can be no disagreement about methodology.

FURTHER READING

Ballstaedt, S-P and Mandl, H. 1987. "Influencing the Degree of Reading Comprehension," in *Knowledge Aided Information Processing*, Van Der Meer, E., and Hoffmann, J., eds. Elsevier Science Publishers: Amsterdam
This collection of essays on recent theories of cognitive psychology is far too technical for most readers, but the cited article gives a good idea of the complex interplay of elements—memory, prior knowledge, semantic analysis, and levels of processing, just to name a few —that enable us to understand what we read.
Chicago Manual of Style, 15[th]ed., 2003. University of Chicago Press: Chicago.
This is the mother ship of style manuals. This big volume contains more than you'll ever want to know about manuscript preparation, documentation, and the publishing process, but it will also have definitive answers for you on all those niggling little questions about style (do you write out the number twelve or use the Arabic numeral?). The sections on "Grammar and Usage" and "Punctuation" are a terrific reference tool for engineers. Most discipline-specific style manuals in engineering are based on the *Chicago Manual*.

Day, C. 2002. "Remotely Sensed Neutrons and Gamma Rays Reveal Ice beneath the Martian Surface" and "Choreographing Wave Propagation in Excitable Media," *Physics Today*, August 2002, vol. 55, no. 8, pp. 16–17 and 21.

Reading science and engineering magazines intended for a mixed audience (technical and semitechnical) can provide models for good technical writing. *Physics Today* is one such magazine; each issue contains thoughtful articles on very technical subjects written for anyone with an interest in physics or in any of the fields deriving from physics (such as engineering). See next entry for another example of good technical writing.

Fitzgerald, R. 2000. "Phase-Sensitive X-Ray Imaging," *Physics Today*, July 2000, vol. 53, no.7, pp. 23–26.

Lanham, R. 2000. *Revising Business Prose*, 4th ed. Allyn & Bacon: Needham Heights, MA.

Richard Lanham's book contains a wonderful discussion of how to tighten your sentences and strengthen your meaning. He calls this procedure the "Paramedic Method" for diagnosing and curing wordy sentences. Read the whole book (it is short), but look especially at the first chapter, "Who's Kicking Who" (if you caught the error in grammar, you are right—Lanham wants to get your attention).

Strunk, W., and White, E.B. 1979. *The Elements of Style*, 3d. ed. Macmillan: New York.

This book is the last word for many technical professionals on style and grammar. It covers only those style guidelines the authors considered most important or most often abused, but the book's frank, direct, and directive style has delighted many people and helped them remember rules such as "Do not join independent clauses with a comma." The effect of this book has been extraordinary for almost a century. It was originally written (by William Strunk) in 1918!

Zinsser, W. K. 1990. *On Writing Well: An Informal Guide to Writing Nonfiction*, 25th anniversary ed. Harper Collins: New York.

William Zinsser is a prolific writer whose books and journalism pieces cover subjects from jazz musicians to the art of Roger Tory Peterson. This book on writing has become a classic for its crisp demonstration of the value of simplicity in writing and for its explanation of writing as a transaction between author and reader. Chapter 15 covers science writing and technical writing.

12

Speaking: Do I Really Have to Stand Up and Talk in Front of All Those People?

1   INTRODUCTION

Engineers have to communicate information orally all the time—sometimes very informally through one-on-one conversations, sometimes a little more formally through project briefings in a conference room, and sometimes much more formally as a speaker in a big auditorium. In all these situations, you want to get comfortable with using body language, voice quality, and visuals to your advantage. You can use those tools to help deliver the message of your talk, whether you are making recommendations to a client, requesting funds for a new project, or giving the results of a research study. It is all about interacting with your audience. If the members of your audience (whether composed of 1 or 100 people) feel you are speaking directly to them and would be willing to *listen* to them in return, you will have succeeded. After all, your audience probably prefers hearing and watching your presentation than having to read a long report on the subject.

HINT

Most people would rather listen to someone explain technical information than read about those same concepts. After all, it is more fun and memorable to look at pictures of butterflies and flowers than to read about the pollination characteristics of butterflies.

OBJECTIVES

By reading this chapter, you will learn the following:

- how to plan and outline your presentation;
- how to plan content and visuals for your talk;
- how to use voice quality and body language to deliver your message;
- how to use the most appropriate delivery mode for your talk;
- how to use your nervousness to prepare for and deliver a talk;
- how to handle questions from the audience;
- how to prepare for a team presentation.

Of course, most people are nervous about speaking in public, especially in a professional situation. But controlled nervousness can be used to your advantage, to give you energy and motivation. In this chapter, we will look at techniques for controlling nervousness. The most important strategy is to be prepared. There is no substitute for planning and rehearsing your talk in advance.

2   PLANNING THE CONTENT OF A PRESENTATION: OUTLINING

The first step in planning a good presentation is usually to make an outline of the contents. The next steps in developing your presentation would be to create the visuals and then rehearse. These steps are not always linear (you might, for instance, start by preparing a graph of test results), but you want to allow time to accomplish all three steps.

Here is a plan for step one, outlining your talk. Consider these items as you outline:

* Know your **audience**.
* Choose **three to five main points** to **highlight**.
* Divide your talk into **three sections:**
  * **Repeat** the main points in each section.
  * Decide where **visuals** will be useful.

As the talks you give become more complex, you may find that you need to make more than three to five main points, but this rule of thumb is useful to keep in mind throughout your career, especially when talking to a less technical audience.

Audience

You never know who will come to a presentation you are giving. Even if the audience is supposed to be just your boss and a couple of other project managers, your boss might rush in at the last minute and tell you he or she is bringing a couple of visitors from corporate headquarters to your talk. Or it might turn out that a couple of inspectors from the regulatory agency want to hear what you have to say about the air-pollution studies you have been conducting. Even at technical conferences, you cannot be sure these days that everyone has the same technical background you do. Interdisciplinary projects and studies are becoming increasingly common, and you have to be sure that everyone understands your information. Sometimes, this diversity of audience means that you must add more background information and explanation than you might think is necessary. Remember, too, that we all hear differently then we read. When we read, we can go back and reread information we do not quite understand. Your listeners cannot do that, so you have to enable them to understand your presentation from the beginning.

Highlighting

When you are presenting, time tends go to by faster than you thought it would. You have to build in time for pauses and (sometimes) more lengthy explanations than you had originally thought. So, do not try to cover too much material! (Some of your professors have probably given you an unintentional lesson in cognitive overkill during a lecture.) You cannot begin to cover all of the material that is in your report, thesis, or proposal. So, choose three to five main points to highlight, and build your talk around them.

HINT

> You only have time to
> present and support
> three to five main points!

Three Sections

That old chestnut about an essay having three main parts—beginning, middle, and end—is really true for a talk. Listeners need a lot of structure to keep their mental place in listening to a talk. Studies have shown that even the most well-intentioned listeners retain less than one-third of the information given in a talk. If you think about how *you* listen, you will realize that you fade in and out of attentiveness and do not even hear everything that is said. Also, you may not understand all of a speaker's information or be able to put it in a meaningful context. Help *your* listeners remember the important points of your talk by repeating the points throughout the presentation. After all, if you state a critical point three times, you are pretty likely to get close to a 100% chance that the listeners will remember it ($3 \times \frac{1}{3} = 1$, which you can think of as 100%).

While you are making your outline, you can also be thinking about where you will need to show visuals and which of these visuals should convey technical information and which should keep listeners on track by indicating what sort of information the talk is about to cover (conclusions, recommendations, etc.).

Plan for a 15-minute talk and you cannot go wrong. Most individual student presentations cannot be longer, and most individual presentations at conferences or meetings are a similar length. At conferences, there will probably be a session moderator keeping track of time, and your talk most likely will be sandwiched in with at least two others during a 60-minute session. Allowing for questions after each talk, this situation means 15 minutes maximum for your talk itself. If you are told that you have more time than that, terrific. If you planned for only 15 minutes, then you can always add a few more details. (Somehow, there is usually more to say about a subject!)

Here is a checklist for the first section of a typical 15-minute presentation:

Introduction (2–3 minutes):

- Introduce yourself.
- Motivate the audience to listen to you.
- Explain the purpose of your work and of the presentation.
- Preview the main ideas.
- Establish key concepts.

Beginnings are important. The impression you initially make will stay with your listeners. Begin in an upbeat manner; remember that you are meeting and greeting this audience. Try to use your voice and movements to convey some excitement about the project you are about to discuss. If you do not sound excited about the work you have done, why would an audience want to listen to you for upwards of a quarter of an hour? In your introduction, preview the main ideas you will discuss and mention any key concepts you want folks to keep in mind while they listen to you. One example of such a key concept might be to remind them that your test results are preliminary and need to be confirmed in the next phase by field studies. Do not forget to introduce yourself if no one does it for you: Who are you, where are you from, and why are you talking to these people?

You do not want to memorize your talk word for word (because you would sound too stilted), but you might want to memorize the first few lines of your own introduction. You will probably be pretty nervous, and if you can begin smoothly, you will become more confident as you go along.

The following is a checklist for the second section of the presentation:

Body (8–10 minutes):

- Use an easy-to-follow organization.
- Use transitions.
- Provide supporting data.
- Bring in key concepts.

Keep the body of your talk well organized with good graphics, and you will probably keep people awake. That is no mean feat in this age of overwork and multitasking! Be sure to discuss your topics and key concepts in the same order that you introduced them in the introduction. Keeping the same sequence is a mnemonic device that helps your listeners remember the information. Especially in the body of your talk, where you present a good number of details to support your main findings or points, you must focus on logical, repetitive organization and repetition of keywords.

Here is a checklist for the third section of the presentation:

Conclusions (2–3 minutes):

- Provide a clear wrap-up.
- Comment on the significance of the results.
- Do not just stop in your tracks!
- Ask for questions.

Never just stop and say, "That's all." Plan a clear ending to your talk that emphasizes the most important fact or conclusion of your work. Remember that many in your audience will probably remember best the last thing you said (other than, "Are there any questions?"). Especially if your talk has been fairly technical, you must use the ending to underline the significance of what you did, found, or concluded. For talks that give instructions of some kind, finish with the most important fact, whether it is a safety warning or a statement of how easy these instructions will make the job or how important the job is. Repetition is your friend here. Do not fail to say something just because you have already said it.

Of course, you always end any talk with a request for questions or comments from your listeners. Your job is to make sure your message came through, and, fortunately, presentation allows you to know for sure whether you succeeded. Asking for questions gives you another chance to be clear if anyone is confused or in doubt about something you have said or done.

Here is a sample outline for a 15–20-minute talk given to the U.S. Environmental Protection Agency. The talk was a progress report on a research project testing a new material for possible use as a landfill liner. You can use this outline as a guide while preparing a talk of your own. The wording you use in your outline may find its way onto your slides, but keep in mind that *these outline sections are not yet slides*! The outline is as follows:

Sample Presentation Outline

INTRODUCTION

<u>Project</u>

Designing and conducting bench-scale hydraulic conductivity tests of manufactured bentonitic blanket materials for landfill liners and caps.

Purpose of Project: To provide data to EPA on whether these new materials are as effective in preventing leachate from escaping into soil (and rain from getting into landfill) as are current liners (three feet of compacted clay).

<u>Purpose of Talk</u>

To update audience on testing and results so far. To solicit feedback on test design and methods and on preliminary conclusions.

<u>List of Main Topics (what I will discuss)</u>

Background on material
Testing equipment
Testing procedure
Current status of testing

<u>List of Key Concepts</u>

Designers in a hurry to use new material
Test designed only for ideal lab conditions
Further testing needs to be done

BODY

<u>Main Points</u>

1. Background on liner material
composition, cost, ease of installation

2. Testing equipment
9 steel tanks, gravel, water, etc.
collection dish under drain

3. Testing procedure and duration
3 sets of tests for each tank
each set takes two months
readings taken weekly
hydraulic flow calculated: $Q = kiA$
test stopped when steady flow is reached

4. Current status
first set of tests complete
hydraulic conductivity values calculated
second set of tests set up

CONCLUSION

<u>Tentative Conclusions</u>

1. Conductivity is within range published by manufacturers of three brands tested.
2. Conductivity is comparable to (actually slightly lower than) that of clay liner.
3. Further testing is needed—e.g., simulating actual landfill conditions.

---

3   PLANNING THE VISUALS

When we get information in both words and images, we understand better. A picture may be worth a thousand words, but we still need words to give us the context for the picture. Be sure that your words and your visuals are in synch all the time: Do not leave a visual up while you talk about something else. Also, it is OK for the presentation screen to be dark or blank sometimes. Remember that *you* are giving the talk, not your fancy pictures.

HINT

Words + Images = 💡

Do not try to use too many visuals; it is better to explain a few things thoroughly than to have to skim through and skip visuals because you are running out of time. You have to allow time for pauses and for potentially more-thorough explanations than you had anticipated because you can see the audience is confused.

HINT

Creating Visuals

- Begin planning visuals as soon as the outline of your presentation is completed.
- Plan on using 10–20 visuals for a 10–15-minute talk.
- Consider all delivery methods:
  - Computer projection is the most professional.
  - There may be reasons to consider other methods as well.

Here is a checklist for designing visuals:

- *Simplify* any hard-copy graphics (graphs, tables, etc.)
- Think big.
- Include mapping visuals.

The following subsections explain these three points.

Simplify

A long table or a complex graph that works in a report will *not* work well in a presentation. The audience does not have enough time to process and understand visuals that are very complex and dense. Remember that each visual will probably be shown for less than one minute. Consider Table 1.

Table 1 does not make a good presentation graphic. There are too many numbers to absorb and understand quickly, and the significance of those numbers is not made instantly visually clear. The numbers showing diameter, for example, look as important as the numbers showing settlement (presumably the critical information). But the main problem with this visual is the small-sized and wordy caption; the labeling is left over from the hard-copy version. Presentation visuals do not need to be numbered, and the titles should be very simple and short, usually without captions. In any case, the caption here is meaningless in the hard-copy, handout version of your slides.

For visuals that are mostly words, remember again that an audience does not have time to read and process information the way a reader of a book can. You must use fewer

TABLE 1   Comparison of Settling for Various Types of Piles. The piles that exceed 0.25 inches of settlement are shown in red. The piles that are shaded in gray were discarded. [*This table is too crowded to make a good presentation visual. Titles for graphics should not have captions.*]

Concrete Pile			Hollow Steel Pile			Concrete-Filled Pile		
Diam (in)	Len (ft)	Sett (in)	Diam (in)	Len (ft)	Sett (in)	Diam (in)	Len (ft)	Sett (in)
12	50	0.19	12	50	0.07	12	50	0.19
12	55	0.37	12	55	0.18	12	55	0.37
12	60	0.36	12	60	0.17	12	60	0.36
12	65	0.61	12	65	0.28	12	65	0.61
14	50	0.20	14	50	0.10	14	50	0.20
14	55	0.33	14	55	0.16	14	55	0.33
14	60	0.43	14	60	0.21	14	60	0.43
14	65	0.68	14	65	0.26	14	65	0.58
16	50	0.23	16	50	0.10	16	50	0.23
16	55	0.32	16	55	0.20	16	55	0.32
16	60	0.41	16	60	0.42	16	60	0.41
16	65	0.43	16	65	0.43	16	65	0.43

words and allow more white space between the words. Here is a general rule of thumb for text on slides:

- No more than seven or eight lines of text per slide.
- No more than seven or eight words per line.

Think Big

One of the prime benefits of using a software presentation-package such as Microsoft PowerPoint is that the default text sizes are always large enough to be seen easily. Because we are so used to judging visual ease of reading from a small screen or from a hard copy, we forget that projecting text and images over distance necessitates a larger scale if the visuals are going to be read easily. If you customize the default font settings for any particular design template in PowerPoint, make sure that you maintain a font size that can be read easily from the back of a large room. If you are using an overhead projector, always enlarge the hard-copy versions of your tables and graphs. Use these minimum font sizes for presentation graphics:

- 18-point minimum font for labeling axes
- 32-point minimum font for titles
- 24-point minimum font for first-level bullet points
- 20-point minimum font for bullet points and main text (only for second- or third-level bullet points)

Use fonts larger than these wherever you can. A good test for readability of your slides is to print them out in slide view, place each one on the floor, and stand back about a foot. If you can read the slide easily, then it is probably large enough for your audience to see easily when it is projected on a screen in front of a large room.

Include Mapping Visuals

You are probably aware of the importance of content visuals in conveying information on the subject you are discussing. For example, the graph in Figure 1 plots the theoretical

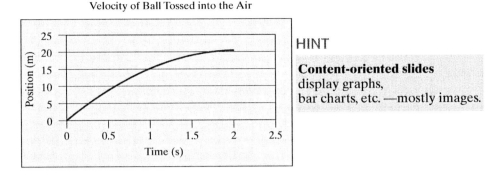

Velocity of Ball Tossed into the Air

HINT

Content-oriented slides display graphs, bar charts, etc. —mostly images.

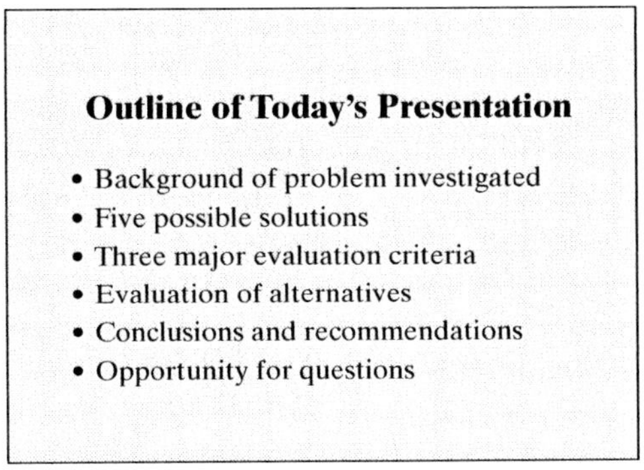

Figure 1. Example of content-oriented slide for a presentation.

Outline of Today's Presentation

- Background of problem investigated
- Five possible solutions
- Three major evaluation criteria
- Evaluation of alternatives
- Conclusions and recommendations
- Opportunity for questions

HINT

Mapping slides map the structure of the talk—mostly words.

Figure 2. Example of a mapping slide for a presentation. You should use both content-oriented and mapping visuals.

speed and position of a ball. The visual shows the exact relationship faster than words alone could explain it. But you may not be aware of the importance of visuals that map your talk and emphasize certain key points (e.g., how the theoretical information was used to solve a problem). You want to tell your audience where you are in the talk and what to expect. A mapping slide that outlines the content and purpose of the talk, as shown in Figure 2, prepares the listener for what is to come, thereby enhancing his or her understanding of topics and ideas as you explain them in more detail.

The first mapping slide should always be your title slide. Tell the members of your audience both orally and visually who you are, where you are from, why you are talking to them, and what is the general subject of your talk. In Figure 3, the font sizes are Arial 40 for the title, Arial 32 for the presenter's name, and Times 24 for the speaker's affiliation and date. Arial is a sans-serif font (meaning that it has no little "feet" at the edges of the letters), so it projects very well. Times is a serif font that should be used carefully for presentation graphics. Use Times for information that is somewhat less important than other information, or else make sure you never use less than a 24-point size.

Following the title slide, an introduction slide should outline in a bit more detail what information you will impart. (See Figure 2.) Similarly, labeling the conclusions

Figure 3.   Sample title slide for a presentation.

slide "Conclusions" and writing the conclusions out in simplified form tells the listener that the talk is almost at an end. If the listener's mind has been drifting, he or she knows that now is the time to listen attentively and get the talk's most important points.

Modes of Delivery

Computer projection has become the professional standard for delivery of most presentations. There are tremendous advantages and a few potential problems with using computer projection. If you have designed your slides using presentation software, you can update them even at the very last minute. There is also no chance of getting the slides out of order (as with transparencies or 35-mm slides). You can also use the full range of multimedia options available to you through your computer and the projection capabilities at the presentation site. To gain these advantages, however, you must understand and be confident about the equipment you will be using. When problems arise, it is generally because you have not checked out the equipment beforehand, especially when you are off site, away from school or the office. It is possible that the projector will not be compatible with your computer or that the right cables will not be at hand. If you have your presentation on disk, the borrowed computer may not have the right software to run your files. Or, if some of your presentation depends on the Internet or other network connections, the correct hookups may not be available. If at all possible, you should rehearse or at least visit with the equipment to be used. Go there the day before and assess the equipment.

At this point in the early 21st century, the most commonly used presentation software is probably Microsoft PowerPoint. This package is very user friendly and very powerful. I have seen students learn to create decent slides within 10 to 15 minutes and then learn the finer points of designing with PowerPoint within the next hour. All you have to do is open the program and start experimenting. Use the templates to give yourself ideas on design and format, but remember that others may be using those very same templates. Your talk should be unique, because both you and the way you present your particular information are unique. PowerPoint is very customizable, so take the trouble to experiment with design and format.

Packages such as PowerPoint help convey information in manageable chunks. This sort of software has revolutionized business and technical presentations by forcing the

HINT

Suggestions for Designing with Presentation Software

- Use the design templates rather than the genre templates ("sales pitch," etc.). Design templates offer a consistent format for slides (font size and type, placement of titles, etc.), but do not try to dictate content.
- Be careful about colors: Use very dark text on a very light background or vice versa.
- Avoid red texts, as it is difficult to read from a distance, no matter how large the text.
- Either keep slides consistent in design or vary the design according to subject matter. For example, if you are introducing a multiphase project, you might make the introduction slides slightly different in format from the body slides. Conclusion slides might then repeat the introduction slides' design.
- Experiment with animations and dimming, but consider your audience before using these effects: A semitechnical audience may appreciate "entertainment" more than would the members of your dissertation committee.

presenter to distill his or her thoughts and information for greatest simplicity and clarity. Bullet points or talking points can be created effortlessly in PowerPoint, and the product has a large selection of clip art just a click away. See how the slide shown in Figure 4 clearly introduces a case study on environmental contamination, using a piece of clip art to render the subject matter more memorable in the mind of the listener.

You can use presentation software not only to create the visuals for your talk but also to organize your thoughts (and therefore your talk) and to create handouts for the audience. Once you start using the software, you will realize how the necessity to type your thoughts in logical order, using short phrases or sentences, helps to organize your thoughts in the first place. You may have thought you knew what you wanted to say about the difficulty of monitoring a site suspected of being contaminated with benzene, but chances are that if you just started extemporizing (speaking off the cuff), you would say a lot more than what's contained in the second bullet point on that slide. Yet, for a general audience, that bullet point contains a good summary of the problem.

Be careful, however, of letting your bullet points speak for you. Those bullets are simply the tip of the iceberg; it is up to you to provide the connections between the bullet

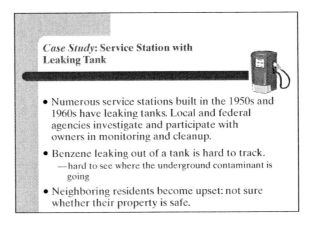

Figure 4. Sample slide for introducing a case study.

points that make them come alive. You want to create *meaning*, not simply a *list*, out of your data and your analysis. *Never stand in front of your audience and read your slides.* Use the slides for your own visual reference, and repeat keywords, phrases, and critical pieces of data, but always add more information, further examples, or a story that illustrates the point indicated by the bullet.

HINT

> ## Do Not Let Your Bullet Points Speak for You
>
> - Your job is to create meaning so the audience understands the significance of your work.
> - Do not simply read your bullet points.
> - Explain: Provide "connective tissue" between bullet points.

Never let your visuals upstage you or the content you are presenting. A package such as PowerPoint supports all sorts of multimedia applications (including animation, video, audio, and other special effects) that can be used to make your talk understandable, memorable, and entertaining. But as you plan your visuals, always consider first the audience to whom you will be presenting. The more technical knowledge the audience members have about your subject matter, the fewer bells and whistles they will need. And remember that bells and whistles should never be used for their own sake, but always in the interest of stressing or explaining a particular point that you are making. For example, the text on the PowerPoint slide shown in Figure 5 does not match the illustration.

There are situations in which computer projection may be unavailable or may not be the best choice for your talk. If you are showing photographs that were not computer generated, you may want to use 35-millimeter slides to achieve the best resolution. If you are leading an interactive meeting or workshop, you may want to use overheads (transparencies) to capture the ideas or modifications suggested by participants. Sometimes, the overhead projector will be the only equipment available to you.

Whatever your mode of delivery, keep these guidelines in mind as you develop your visuals: Make sure that each visual makes the right point. Do not get carried away with the possibilities offered by clip art and by all the many pictures you can download from the Web. Let your talk's content guide you, and then try to build in a little gentle humor here and there.

Figure 5.   Example of a possibly frivolous slide.
[If this slide is not meant to illustrate something about cats or catlike qualities, then find another picture. Never use a picture just because it is "cool" or you like it.]

HINT

Guidelines for Designing Visuals in All Modes

- **Design each visual to make one main point.**
- **Two visuals may be better than one.**
- **Be sure each visual makes the right point.**
- **Leave a visual up only as long as you are talking about it.**
- **Remember that *you* must still be the focus, not your visuals.**
- **Avoid clutter. On graphs, be sure to omit needless gridlines, tick marks, etc.**
- **Check your visuals for distortion, spelling errors, and computational mistakes.**
- **Think big. Follow software guides. Most text should be in at least 24-point font. The bigger the presentation room, the bigger the font size should be.**
- **Use few words, and separate them with lots of white space. The benchmark maximum lengths are as follows:**
  - **Seven to eight lines of text per slide**
  - **Seven to eight words per line**

PRACTICE QUESTION: DESIGNING SLIDES

How could the slide shown in Figure 6 be improved? Identify specific problems with it.

> **Job Experience**
>
> ❖ Use specific keywords that highlight particular technical, organizational, or people/communication skills:
>   - "pavement distress mechanisms," "life-cycle costs," "multimedia presentations"
> ➣ a past- or present-tense verb should be used to begin each job description.
>   - Check the list of action words for suggested verbs.
> ❖ Highlight job title, employer, location, and dates employed. Be sure to put all dates in same column on resume.

Figure 6. Example of badly designed slide.

SUGGESTED ANSWER

Some of the problems with the slide include the following:
- too much text
- awkward placement of text

- inappropriate background for a text-laden slide—the lines are distracting
- the size of text doesn't always reflect the level of bullet
- the bullet design is not consistent
- capitalization is not consistent

Figure 7 shows a suggested revision.

> **Job Experience**
>
> • Use keywords to highlight specific technical, organizational, or communication skills:
>   - "pavement distress mechanisms," "life-cycle costs," "multimedia presentations"
> • Use past-or present-tense verb to begin each job description.
>   - Check list of action words for suggested verbs.
> • Highlight *job title, employer, location,* and *dates employed.*

Figure 7. Example of improved slide design.

4   PLANNING THE DELIVERY

Remember that your audience will need your help to understand clearly what you are saying. After all, readers can read at their own pace and stop whenever they want to.

Listeners, on the other hand, are at the mercy of the speaker's pace and level of detail. Remember this factor when you give a talk. Plan not to talk too quickly, and keep an eye on the audience members to see if they are understanding you. For many people, it is more difficult to retain large amounts of information when listening than when reading. When we listen to a talk, we are also listening to what is in our own heads—all that inner conversation that most of us have going on almost all the time. Use voice quality, body language, visuals, and transitions—the tools described here—to help keep your listeners with you during your talk.

You have some powerful tools to use when giving a talk. Aside from the words you speak and the visuals you show about the topics indicated in your outline, you have your own voice quality and body language. You can use these tools to convince an audience of your credibility, intelligence, and enthusiasm for the work you have done. Enthusiasm may be the most important ingredient of your talk: If you show that you care intensely about the subject and the work, chances are your audience will also care. Conversely, if you speak in a monotonous, flat tone and if you stand in one place or slouch, the audience members will get the message that you do not care that much, so *neither will they.* The best way to improve your delivery strategies is to harness the enthusiasm that should already be there inside you (though perhaps rather buried). Positive energy communicates best. But first you need to get feedback on how you come across to an audience. You can use rehearsing, videotaping, and anticipating questions as strategies for eliciting feedback.

Rehearsing

The best way to improve the delivery of your talk is to rehearse in front of someone. Rehearsing in front of at least one other person enables you to get constructive feedback—on what you are doing right and what you are doing wrong—that will help you communicate effectively with your audience. Ask your classmates or coworkers to watch you run through your talk, and offer to do the same for them. Rehearsing at least three times is a good idea for less experienced presenters: Rehearse once on your own, once standing up in front of someone, and once (ideally) with your audiovisual equipment in the space where you will be giving your talk. Ask your surrogate audience members to critique your delivery. Could they hear and understand everything you said? Could they follow the talk, and did you make it interesting? The HINT box contains a suggested checklist of questions for your reviewers to answer:

HINT

Questions for Your Rehearsal Reviewer to Answer about You

Is the structure of the talk evident?

Do the various sections hang together and form a whole?

Does the pace seem right?

Is the subject matter clear and compelling?

Are the visuals clear and compelling?

Does the presenter sound enthusiastic?

Does the presenter speak to the point without using verbal fillers, such as "um" and "you know"?

Does the speaker maintain eye contact?

Does the speaker move naturally, without fidgeting?

Could I hear every word of the presentation?

Does the talk hold my interest?

Voice Quality

Tone of voice is so very important in any interpersonal communication. Think of how many times you may have been misunderstood because your listener thought you were being sarcastic or bored when you really were not—your voice just somehow sounded that way. A good voice is an enormous personal asset. Your career will truly benefit if you can learn to control, modulate, and use your voice to be persuasive, informative, or inspiring, as the occasion demands. In a presentation, you have to ensure first of all that you are speaking loudly enough for everyone in the room to hear you—everyone, even those people in the very back rows. Every speaker can learn to speak more loudly. Try the exercise explained in the upcoming box to increase the volume of your voice. The trick is not to put more pressure on your throat—that is not where your voice originates—but rather to apply pressure to your diaphragm, where your voice originates. Your diaphragm is like a bellows that can heat up your voice to a roaring fire.

PRACTICE EXERCISE: INCREASE VOICE VOLUME AND RESONANCE

- Stand with your feet shoulder width apart and your hands on your diaphragm, between your belly button and breastbone. Open your mouth and emit a constant sound at the same pitch. Press on your diaphragm and see how your voice volume increases without your even trying. The harder you press, the louder is the sound.

- Remember that your voice does not come from your throat; it rises up from your diaphragm and gains power from the air in your lungs.

Second, you want to work on the richness, pleasantness, and variety of your voice. These qualities are controlled by what sound experts call *tone*, *pitch*, and *dynamics*. Some of us naturally have a rather monotonous voice, one that stays at the same pitch, tone, and dynamic. In any talk, we want, however, to use our voice as an instrument that conveys emphasis, importance, humor, and sometimes even emotion. *Tone* is the resonance of your voice. If you have a squeaky or thin voice, check out that voice exercise in the previous box for a method of strengthening your voice so it sounds richer and more resonant. *Pitch* is the highness or lowness of your voice. Try to vary your pitch to emphasize important points. Remember that your audience understands meaning by the way that your voice rises and falls. A rising voice at the end of a sentence is the way that we understand you are asking a question, for instance. Do not make or let your voice rise at the end if you are not asking a question. However, do not let your voice fall so low at the end of a sentence that the listener cannot catch the last few words. Be careful not to run out of energy (and therefore volume) at the end of your sentences. *Dynamics* refers to loudness and softness of a voice. Again, you can emphasize important points by raising your voice volume a little.

Also be careful not to speak too fast. Nervousness makes us speed up. On the other hand, if the pace of your talk is slow, it may seem that you are unsure of what you are going to say next. Strive for a medium pace, one that carries listeners along without losing any information because you are whizzing over the words.

Body Language

You want to show that you care by leaning slightly forward, toward the audience, and using your hands appropriately to emphasize points and to include the audience in your

HINT

Voice Quality

- Speak loudly enough for all to hear.
- Make sure your voice is varied in pitch and dynamics.
- Speak in a resonant tone.
- Make your voice rise and fall appropriately; don't run out of steam at the end of a sentence.
- Speak at a medium pace. Generally, speak more carefully and slowly than you normally do.
- Speak *toward* the audience. Glance toward slides only briefly.

thoughts. If you stand with your arms crossed, lean away from the audience, or slouch against the table or podium, your gestures are excluding the audience and creating a barrier between you and those to whom you are speaking. Any audience member wants to feel as though you are speaking directly to him or her. If you stand in one place all the time, your audience will become bored, and chances are you will become increasingly nervous. Moving around helps control nervousness, because movement relieves stress. Be careful as you move around, however: Move naturally, and do not develop annoying repetitive movements without realizing it. I once watched a young speaker drive her audience crazy by continually scratching behind her left knee. She had no idea she was doing this, but the audience was mesmerized by this repeated nervous motion and consequently could not pay attention to the admirable content of her talk.

The other way to distance yourself from and alienate an audience is by failing to make eye contact. In the United States, if someone does not look at us, we either lose interest in what he or she is saying or feel that the speaker is untrustworthy. The same reaction may not occur in other cultures however; in fact, if you are from a non-Western country, you may be uncomfortable looking directly at your audience. Nevertheless, if you are speaking in the United States, you should know that looking someone in the eye is considered to be a trait of truth and strength. If you gaze over the heads of your audience, down at the floor, or, worse, out the window, your audience will probably simply stop listening to you. If you are not looking at your audience because you are afraid of what you will see, relax. Most listeners are glad to be hearing your information delivered in an accessible and visually appealing way. They are on your side, and if you look out at that sea of faces, you will probably see a lot of friendly, positive expressions. You can get a nice charge of energy by looking at your listeners and seeing someone nod as though he or she understands or even smile as though he or she is happy to have this information. Do not cut yourself off from this positive energy by failing to look out at your audience. On the other hand, do not stare at just one or a couple of people. Practice a sweeping motion, resting your eyes for just a couple of seconds on each face. Try to include the entire room in this sweeping motion.

HINT

Body Language

- Use appropriate movement. Move and position your hands naturally.
- Use inclusive gestures (no crossed arms).
- Maintain good posture (no leaning against the podium or shoving both hands in pockets).
- Do not make distracting tics or noises.
- Maintain good eye contact.

Stand and face the audience!

Using Visuals

It is easy to use too many visuals, now that they are relatively easy to create. Check yourself during rehearsal by timing your talk *while using* visuals. A good rule of thumb for the number of visuals is to use no more than 1 per minute, or 10–20 for a 15–20-minute talk. Be careful of a natural tendency to include more visuals than you really need to make your points. Ask a reviewer whether your visuals support your points well, raise further questions, or seem rather empty of content. Practice displaying the visuals using whatever technology you have chosen; the last thing you want to do is to have to fiddle with the equipment during the presentation. Learn how to use a laser pointer so that you do not flash it around needlessly.

Using Transitions

Moving a reader along from point to point is difficult to do in writing; in a presentation, you have more tools—pitch and tone of voice, gestures, etc.—to help. And you have another tool that you also use in writing: transitional words and phrases. These words and phrases can be more direct and informal, however, in speech than in writing. Rhetorical questions work really well to sum up one section of information and point to the next section: "So, what did we find once we had completed the lab experiments?" "What did our studies show us about the load-bearing properties of this material?"

Remember that in speech, you will want to use active voice—e.g., "we found deformation"—much more than passive voice—e.g., "deformation was found." Active voice will help your speech be clearer, more concise, and more direct.

Videotaping

An excellent way to improve your presentation skills is to have someone videotape you so that you can see for yourself what your strong and weak points are. As you watch the tape later, ask yourself these questions:

- What is my greatest strength as a speaker?
- What is the weakest part of my presentation? Why?
- What, specifically, can I do to improve? Should I do voice exercises? Practice more? Reorganize?
- What should be the result of my improvement efforts in my next talk?

Always notice what you do right as well as what you do wrong. Some students realize, for instance, that even though they were very nervous giving the talk, the tape shows a person seemingly in control, with few signs of nervousness. This is great information to have: You do not *show* your nervousness nearly as much as you *feel* it. Knowing that should give you more confidence the next time around.

When it comes to improving certain aspects of your presentation (increasing voice volume, for instance), practice strategies for planning, rehearsing, and answering questions and see what difference the strategies make the next time around. Set realistic goals for yourself. Your voice does not have to be broadcast quality, like your favorite news reporter's. It just has to be loud enough and resonant enough to get your meaning across. Listen closely to your tape, and pretend to be someone in an audience listening to you. Take notes on your performance. When you tape yourself again, compare the new notes with the old. *Any* improvement is a significant improvement.

Anticipating Questions

The question-and-answer (Q&A) session that inevitably follows almost every presentation is an important mechanism for exchanging information. The audience gets to clarify or learn more about your subject matter, and you get to discuss some details that had to be left out of your talk or to correct any misunderstandings that may have arisen. You, as well as the audience, can learn a lot during this session. Unfortunately, many speakers are afraid of Q&A and do not even want to think about it beforehand. That is unfortunate, because preparing for Q&A will give you a good level of confidence. How do you prepare?

You can ask your rehearsal reviewers questions about the content of your talk: What is not quite clear to them, or what do they want to know more about? The first type of question will lead you to reorganize or clarify some part of your talk, and the latter type will give you a heads-up on possible questions your audience will have following your actual talk. You cannot prepare information on every topic related to yours, but being aware of future directions or similar work in other areas would enable you to answer very nicely such a "tell me more" kind of question.

As you look over your outline and rehearse your talk, think to yourself about questions that might arise from your content. Jot them down, and spend a little time thinking about them. Don't spend too much time—you cannot prepare for every type of question, nor should you have to. Your job is not to know everything, just to have done your homework on the subjects you are presenting.

5   CONTROLLING NERVOUSNESS

Everyone gets nervous at some point before giving a talk. The trick is to use your nervousness as a source of energy without becoming overly anxious. Let your nervousness give you energy. Being nervous means at least you are not apathetic; after all, people who are bored and indifferent are going to *sound* boring. But do not let nervousness overwhelm you. Look over the upcoming strategies for coping with nervousness before and during your talk, and see which ones might work for you. Different strategies work better for different people. The goal is to keep your nervousness within reasonable limits at the same time that you harness it for energy, motivation, and the willingness to go the extra mile in preparing.

Before Your Talk

Deep breathing is something you can do right before your talk or anytime you feel anxious. Simply breathe in slowly on a count of, say, four, and then breathe out on double that amount, or eight counts. Counting slows your breathing down, and soon your body will feel more relaxed. When the body relaxes, the mind tends to follow suit.

Mental imaging is a technique used widely by coaches for teams and individual players to buttress their confidence. For example, a kicker might use this technique before being brought in to attempt the extra point in a football game. He would create a mental movie that shows him moving his foot back, swinging forward, and connecting with the ball at exactly the right point. He would watch mentally as the ball arcs up into the air and sails over the goal right between the goalposts to thunderous applause from the spectators. In your case, imagine yourself getting up to give a talk, beginning confidently, and speaking at exactly the right pace, with people looking pleased and affirming by nodding their heads. Your mental movie would include your finishing on time with good energy, a definite conclusion, and perhaps a smile as you ask for questions. Remember also to picture the audience—a group of people with glints in their eyes of understanding and even admiration for you and the work you have done. Such a mental movie builds confidence, and confidence enables you to make the movie come true.

Mind games can help divert your mind from focusing on your own fears and anxieties. Count the chairs in the room, or say people's names backward, for example. Bring a crossword puzzle to occupy you during the time before you get up to speak. Or really concentrate on the other talks and think about their content instead of on your own talk. Last-minute cramming and memorization usually does not work and ends up making you feel more nervous by the time you actually come to the podium.

HINT

Tips for controlling nervousness before your talk:

- Try exercising.
- Avoid caffeine the day of your talk.
- Replace negative self-assessments with positive self-talk.
- Check all equipment in advance.

Just Before and during Your Talk

Here is a strategy for settling yourself down right before your talk: As you come up to the podium, speak to a few folks along the way. If you know someone in the audience, be sure and say hi to them as you move to the front; if you do not know anyone, speak to the moderator or to the speaker who went before you—tell her what a good job he or she did. You could even admit to the moderator that you are nervous; chances are he or she will say something reassuring. The point is that by carrying on these small conversations, you ready yourself psychologically to behave during your talk as though you are simply continuing a conversation, only now with lots of people. Conversing with people is different than thinking of them as some sort of enemy from whom you would like to hide. This strategy should make facing the audience less intimidating and put you in the right frame of mind to relax, focus on what you want to say, stay connected with your audience, and even have fun.

Once you are at the podium, take a moment before speaking to get relaxed and adjusted to your audience. Think of the audience as a group of friends, even if you have never seen any of the people before. As you talk, keep an eye on the audience members' reactions, and slow down or ask for questions if some of them are looking puzzled. This checking takes practice; do not let the reactions of a few folks alarm or throw you. You can hardly ever make *everyone* understand *all* of your points; do not even try. There are always some people who will look bored or distracted for particular reasons. Think about that 8:00 AM class you took; you were probably not the most lively looking listener.

Remember, your audience always wants you to succeed! They will give you the benefit of the doubt because they are happy sitting there being informed and, perhaps, even slightly entertained.

PRACTICE QUESTION: HARNESSING NERVOUSNESS

In what ways is nervousness a useful quality for you as a speaker?

SUGGESTED ANSWER

Nervousness gives you energy. It makes you more alert. Use your nervousness as a source of strength and enthusiasm. Nervousness encourages you to rehearse more.

6 HANDLING QUESTIONS

Audience questions can give you, the speaker, very valuable feedback on the direction and methodology of your work. Here are some strategies for handling questions as they come at you:

Tips for Answering Audience Questions

1. Remain standing at the front of the room following your presentation. Do not run off or start heading to the edge of the speaking area. Convey confidence and a willingness to entertain questions.

2. Be aware of your body position; the audience is watching you. Avoid playing with your clothing, hair, notes, or writing implements. If your partner is answering a question, pay respectful attention.

3. Try to select questions from different parts of the room. In most Q&A situations, it is best to try to include the entire audience by using this method. Even if a particular person does not get a question answered, he or she won't feel ignored.

4. Repeat the question before you answer it, so everyone can hear it. Paraphrasing serves three crucial functions: (1) It allows everyone in the audience to hear the question; (2) it gives you time to think of your response; (3) it ensures that you understand exactly what is being asked of you.

5. Answer each question clearly and then move on. Provide an efficient and accurate response, and move to the next question. Try not to ramble or wander into a related topic.

6. Signal when you will accept one last question. To avoid the perception that you are trying to escape a particularly nasty question, warn the audience in advance that your time for questions is quickly passing. In a classroom setting, however, this role usually falls to the instructor.

7. Brainstorm possible questions in advance. The best way to prepare for a Q&A period is to think of possible questions ahead of time. You may not accurately guess what your audience will ask, but you will feel more confident. In addition, you may very well guess accurately, and then your answer will sparkle with professionalism.

8. Do not assume that tough questions are hostile questions. You may have simply gotten someone really thinking! If a question is long, and complicated, or you just do not understand it, do not try to bluff your way through an answer. Admit that you had not thought of that or studied that as part of your work, and *offer to speak with the questioner privately* after the session.

9. Practice answering questions as a part of rehearsal. If you practice with a potential audience member (and you should), have that person ask you questions about the presentation. This practice will help simulate the actual presentation experience and will boost your confidence.

Remember that the Q&A session can be the most valuable and the most enjoyable part of the presentation for you. You can learn new perspectives and ideas, and you will get feedback on the direction of your work or approach to a problem. Stay upbeat and positive, even when you are confused by a long, complex, or unforeseen question. Most listeners are not trying to test your knowledge; they really want to learn from your talk. But they have their own individual agendas, and their concerns and backgrounds are often not the same as yours. So each listener is trying to fit your information into the framework of what he or she knows and works on. Sometimes the fitting process takes some work on the part of speaker and listener, but especially in science and engineering, listeners and speaker usually share a strong bond: Everyone wants to see progress in solving that particular problem or in advancing the body of knowledge about that particular field. And when someone says publicly (as will happen to you sometime) that he or she really enjoyed your presentation, you will feel *great*.

7   PREPARING FOR A TEAM PRESENTATION

Many presentations in engineering practice are given by teams of engineers or by multi-disciplinary teams that may include engineers, architects, planners, marketing experts, salespeople, attorneys, academic researchers, regulators, and other types of professionals. In many college courses, presentations of research are also done by teams—usually, teams of students with varying backgrounds and areas of expertise. So, learning to present well involves learning how to coordinate with other speakers as well as how to plan and deliver your own material.

All of the same strategies you might use for planning, rehearsing, and controlling nervousness apply to team presentations as well as individual ones. What changes a bit is the delivery. You have to consider not only where you will stand and how you will move and run the equipment, but also where your teammates will stand and move, etc. And you have to plan what you will do when you are not the one talking. At many presentation venues, the entire team will either sit or stand at the front of the room, so you will need to practice keeping your hands calm and trying not to fidget when you are not talking. Because a team presentation has to be even more "choreographed" than a solo presentation, rehearsing with the rest of your team, probably several times, is even more important for success.

What, then, are some special strategies for preparing a team presentation? First of all, you must be sure to share contact and schedule information with each other at the beginning of the project. Meet as often as you can to plan and rehearse the talk. Second, divide up the responsibilities and the work in such a way that draws on each member's particular strengths. Each of you will most likely be responsible for a particular part of the presentation's content, but it might be best to have one person creating the slides, so that they are uniform in design. If you have the choice, you will want to select the person with the most outgoing, upbeat personality to introduce the talk (and possibly also to conclude it). It may be best to have this person act as a sort of emcee, directing audience questions to the most appropriate speaker, for instance.

During rehearsals, be supportive, but constructively critical, of each other's content and delivery style. Sometime before the dress rehearsal, go out into the room, sit at the back, and see whether you can hear everything each speaker is saying. Pretend you are an audience member who does not already know a lot about the project. Do the slides and the flow of information make sense? Are the points easy to understand? Does each speaker provide transitions between important points? At the dress rehearsal, of course, the entire team should be up front, and you should all be practicing how to "pass the baton" to each other. Remember to remind the audience of the name of the speaker who will be speaking after you; no one is going to remember an entire list of names on a title slide. Enjoy the synergy of presenting with a group. You will find that the audience will also enjoy that energy. Your tone with your teammates should be natural and relatively informal, and small touches of humor may be used here and there. Ask at least one non-team member to watch a rehearsal and comment about the humor to ensure that it is appropriate and relevant.

HINT

Tips for Presenting with a Team

Preparation

- Share contact information at the first meeting. Stay in touch!
- Divide up the preparation according to individual strengths:
  - Who is the best slide designer?
  - Who knows the best sources of information for each topic?

- Divide up speaker roles according to individual strengths:
  - Who knows most about each section or topic?
  - Who is the most upbeat?

- Rehearse often, and seek constructive criticism.
- Work on transitioning smoothly between sections and speakers; do not get in each other's way. Does it make sense to have one person running the computer projection?
- Practice answering questions the team has brainstormed.

Delivery

- "Pass the baton" to each other by mentioning the next speaker's name. Consider previewing what he or she will discuss.
- Answer those audience questions with which you feel most comfortable. If no one can answer a particular question, offer to find out the answer and get back to the questioner later.
- Stay upbeat and enjoy the synergy of presenting with colleagues!

SUMMARY

- Planning an effective presentation means thinking about your audience and their level of familiarity with and interest in your subject matter. You should design visuals and adjust your language to make technical concepts and data clear to that audience.
- Testing your presentation on a sample audience is a great way to prepare. Ask for feedback from the test audience-members on your voice, delivery, and visuals. Was your talk interesting to them, and did they understand everything?
- Visuals for a talk should generally be bigger, with less text, than you think, so that people can read them easily from the back of the room.
- You can use nervousness as a source of energy to make your presentation more vivid and keep yourself alert and on the ball.
- There are many strategies for controlling the level of nervousness that threatens to overwhelm you. Learn which strategies work best for you, and practice using them before and during your delivery.
- Preparing for a team presentation requires rehearsal with your teammates, not just by yourself.

Problems

1. Along with several other students (if possible), attend a talk given at your college or in the community. Take notes on the speaker's delivery, the visuals shown, and your general reaction to the tone and content of the talk. Answer the following questions:

    Was the talk interesting? Did it hold your attention?
    Did you understand all the information?
    Did the visuals enhance your understanding? If so, how?
    How did the speaker's voice and body language enhance or detract from your understanding or your interest?

2. If you attended the talk in #1 with at least one other student, compare your notes with the other students'. Answer the following questions:

    Did you all agree on which aspects (visuals, language, body language, voice, etc.) were most effective?
    What differences do you note in your reactions to the talk? Can you postulate any reasons for those differences?

3. Make an outline for a presentation you will deliver in one of your classes. Begin the outline by summarizing in 30 words (or less) your objective in giving the talk. Phrase your objective using an active verb, e.g.: "In this talk, I want to *demonstrate/persuade/inform/show* my audience *something*." Show the outline to your instructor or another student for feedback.

4. Pick your favorite design template in MS Powerpoint (or another presentation software package) and create a slide (not the title slide). Try to use a projector to look at the slide on a big screen (rather than on your computer screen). Ask a friend to look with you. Then, answer these questions:

    If your slide has text on it, does the design get in the way of reading the text?
    If your slide has a visual, does the design get in the way of seeing and understanding the visual?
    If you use this design, which slide formats or layouts will you need to avoid?

5. Using MS Powerpoint or another presentation software, create a slide with nothing but red, 24-point text. Then project the slide on a big screen in as big a room as you can find. How close to the screen do you have to sit to be able to read the red text?

6. Along with a friend, find a big room or, preferably, an auditorium somewhere on campus or in your town. Ask your friend to sit in the back of the room while you stand in the front or on the stage. Talk in a normal voice. If your friend cannot hear you very well, ask him or her to keep moving closer to the front. How close to the front does your friend have to move to be able to hear you easily?

7. True or false? I should work hard to eliminate all traces of nervousness in myself before I give a talk.

8. The most important quality in giving a successful presentation is which *one* of the following?

    Showing only one visual per minute (on average)
    Never saying "uhm"
    Being enthusiastic
    Always remembering to step to the side of the big screen

FURTHER READING

Gurak, L.J. 2000. *Oral Presentations for Technical Communication*. Allyn & Bacon: Boston.

This is probably the best book available that is devoted entirely to technical presentations; most publications on presentations are overgeneralized and geared to the sales pitch or after-dinner situation. Presentation of complex technical information requires much more thought about the background of your audience and the best way to display data. Chapters 16, 17, and 18, on visuals in presentations, are particularly helpful.

Houp, K.W., Pearsall, T.E., Tebeaux, E., and Dragga, S. 2002. *Reporting Technical Information*, 10th ed. Oxford University Press: New York.

This venerable textbook, now in its 10th edition, covers all aspects of writing and presenting technical information. The chapters on techniques and applications of writing are excellent, and of all the many technical-communication textbooks out there, this one does the best job on presentations. Make sure to read Chapter 19, "Oral Reports."

Tufte, E.R. 2003. *The Cognitive Style of PowerPoint*. Graphics Press: Cheshire, CT.

This pamphlet argues that overuse of PowerPoint has led to a sort of dumbing down of business and professional audiences. Relying on bullet points to convey complex messages, Tufte argues, allows the speaker to avoid his or her responsibility to analyze and describe complexity—the "connective tissue" between those bullets that is the real information.

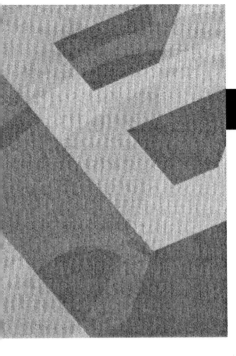

APPENDIX

13

Codes of Ethics of Professional Engineering Societies

THE INSTITUTE OF ELECTRICAL AND ELECTRONICS ENGINEERS, INC.* (IEEE)

We, the members of the IEEE, in recognition of the importance of our technologies affecting the quality of life throughout the world, and in accepting a personal obligation to our profession, its members and the communities we serve, do hereby commit ourselves to the highest ethical and professional conduct and agree:

1. to accept responsibility in making decisions consistent with the safety, health and welfare of the public, and to disclose promptly factors that might endanger the public or the environment;
2. to avoid real or perceived conflicts of interest whenever possible, and to disclose them to affected parties when they do exist;
3. to be honest and realistic in stating claims or estimates based on available data;
4. to reject bribery in all its forms;
5. to improve the understanding of technology, its appropriate application, and potential consequences;
6. to maintain and improve our technical competence and to undertake technological tasks for others only if qualified by training or experience, or after full disclosure of pertinent limitations;
7. to seek, accept, and offer honest criticism of technical work, to acknowledge and correct errors, and to credit properly the contributions of others;
8. to treat fairly all persons regardless of such factors as race, religion, gender, disability, age, or national origin;
9. to avoid injuring others, their property, reputation, or employment by false or malicious action;
10. to assist colleagues and co-workers in their professional development and to support them in following this code of ethics.

Approved by the IEEE Board of Directors, February 2006

*Code of Ethics (© 2006 IEEE. Reprinted with permission.)

NATIONAL SOCIETY OF PROFESSIONAL ENGINEERS (NSPE) CODE OF ETHICS FOR ENGINEERS

Preamble

Engineering is an important and learned profession. As members of this profession, engineers are expected to exhibit the highest standards of honesty and integrity. Engineering has a direct and vital impact on the quality of life for all people. Accordingly, the services provided by engineers require honesty, impartiality, fairness and equity, and must be dedicated to the protection of the public health, safety, and welfare. Engineers must perform under a standard of professional behavior that requires adherence to the highest principles of ethical conduct.

I. Fundamental Canons

Engineers, in the fulfillment of their professional duties, shall:

1. Hold paramount the safety, health, and welfare of the public.
2. Perform services only in areas of their competence.
3. Issue public statements only in an objective and truthful manner.
4. Act for each employer or client as faithful agents or trustees.
5. Avoid deceptive acts.
6. Conduct themselves honorably, responsibly, ethically, and lawfully so as to enhance the honor, reputation, and usefulness of the profession.

II. Rules of Practice

1. Engineers shall hold paramount the safety, health, and welfare of the public.

   a. If engineers' judgment is overruled under circumstances that endanger life or property, they shall notify their employer or client and such other authority as may be appropriate.

   b. Engineers shall approve only those engineering documents that are in conformity with applicable standards.

   c. Engineers shall not reveal facts, data or information without the prior consent of the client or employer except as authorized or required by law or this Code.

   d. Engineers shall not permit the use of their name or associate in business ventures with any person or firm that they believe are engaged in fraudulent or dishonest enterprise.

   e. Engineers having knowledge of any alleged violation of this Code shall report thereon to appropriate professional bodies and, when relevant, also to public authorities, and cooperate with the proper authorities in furnishing such information or assistance as may be required.

2. Engineers shall perform services only in the areas of their competence.

   a. Engineers shall undertake assignments only when qualified by education or experience in the specific technical fields involved.

   b. Engineers shall not affix their signatures to any plans or documents dealing with subject matter in which they lack competence, nor to any plan or document not prepared under their direction and control.

   c. Engineers may accept assignments and assume responsibility for coordination of an entire project and sign and seal the engineering documents for the entire project, provided that each technical segment is signed and sealed only by the qualified engineers who prepared the segment.

3. Engineers shall issue public statements only in an objective and truthful manner.

   a. Engineers shall be objective and truthful in professional reports, statements, or testimony. They shall include all relevant and pertinent information in such reports, statements, or testimony, which should bear the date indicating when it was current.

   b. Engineers may express publicly technical opinions that are founded upon knowledge of the facts and competence in the subject matter.

   c. Engineers shall issue no statements, criticisms, or arguments on technical matters that are inspired or paid for by interested parties, unless they have prefaced their comments by explicitly identifying the interested parties on whose behalf they are speaking, and by revealing the existence of any interest the engineers may have in the matters.

4. Engineers shall act for each employer or client as faithful agents or trustees.

   a. Engineers shall disclose all known or potential conflicts of interest that could influence or appear to influence their judgment or the quality of their services.

   b. Engineers shall not accept compensation, financial or otherwise, from more than one party for services on the same project, or for services pertaining to the same project, unless the circumstances are fully disclosed and agreed to by all interested parties.

   c. Engineers shall not solicit or accept financial or other valuable consideration, directly or indirectly, from outside agents in connection with the work for which they are responsible.

   d. Engineers in public service as members, advisors, or employees of a governmental or quasi-governmental body or department shall not participate in decisions with respect to services solicited or provided by them or their organizations in private or public engineering practice.

   e. Engineers shall not solicit or accept a contract from a governmental body on which a principal or officer of their organization serves as a member.

5. Engineers shall avoid deceptive acts.

   a. Engineers shall not falsify their qualifications or permit misrepresentation of their or their associates' qualifications. They shall not misrepresent or exaggerate their responsibility in or for the subject matter of prior assignments. Brochures or other presentations incident to the solicitation of employment shall not misrepresent pertinent facts concerning employers, employees, associates, joint venturers, or past accomplishments.

   b. Engineers shall not offer, give, solicit or receive, either directly or indirectly, any contribution to influence the award of a contract by public authority, or which may be reasonably construed by the public as having the effect of intent to influencing the awarding of a contract. They shall not offer any gift or other valuable consideration in order to secure work. They shall not pay a commission, percentage, or brokerage fee in order to secure work, except to a bona fide employee or bona fide established commercial or marketing agencies retained by them.

III. Professional Obligations

1. Engineers shall be guided in all their relations by the highest standards of honesty and integrity.

   a. Engineers shall acknowledge their errors and shall not distort or alter the facts.

   b. Engineers shall advise their clients or employers when they believe a project will not be successful.

   c. Engineers shall not accept outside employment to the detriment of their regular work or interest. Before accepting any outside engineering employment they will notify their employers.

   d. Engineers shall not attempt to attract an engineer from another employer by false or misleading pretenses.

   e. Engineers shall not actively participate in strikes, picket lines, or other collective coercive action.

   f. Engineers shall not promote their own interest at the expense of the dignity and integrity of the profession.

2. Engineers shall at all times strive to serve the public interest.

   a. Engineers shall seek opportunities to participate in civic affairs; career guidance for youths; and work for the advancement of the safety, health and well-being of their community.

   b. Engineers shall not complete, sign, or seal plans and/or specifications that are not in conformity with applicable engineering standards. If the client or employer insists on such unprofessional conduct, they shall notify the proper authorities and withdraw from further service on the project.

   c. Engineers shall endeavor to extend public knowledge and appreciation of engineering and its achievements.

3. Engineers shall avoid all conduct or practice that deceives the public.

   a. Engineers shall avoid the use of statements containing a material misrepresentation of fact or omitting a material fact.

   b. Consistent with the foregoing, Engineers may advertise for recruitment of personnel.

   c. Consistent with the foregoing, Engineers may prepare articles for the lay or technical press, but such articles shall not imply credit to the author for work performed by others.

4. Engineers shall not disclose, without consent, confidential information concerning the business affairs or technical processes of any present or former client or employer, or public body on which they serve.

   a. Engineers shall not, without the consent of all interested parties, promote or arrange for new employment or practice in connection with a specific project for which the Engineer has gained particular and specialized knowledge.

   b. Engineers shall not, without the consent of all interested parties, participate in or represent an adversary interest in connection with a specific project or proceeding in which the Engineer has gained particular specialized knowledge on behalf of a former client or employer.

5. Engineers shall not be influenced in their professional duties by conflicting interests.

   a. Engineers shall not accept financial or other considerations, including free engineering designs, from material or equipment suppliers for specifying their product.

   b. Engineers shall not accept commissions or allowances, directly or indirectly, from contractors or other parties dealing with clients or employers of the Engineer in connection with work for which the Engineer is responsible.

6. Engineers shall not attempt to obtain employment or advancement or professional engagements by untruthfully criticizing other engineers, or by other improper or questionable methods.

   a. Engineers shall not request, propose, or accept a commission on a contingent basis under circumstances in which their judgment may be compromised.

   b. Engineers in salaried positions shall accept part-time engineering work only to the extent consistent with policies of the employer and in accordance with ethical considerations.

   c. Engineers shall not, without consent, use equipment, supplies, laboratory, or office facilities of an employer to carry on outside private practice.

7. Engineers shall not attempt to injure, maliciously or falsely, directly or indirectly, the professional reputation, prospects, practice, or employment of other engineers. Engineers who believe others are guilty of unethical or illegal practice shall present such information to the proper authority for action.

   a. Engineers in private practice shall not review the work of another engineer for the same client, except with the knowledge of such engineer, or unless the connection of such engineer with the work has been terminated.

   b. Engineers in governmental, industrial, or educational employ are entitled to review and evaluate the work of other engineers when so required by their employment duties.

   c. Engineers in sales or industrial employ are entitled to make engineering comparisons of represented products with products of other suppliers.

8. Engineers shall accept personal responsibility for their professional activities provided, however, that Engineers may seek indemnification for services arising out of their practice for other than gross negligence, where the Engineer's interests cannot otherwise be protected.

   a. Engineers shall conform with state registration laws in the practice of engineering.

   b. Engineers shall not use association with a nonengineer, a corporation, or partnership as a "cloak" for unethical acts.

9. Engineers shall give credit for engineering work to those to whom credit is due, and will recognize the proprietary interests of others.

   a. Engineers shall, whenever possible, name the person or persons who may be individually responsible for designs, inventions, writings, or other accomplishments.

b. Engineers using designs supplied by a client recognize that the designs remain the property of the client and may not be duplicated by the Engineer for others without express permission.

c. Engineers, before undertaking work for others in connection with which the Engineer may make improvements, plans, designs, inventions, or other records that may justify copyrights or patents, should enter into a positive agreement regarding ownership.

d. Engineers' designs, data, records, and notes referring exclusively to an employer's work are the employer's property. Employer should indemnify the Engineer for use of the information for any purpose other than the original purpose.

As Revised July 1996

"By order of the United States District Court for the District of Columbia, former Section 11(c) of the NSPE Code of Ethics prohibiting competitive bidding, and all policy statements, opinions, rulings or other guidelines interpreting its scope, have been rescinded as unlawfully interfering with the legal right of engineers, protected under the antitrust laws, to provide price information to prospective clients; accordingly, nothing contained in the NSPE Code of Ethics, policy statements, opinions, rulings or other guidelines prohibits the submission of price quotations or competitive bids for engineering services at any time or in any amount."

Statement by NSPE Executive Committee

In order to correct misunderstandings which have been indicated in some instances since the issuance of the Supreme Court decision and the entry of the Final Judgment, it is noted that in its decision of April 25, 1978, the Supreme Court of the United States declared: "The Sherman Act does not require competitive bidding."

It is further noted that as made clear in the Supreme Court decision:

1. Engineers and firms may individually refuse to bid for engineering services.
2. Clients are not required to seek bids for engineering services.
3. Federal, state, and local laws governing procedures to procure engineering services are not affected, and remain in full force and effect.
4. State societies and local chapters are free to actively and aggressively seek legislation for professional selection and negotiation procedures by public agencies.
5. State registration board rules of professional conduct, including rules prohibiting competitive bidding for engineering services, are not affected and remain in full force and effect. State registration boards with authority to adopt rules of professional conduct may adopt rules governing procedures to obtain engineering services.
6. As noted by the Supreme Court, "nothing in the judgment prevents NSPE and its members from attempting to influence governmental action ... "

NOTE: In regard to the question of application of the Code to corporations vis-à-vis real persons, business form or type should not negate nor influence conformance of individuals to the Code. The Code deals with professional services, which services must be performed by real persons. Real persons in turn establish and implement policies within business structures. The Code is clearly written to apply to the Engineer and items incumbent on members of NSPE to endeavor to live up to its provisions. This applies to all pertinent sections of the Code.

NOTE: There is also the NSPE Ethics Reference Guide, which fleshes out some of this information.

AMERICAN SOCIETY OF MECHANICAL ENGINEERS (ASME)

Ethics

ASME requires ethical practice by each of its members and has adopted the following Code of Ethics of Engineers as referenced in the ASME Constitution, Article C2.1.1.

Code of Ethics of Engineers

The Fundamental Principles

Engineers uphold and advance the integrity, honor and dignity of the engineering profession by:

   I. Using their knowledge and skill for the enhancement of human welfare;
   II. Being honest and impartial, and serving with fidelity the public, their employers and clients; and
   III. Striving to increase the competence and prestige of the engineering profession.

The Fundamental Canons

1. Engineers shall hold paramount the safety, health, and welfare of the public in the performance of their professional duties.
2. Engineers shall perform services only in the areas of their competence.
3. Engineers shall continue their professional development throughout their careers and shall provide opportunities for the professional and ethical development of those engineers under their supervision.
4. Engineers shall act in professional matters for each employer or client as faithful agents or trustees, and shall avoid conflicts of interest or the appearance of conflicts of interest.
5. Engineers shall build their professional reputation on the merit of their services and shall not compete unfairly with others.
6. Engineers shall associate only with reputable persons or organizations.
7. Engineers shall issue public statements only in an objective and truthful manner.
8. Engineers shall consider environmental impact in the performance of their professional duties.
9. Engineers shall consider sustainable development in the performance of their professional duties.

   Adopted: March 7, 1976
   Revised: December 9, 1976
             December 7, 1979
             November 19, 1982
             June 15, 1984
             (editorial changes 7/84)
             June 16, 1988
             September 12, 1991
             September 11, 1994

June 10, 1998
September 21, 2002
September 13, 2003
(editorial changes 6/1/05)

The ASME Criteria for Interpretation of the Canons

The ASME criteria for interpretation of the Canons are guidelines and represent the objectives toward which members of the engineering profession should strive. They are principles which an engineer can reference in specific situations. In addition, they provide interpretive guidance to the ASME Board on Professional Practice and Ethics on the Code of Ethics of Engineers.

1. Engineers shall hold paramount the safety, health, and welfare of the public in the performance of their professional duties.

    a. Engineers shall recognize that the lives, safety, health, and welfare of the general public are dependent upon engineering judgments, decisions and practices incorporated into structures, machines, products, processes and devices.

    b. Engineers shall not approve or seal plans and/or specifications that are not of a design safe to the public health and welfare and in conformity with accepted engineering standards.

    c. Whenever the Engineers' professional judgments are overruled under circumstances where the safety, health, and welfare of the public are endangered, the Engineers shall inform their clients and/or employers of the possible consequences.

    (1) Engineers shall endeavor to provide data such as published standards, test codes, and quality control procedures that will enable the users to understand safe use during life expectancy associated with the designs, products, or systems for which they are responsible.

    (2) Engineers shall conduct reviews of the safety and reliability of the designs, products, or systems for which they are responsible before giving their approval to the plans for the design.

    (3) Whenever Engineers observe conditions, directly related to their employment, which they believe will endanger public safety or health, they shall inform the proper authority of the situation.

    d. If engineers have knowledge of or reason to believe that another person or firm may be in violation of any of the provisions of these Canons, they shall present such information to the proper authority in writing and shall cooperate with the proper authority in furnishing such further information or assistance as may be required.

2. Engineers shall perform services only in areas of their competence.

    a. Engineers shall undertake to perform engineering assignments only when qualified by education and/or experience in the specific technical field of engineering involved.

    b. Engineers may accept an assignment requiring education and/or experience outside of their own fields of competence, but their services shall be restricted to other phases of the project in which they are qualified. All other phases of such project shall be performed by qualified associates, consultants, or employees.

3. Engineers shall continue their professional development throughout their careers, and should provide opportunities for the professional and ethical development of those engineers under their supervision.

4. Engineers shall act in professional matters for each employer or client as faithful agents or trustees, and shall avoid conflicts of interest or the appearance of conflicts of interest.

   a. Engineers shall avoid all known conflicts of interest with their employers or clients and shall promptly inform their employers or clients of any business association, interests, or circumstances which could influence their judgment or the quality of their services.

   b. Engineers shall not undertake any assignments which would knowingly create a potential conflict of interest between themselves and their clients or their employers.

   c. Engineers shall not accept compensation, financial or otherwise, from more than one party for services on the same project, or for services pertaining to the same project, unless the circumstances are fully disclosed to, and agreed to, by all interested parties.

   d. Engineers shall not solicit or accept financial or other valuable considerations, for specifying products or material or equipment suppliers, without disclosure to their clients or employers.

   e. Engineers shall not solicit or accept gratuities, directly or indirectly, from contractors, their agents, or other parties dealing with their clients or employers in connection with work for which they are responsible. Where official public policy or employers' policies tolerate acceptance of modest gratuities or gifts, engineers shall avoid a conflict of interest by complying with appropriate policies and shall avoid the appearance of a conflict of interest.

   f. When in public service as members, advisors, or employees of a governmental body or department, Engineers shall not participate in considerations or actions with respect to services provided by them or their organization(s) in private or product engineering practice.

   g. Engineers shall not solicit an engineering contract from a governmental body or other entity on which a principal, officer, or employee of their organization serves as a member without disclosing their relationship and removing themselves from any activity of the body which concerns their organization.

   h. Engineers working on codes, standards, or governmental sanctioned rules and specifications shall exercise careful judgment in their determinations to ensure a balanced viewpoint, and avoid a conflict of interest.

   i. When, as a result of their studies, Engineers believe a project(s) will not be successful, they shall so advise their employer or client.

   j. Engineers shall treat information coming to them in the course of their assignments as confidential, and shall not use such information as a means of making personal profit if such action is adverse to the interests of their clients, their employers, or the public.

(1) They will not disclose confidential information concerning the business affairs or technical processes of any present or former employer or client or bidder under evaluation, without his consent, unless required by law or court order.

(2) They shall not reveal confidential information or finding of any commission or board of which they are members unless required by law or court order.

(3) Designs supplied to Engineers by clients shall not be duplicated by the Engineers for others without the express permission of the client(s).

k. Engineers shall act with fairness and justice to all parties when administering a construction (or other) contract.

l. Before undertaking work for others in which Engineers may make improvements, plans, designs, inventions, or other records which may justify seeking copyrights, patents, or proprietary rights, Engineers shall enter into positive agreements regarding the rights of respective parties.

m. Engineers shall admit their own errors when proven wrong and refrain from distorting or altering the facts to justify their mistakes or decisions.

n. Engineers shall not accept professional employment or assignments outside of their regular work without the knowledge of their employers.

o. Engineers shall not attempt to attract an employee from other employers or from the marketplace by false or misleading representations.

5. Engineers shall build their professional reputation on the merit of their services and shall not compete unfairly with others.

a. Engineers shall negotiate contracts for professional services on the basis of demonstrated competence and qualifications for the type of professional service required.

b. Engineers shall not request, propose, or accept professional commissions on a contingent basis if, under the circumstances, their professional judgments may be compromised.

c. Engineers shall not falsify or permit misrepresentation of their, or their associates', academic or professional qualification. They shall not misrepresent or exaggerate their degrees of responsibility in or for the subject matter of prior assignments. Brochures or other presentations used to solicit personal employment shall not misrepresent pertinent facts concerning employers, employees, associates, joint venturers, or their accomplishments.

d. Engineers shall prepare articles for the lay or technical press which are only factual. Technical Communications for publication (theses, articles, papers, reports, etc.), which are based on research involving more than one individual (including students and supervising faculty, industrial supervisor/researcher, or other co-workers) must recognize all significant contributors. Plagiarism, the act of substantially using another's ideas or written materials without due credit, is unethical. (See Appendix.)

e. Engineers shall not maliciously or falsely, directly or indirectly, injure the professional reputation, prospects, practice or employment of another engineer, nor shall they indiscriminately criticize another's work.

f. Engineers shall not use equipment, supplies, laboratory, or office facilities of their employers to carry on outside private practice without consent.

6. Engineers shall associate only with reputable persons or organizations.

   a. Engineers shall not knowingly associate with or permit the use of their names or firm names in business ventures by any person or firm which they know, or have reason to believe, are engaging in business or professional practices of a fraudulent or dishonest nature.

   b. Engineers shall not use association with nonengineers, corporations, or partnerships to disguise unethical acts.

7. Engineers shall issue public statements only in an objective and truthful manner.

   a. Engineers shall endeavor to extend public knowledge, and to prevent misunderstandings of the achievements of engineering.

   b. Engineers shall be completely objective and truthful in all professional reports, statements, or testimony. They shall include all relevant and pertinent information in such reports, statements, or testimony.

   c. Engineers, when serving as expert or technical witnesses before any court, commission, or other tribunal, shall express an engineering opinion only when it is founded on their adequate knowledge of the facts in issue, their background of technical competence in the subject matter, and their belief in the accuracy and propriety of their testimony.

   d. Engineers shall issue no statements, criticisms, or arguments on engineering matters which are inspired or paid for by an interested party, or parties, unless they preface their comments by identifying themselves, by disclosing the identities of the party or parties on whose behalf they are speaking, and by revealing the existence of any financial interest they may have in matters under discussion.

   e. Engineers shall be truthful in explaining their work and merit, and shall avoid any act tending to promote their own interest at the expense of the integrity and honor of the profession or another individual.

8. Engineers shall consider environmental impact in the performance of their professional duties.

   a. Engineers shall concern themselves with the impact of their plans and designs on the environment. When the impact is a clear threat to health or safety of the public, then the guidelines for this Canon revert to those of Canon 1.

9. Engineers shall consider sustainable development in the performance of their professional duties.

   a. Engineers shall consider development that meets the needs of the present without compromising the ability of future generations to meet their own needs. When the impact of the trade-off between economic, ecological, and social issues forms a clear threat to health or safety of the public, then the guidelines for this Canon revert to those of Canon 1.

10. Engineers accepting membership in The American Society of Mechanical Engineers by this action agree to abide by this Society Policy on Ethics and procedures for its implementation.

July 25, 2005

AMERICAN SOCIETY OF CIVIL ENGINEERS* (ASCE)

The Engineering Code of Ethics

Fundamental Principles

Engineers uphold and advance the integrity, honor, and dignity of the engineering profession by:
using their knowledge and skill for the enhancement of human welfare;
being honest and impartial and serving with fidelity the public, their employers, and clients;
striving to increase the competence and prestige of the engineering profession;
and supporting the professional and technical societies of their disciplines.

Fundamental Canons

Engineers shall hold paramount the safety, health, and welfare of the public and shall strive to comply with the principles of sustainable development in the performance of their professional duties.
Engineers shall perform services only in areas of their competence.
Engineers shall issue public statements only in an objective and truthful manner.
Engineers shall act in professional matters for each employer or client as faithful agents or trustees, and shall avoid conflicts of interest.
Engineers shall build their professional reputation on the merit of their services and shall not compete unfairly with others.
Engineers shall act in such a manner as to uphold and enhance the honor, integrity, and dignity of the engineering profession.
Engineers shall continue their professional development throughout their careers, and shall provide opportunities for the professional development of those engineers under their supervision.

AMERICAN INSTITUTE OF CHEMICAL ENGINEERS (AICHE)

AIChE Code of Ethics

American Institute of Chemical Engineers

Members of the American Institute of Chemical Engineers shall uphold and advance the integrity, honor, and dignity of the engineering profession by: being honest and impartial and serving with fidelity their employers, their clients, and the public; striving to increase the competence and prestige of the engineering profession; and using their knowledge and skill for the enhancement of human welfare. To achieve these goals, members shall:

- Hold paramount the safety, health, and welfare of the public and protect the environment in performance of their professional duties.
- Formally advise their employers or clients (and consider further disclosure, if warranted) if they perceive that a consequence of their duties will adversely affect the present or future health or safety of their colleagues or the public.

*Courtesy of ASCE

- Accept responsibility for their actions, seek and heed critical review of their work, and offer objective criticism of the work of others.
- Issue statements or present information only in an objective and truthful manner.
- Act in professional matters for each employer or client as faithful agents or trustees, avoiding conflicts of interest and never breaching confidentiality.
- Treat fairly and respectfully all colleagues and co-workers, recognizing their unique contributions and capabilities.
- Perform professional services only in areas of their competence.
- Build their professional reputations on the merits of their services.
- Continue their professional development throughout their careers, and provide opportunities for the professional development of those under their supervision.
- Never tolerate harassment.
- Conduct themselves in a fair, honorable, and respectful manner.

(Revised January 17, 2003)

Index